Relax.

You've opened the right book.

Once upon a time, people were wrong. They thought the automobile was an electric death-trap that would never replace the buggy, the Internet was only for academic shut-ins, and people who used study guides were simply *cheaters*. Then cars stopped exploding every time you started the engine, people realized you could use computers for more than just calculating the digits of *pi*, and the "cheaters" with the study guides… well, they started getting it. They got better grades, got into better schools, and just plain ol' got better. Times change. Rules change. *You snooze, you lose, buggy-drivers.*

SparkNotes is different. We've always been thinking ahead. We were the first study guides on the Internet back in 1999— you've been to SparkNotes.com haven't you? If not… Why!? This book might be posted online for free! You'll also find busy message boards, diagnostic test-prep, and all kinds of tools you'll need to get your act together and your grades up. And if your act's already together, SparkNotes will help you brutalize the competition. Or work for peace. Your call.

We're inexpensive, not cheap. Not only are our books the best bang for the buck, they're the best bang, period. Our reputation is based on staying smart and trustworthy—one step ahead, making tough topics understandable. We explain, we strategize, we translate. We get you where you want to go: smarter, better, faster than anyone else.

If you've got something to say, tell us. Your input makes us better. Found a mistake? Check www.sparknotes.com/errors. Have a comment? Go to www.sparknotes.com/comments. Did you read all the way to the bottom? Awesome. We love you. You're gonna do just fine.

SPARKNOTES™

Left

SPARKNOTES®

SAT II Chemistry

A Barnes & Noble Publication

SPARKNOTES is a registered trademark of SparkNotes LLC.

Spark Educational Publishing
A Division of Barnes & Noble Publishing
120 Fifth Avenue
New York, NY 10011

Please submit all comments and questions or report errors to *www.sparknotes.com/errors*.

Printed and bound in Canada.

ISBN 1-58663-889-0

SparkNotes is neither affiliated with nor endorsed by Harvard University.

SAT II is a registered trademark of the College Entrance Examination Board, which was not involved with the production of and does not endorse this product.

Welcome to SparkNotes Test Preparation

The competition to get into a college is fierce, but fear not: SparkNotes SAT II guides are here to help. Often referred to as the "evil twin sisters" of the SAT I, the SAT IIs are required by the most selective schools, and the pressure is on to do well and outshine your peers.

No problem—at SparkNotes, we believe you should always aim for earning the highest possible score. Our SAT II Chemistry book helps you achieve your goals by giving you the exact tools you need to succeed:

- **The chemistry topics you need to know for the test.** This book isn't designed to teach you all of chemistry; it's designed to teach you the chemistry you need to know to do well on the SAT II Chemistry test. We won't waste your time with material the test doesn't cover. Instead, we've tailored the lessons around the content you're most likely to face, and we'll make sure you actually *understand* (not just memorize) the material.
- **Specific SAT II Chemistry test-taking strategies.** Understanding chemistry is the most important ingredient to a good score on the SAT II Chemistry test, but it pays to know how to approach the test as well. We'll teach you specific skills and strategies that can help you net the valuable points that will distinguish you from the crowd.

- **Three full-length practice tests, and how to transform them into powerful study tools.** Practice tests are an important part of your preparation for any standardized test. They help you to hone your test-taking skills, track your progress, and familiarize you with the test's format and time limits. In addition, our methods for studying the practice tests you take will help you to pinpoint and eliminate your weaknesses.
- **General information about SAT II Subject Tests.** SparkNotes teaches you everything you need to know to do well on a particular SAT II test, but we think it's also important to discuss the SAT IIs in general. The first chapter of this book helps you figure out how colleges use the SAT II tests , which SAT II tests are right for you, when to take the tests, and how to register for them.

While other companies write test prep books to market their expensive courses, SparkNotes' goal is to teach you what you need to know through our books, so so you don't have to take those expensive classes. Our only agenda is to help you get the best score you can.

Contents

Introduction to the SAT II

T he SAT II Subject Tests are created and administered by the College Board and the Educational Testing Service (ETS), the two organizations responsible for producing the dreaded SAT I (which most people call the SAT). The SAT II Subject Tests were created to act as complements to the SAT I. Whereas the SAT I tests your critical thinking skills by asking math and verbal questions, the SAT II Subject Tests examine your knowledge of a particular subject, such as Writing, U.S. History, Physics, or Biology. The SAT I takes three hours; the Subject Tests take only one hour.

In our opinion, the SAT II Subject Tests are better tests than the SAT I because they cover a definitive topic rather than ambiguous critical thinking skills that are difficult to define. However, just because the SAT II Subject Tests do a better job of testing your knowledge of a useful subject doesn't mean the tests are necessarily easier or demand less studying. A "better" test isn't necessarily better for you in terms of how easy it will be.

Chapter Contents

The Good

- Because SAT II Subject Tests cover specific topics such as Grammar, Chemistry, and Biology, you can study for them effectively. If you don't know the structure of DNA, you can look it up and learn it. The SAT IIs are therefore straightforward tests: if you know your stuff, you'll do fine.
- Often, the classes you've taken in school have already prepared you well for the SAT IIs. If you've taken a Chemistry class, you've probably covered most of

the topics that are tested on the SAT II Chemistry test. All you need is some refreshing and refocusing, which this book provides.

The Bad

- Because SAT II Subject Tests quiz you on specific knowledge, it is much harder to "beat" or "outsmart" an SAT II test than it is to outsmart the SAT I. For the SAT I, you can use all sorts of tricks and strategies to figure out an answer. There are far fewer strategies to help you on the SAT II. Don't get us wrong: having test-taking skills will help you on an SAT II, but knowing the subject will help you much, much more. In other words, to do well on the SAT II, you can't just rely on your quick thinking and intelligence. You need to study.

Colleges and the SAT II Subject Tests

We're guessing you didn't sign up to take the SAT II just for the sheer pleasure of it. You probably want to get into college and know that the only reason for taking this test is that colleges want or require you to do so.

Colleges care about SAT II Subject Tests for two reasons. First, the tests demonstrate your interest, knowledge, and skill in specific subjects. Second, because SAT II tests are standardized, they show how your knowledge of Chemistry (or History or Math) measures up to that of high school students nationwide. The grades you get in high school don't offer such a measurement to colleges: some high schools are more difficult than others, and students of equal ability might receive different grades, even in classes with a relatively similar curriculum.

When it comes down to it, colleges like the SAT IIs because the tests make the colleges' job easier. SAT II tests allow colleges to easily compare you to other applicants and provide you with an excellent chance to shine. If you got a 93% on your Chemistry final and a student at another high school across the country got a 91%, colleges don't know how to compare the two grades. They don't know whose class was harder or whose teacher was a tougher grader. But if you get a 720 on the SAT II Chemistry and that other kid gets a 650, colleges *will* recognize the difference in your scores.

College Placement

Occasionally, colleges use SAT II tests to determine placement. For example, if you do very well on the SAT II Chemistry, you might be exempted from a basic science class. It's worth finding out whether the colleges you're applying to use the SAT II tests for this purpose.

Scoring the SAT II Subject Tests

There are three different versions of your SAT II score. The "raw score" is a simple score of how you did on the test, like the grade you might receive on a normal test in school. The "percentile score" compares your raw score to all the other raw scores in the country, letting you know how you did on the test in relation to your peers. The "scaled score," which ranges from 200 to 800, compares your score to the scores received by all students who have ever taken that particular SAT II.

The Raw Score

You will never know your SAT II raw score because it is not included in the score report. But you should understand how the raw score is calculated because this knowledge can affect your strategy for approaching the test.

A student's raw score is based solely on the number of questions that student got right, wrong, or left blank:

- You earn 1 point for every correct answer
- You lose $\frac{1}{4}$ of a point for each incorrect answer
- You receive zero points for each question left blank

Calculating the raw score is easy. Count the number of questions answered correctly and the number of questions answered incorrectly. Then multiply the number of wrong answers by $\frac{1}{4}$, and subtract this value from the number of right answers.

$$\text{raw score} = \text{right answers} - (\tfrac{1}{4} \times \text{wrong answers})$$

The Percentile Score

A student's percentile is based on the percentage of the total test takers who received a lower raw score than he or she did. Let's say, for example, you had a friend named Gregor Mendel, and he received a score that placed him in the 93rd percentile. That percentile tells Gregor that he scored better on the SAT II than 92 percent of the other students who took the same test; it also means that 7 percent of the students taking that test scored as well as or better than he did.

The Scaled Score

ETS takes your raw score and uses a formula to turn it into the scaled score of 200 to 800 that you've probably heard so much about.

The curve to convert raw scores to scaled scores differs from test to test. For example, a raw score of 33 on the Biology might scale to a 600, while the same raw score of 33 on the Chemistry will scale to a 700. In fact, the scaled score can even vary between different editions of the *same* test. A raw score of 33 on the February 2004 Math IIC might scale to a 710, while a 33 in June 2004 might scale to a 690. These differences in scaled scores exist to accommodate varying levels of difficulty and student performance from year to year.

Which SAT II Subject Tests to Take

There are three types of SAT II test: those you must take, those you should take, and those you shouldn't take.

- The SAT II tests you *must* take are those required by the colleges you are interested in.
- The SAT II tests you *should* take are tests that aren't required, but that you'll do well on, thereby impressing the colleges looking at your application.
- The SAT II tests you *shouldn't* take are those that aren't required and cover a subject you don't feel confident about.

Determining Which SAT II Tests Are Required

You'll need to do a bit of research to find out if the colleges you're applying to require that you take a particular SAT II test. Call the schools you're interested in, look at their web sites, or talk to your guidance counselor. Often, colleges require that you take the following SAT II tests:

- The SAT II Writing test
- One of the two SAT II Math tests (either Math IC or Math IIC)
- Another SAT II in a subject of your choice

The SAT II Chemistry is not usually required by colleges. But taking it and doing well can show a liberal arts college that you are well-rounded or a science-oriented college that you are serious about science. In general, it is a good idea to take one science-based SAT II, such as Biology, Chemistry, or Physics.

Deciding If You Should Take an SAT II That Isn't Required

There are two rules of thumb for deciding which additional test to take beyond the Writing and Math tests:

1. **Go with what you know.** If history is your field, a strong score on the American History test will impress admissions officers far more than a bold but mediocre effort on the Physics test.
2. **Try to show breadth.** Scoring well on similar subject tests such as Math, Biology, and Chemistry will not be as impressive as good scores in more diverse subjects, such as Math, Writing, World History, and Biology.

Of course, you also have to know what is considered a good score and whether or not you can get that score (or higher).

Below we have included a list of the most commonly taken SAT II tests and the average scaled score on each. If you feel confident that you can get a score that is above the average (50 points or more), taking the test will probably strengthen your college application. Please note that if you are planning to attend an elite school, you might have to score significantly higher than the national average. The following table is just a general guideline. It's a good idea to call the schools that interest you or talk to a guidance counselor to get a more precise idea of what score you should be shooting for.

Test	Average Score	
Writing	590–600	✓
Literature	590–600	
American History	580–590	
World History	570–580	
Math IC	580–590	✓
Math IIC	655–665	✓
Biology E&M	590–600	
Chemistry	605–615	✓
Physics	635–645	✓

As you decide which test to take, be realistic with yourself. Don't just assume you're going to do great without at least taking a practice test and seeing where you stand.

When to Take an SAT II Subject Test

The best time to take an SAT II Subject Test is right after you've finished a year-long class in that subject. If, for example, you take Chemistry in eleventh grade, then you should take the SAT II Chemistry near the end of that year, when the material is still fresh in your mind. (This rule does not apply for the Writing, Literature, and Foreign Language SAT II tests; it's best to take those after you've had as much study in the area as possible.)

Unless the colleges you're applying to use the SAT II for placement purposes, there is no point in taking any SAT II tests after November of your senior year, since you won't get your scores back from ETS until after the college application deadline has passed.

ETS usually sets testing dates for SAT II Subject Tests in October, November, December, January, May, and June. However, not every subject test is administered in each of these months. To check when the test you want to take is being offered, visit the College Board Web site at www.collegeboard.com or do some research in your school's guidance office.

Registering for SAT II Tests

To register for the SAT II test(s) of your choice, you have to fill out some forms and pay a registration fee. We know, we know—it's ridiculous that *you* have to pay for a test that colleges require you to take in order to make *their* jobs easier, but, sadly, there isn't anything we, or you, can do about it. (It's acceptable here to grumble about the unfairness of the world.)

After grumbling, however, you still have to register. There are two ways to go about it: online or by mail. To register online, go to www.collegeboard.com. To register by mail, fill out and send in the forms enclosed in the *Registration Bulletin*, which should be available in your high school's guidance office. You can also request a copy of the *Bulletin* by calling the College Board at (609) 771-7600 or writing to:

College Board SAT Program
P.O. Box 6200
Princeton, NJ 08541–6200

You can register to take up to three SAT II tests for any given testing day. Unfortunately, even if you decide to take three tests in one day, you'll still have to pay a separate registration fee for each.

Introduction to the SAT II Chemistry Test

Chapter Contents

The best way to do well on the SAT II Chemistry test is to be really good at chemistry. For that, there is no substitute. But the chemistry geek who spends the night before taking the SAT II cramming all of the nuances of crystal-field theory and coordination compounds probably won't fare any better on the test than the average student who reviews this book carefully. Why? Because the SAT II Chemistry test doesn't cover crystal-field theory and coordination compounds.

Happy? Good. This chapter will tell you precisely what the SAT II Chemistry test *will* test you on, how the test breaks down, and what format the questions will take. Take this information to heart and base your study plan around it. There's no use spending hours on end studying topics you won't be tested on.

Content of the SAT II Chemistry Test

The SAT II Chemistry test is written to test your understanding of the topics of chemistry that are typically taught in a one-year college-preparatory-level high school chemistry course.

Well, math and chemistry go hand in hand, right? You might be surprised, then, to learn that you aren't allowed to use a calculator on the SAT II Chemistry test. The math you'll need to do on the test never goes beyond simple arithmetic and manipulation of equations, which is good news for you—you won't be a victim of careless errors made on your calculator.

That said, you should be able to solve problems using ratios, direct and inverse proportions, scientific notation, and some simpler exponential functions. Since the test is an hour long, this means you have an average of 42 seconds to answer each of the 85 questions—the people at ETS realize that isn't enough time to delve into problems involving simultaneous equations or complex algebra. They're more interested in testing your grasp of the basic concepts of chemistry. If you've grasped these concepts, your weakness in math problem solving isn't going to hurt you. You *will*, however, be provided with a simple periodic table. This periodic table will probably look more bare-boned than the one you're used to using: it will have only the symbols of the elements along with their atomic numbers and masses.

Now let's get into the nuts and bolts of what you'll see on the exam. ETS provides the following breakdown of the test, covering eight basic categories, and as you can see, we've arranged the content review in this book according to ETS's outline:

Their Topic	Our Section	Approximate % of the test devoted to these topics.	Approximate no. of questions you'll see on these topics.
Structure of Matter Includes atomic theory and structure, chemical bonding, and molecular structure; nuclear reactions	Structure of Matter	25	21
States of Matter Includes kinetic molecular theory of gases, gas laws, liquids, solids, and phase changes; solutions, concentration units, solubility, conductivity, and colligative properties	States of Matter	15	13
Reaction Types Includes acids and bases, oxidation-reduction, and precipitation	Reaction Types	14	12

Stoichiometry Includes the mole concept, Avogadro's number, empirical and molecular formulas, percentage composition, stoichiometric calculations, and limiting reagents	Stoichiometry	12	10
Equilibrium and Reaction Rates Including gas equilibria, ionic equilibria, Le Chatelier's principle, equilibrium expressions; factors affecting rate of reaction	Equilibrium and Reaction Rates	7	6
Thermodynamics Includes energy changes in chemical reactions and physical processes, Hess's law, and randomness	Thermodynamics	6	5
Descriptive Chemistry Includes physical and chemical properties of elements and their more familiar compounds, chemical reactivity and products of chemical reactions, simple examples from organic chemistry and environmental chemistry	Descriptive Chemistry	13	11
Laboratory Includes equipment, measurement, procedures, observations, safety, calculations, and interpretation of results	Laboratory	8	7

The fact that this book is organized according to these basic categories will give you the ability to focus on each topic to whatever degree you feel necessary: if you know you're weak on gas law questions, take extra time going through "The States of Matter" section, for example. Also, each question in the practice tests at the back of this book has been categorized according to these eight categories so you can precisely identify your weaknesses and then concentrate on the areas you need to study most.

Format of the SAT II Chemistry Test

The 85 multiple-choice-type questions that make up the SAT II Chemistry exam fall into three types, and according to the College Board Web site, these types test three types of skill.

Skill Being Tested	Approximate % of test that this question type makes up	Approximate no. of questions of this type that you'll see
Recall of knowledge: remembering fundamental concepts and specific information; demonstrating familiarity with terminology	20	17
Application of knowledge: Applying a single principle to unfamiliar and/or practical situations to obtain a qualitative result or solve a quantitative problem	45	38
Synthesis of knowledge: Inferring and deducing from qualitative and/or quantitative data; integrating two or more relationships to draw conclusions or solve problems	35	30

As you can see, the SAT II test tests your knowledge of chemistry in three different ways. This test also contains three different types of questions: classification questions, relationship-analysis questions, and five-choice completion questions. Next we'll talk about exactly what these three types of questions look like.

Classification Questions

Classification questions are basically reverse-multiple-choice questions. They consist of five answer choices followed by a string of three to five questions. To make things more confusing, the answer choices may be used once, more than once, or not at all—so although a classification question often looks like simple matching, it isn't!

The level of difficulty in any one set of classification questions is generally pretty random: you can't expect the first question in a set to be easier than the last. However, in the test as a whole, each set of classification questions is generally a bit harder than the one that came before.

Familiarize yourself with the following set of directions—if you read and understand them now, you won't waste precious time on test day.

<u>Directions:</u> Each set of lettered choices below refers to the numbered questions or statements immediately following it. Select the one lettered choice that best answers each question or best fits each statement and then fill in the corresponding oval on the answer sheet. A choice may be used once, more than once, or not at all in each set.

<u>Questions 1–3</u>

(A) Zinc
(B) Iron
(C) Helium
(D) Copper
(E) Fluorine

1. A highly electronegative element

2. Forms colored solutions when dissolved in water

3. Normally exists as a diatomic molecule but can react to form a 2⁻ ion

You can usually answer classification questions a bit more quickly than the standard five-choice completion questions since you need to review only one set of answer choices to answer a series of questions. The answer to number 1 is **E**. Electronegativity is a measure of the ability of an atom in a chemical bond to attract electrons to itself; in chapter 4 you'll learn how to use your periodic table to answer questions like this one. The answer to number 2 is **D**, copper. Copper often forms green/blue solutions. The answer to number 3 is **A**, zinc. Also in chapter 4, you'll learn to predict what ions certain elements will form and in what state they are normally found in nature. Don't worry if you don't know the answers to these questions right now. This example is meant mainly to show you how a classification question is formatted.

Relationship-Analysis Questions

Relationship-analysis questions consist of a specific statement, statement I, followed by another statement, statement II. To answer these questions, you must determine first whether statement I is true or false and then whether statement II is true or false. Next you must decide whether the second statement is the reason for the first statement being true. These questions may appear intimidating to you since they're probably unfamiliar, but after taking the practice exams in this book, you should feel as comfortable with them as you do with the other question types.

One more thing about this question type: strangely enough, on the SAT II Chemistry test, the section containing relationship-analysis questions is always numbered starting with 101. There will be one section of these on each of the tests, and they also get their own special section on your answer sheet—also beginning with number 101. There are usually about 16 or 17 questions of this type on the SAT II Chemistry exam. Again, take the time to familiarize yourself with these directions so you won't have to even look at them on test day.

<u>Directions:</u> Each question below consists of two statements, statement I in the left-hand column and statement II in the right-hand column. For each question, determine whether statement I is true or false <u>and</u> whether statement II is true or false and fill in the corresponding T or F ovals on your answer sheet. <u>Fill in oval CE only if statement II is a correct explanation of statement I.</u>

I		II
101. A 1.0 M solution of HCl has a low pH.	BECAUSE	HCl contains chlorine.
102. An atom of chlorine is smaller than an atom of sulfur.	BECAUSE	Chlorine has a greater effective nuclear charge than sulfur.

Look at question 101. Statement I is true: HCl is an acid, which is a substance that's capable of donating H^+ ions in solution. Acids have a pH that's lower than 7, while bases have a pH above 7. Statement II is also true: HCl is made up of a hydrogen atom and a chlorine atom. Now do the final step—is the pH of HCl directly related to the concentration of the chlorine ions in solution? No, it is directly related to the number of H^+ ions given off by HCl in solution—you would not fill in the bubble marked **CE** (correct explanation).

Now the answer to question 102. Statement I is true. Statement II is true. As you'll learn in "The Structure of Matter," atomic radius decreases from left to right across the periodic table because the more protons in the nucleus of the atom, the more tightly and more closely held are the atom's electrons. This is an example of another way you can use the periodic table while taking the test. If you understand periodic trends, you won't have to memorize the atomic radii of all of the elements. The **CE**, for "correct explanation," should be bubbled in.

Five-Choice Completion Questions

These are the multiple-choice questions we all know and love, and which are the lifeblood of any multiple-choice exam. You know the drill: they ask a question and give you five possible answer choices, and you pick the best one. This will be the third and final part of the exam.

Here are the directions you'll see on the exam:

Directions: Each of the questions or incomplete statements below is followed by five suggested answers or completions. For each question, select the one choice that is the best answer to the question and then fill in the corresponding oval on the answer sheet.

24. Which of the following molecules does not match its geometric shape?

(A) BF_3 trigonal planar
(B) $CHCl_3$ tetrahedral
(C) H_2O V shape (bent)
(D) CO_2 linear
(E) PCl_3 trigonal planar

The answer is **E**—the shape of this compound is irregular tetrahedron (also known as trigonal pyramid). You'll learn rules for predicting molecular structures in chapter 4. Now, the above question is a straightforward multiple choice, but there's another type of five-choice completion question on the test, and it looks like the question below:

25. Which of the following statements correctly describe the information necessary for finding the concentration of an unknown monoprotic acid by titration with KOH?

    I.   The concentration of the base
    II.   The total starting volume of acid
    III.   The volume of the base used to reach the equivalence point

(A)   I only
(B)   II only
(C)   I and II only
(D)   I and III only
(E)   I, II, and III

Let's analyze it. To find the concentration of the unknown acid, you'll need to know the molarity of the base used in the titration or, put in simpler language, the moles of base per liter of solution. So, statement I is necessary. We'll also need the information in statements II and III, as you'll learn in "Laboratory." The correct answer is **E**.

While knowing your chemistry inside and out is the best way to ensure that you'll do well on this test, it will also help you on test day if you've developed a strategy that enables you to answer all the questions that test you on chemistry you feel confident about and to guess intelligently on the questions on areas in which you feel less confident. We will talk about some strategies for how to deal with these harder questions in the next chapter.

Introduction

Scoring the SAT II Chemistry

Scoring on the SAT II Chemistry is the same as scoring for all other SAT II tests. For every right answer, you earn one point. For every wrong answer, you lose $1/4$ of a point. For each question you leave blank, you earn zero points. These points combined equal your raw score. ETS converts your raw score to a scaled score using a curve tailored to the particular test you take. We've included a raw-to-scaled conversion chart below so you can translate your raw score on a practice test into scaled scores.

Raw Score	Scaled Score	Raw Score	Scaled Score	Raw Score	Scaled Score
80	800	49	600	18	420
79	800	48	590	17	410
78	790	47	590	16	410
77	780	46	580	15	400
76	770	45	580	14	390
75	770	44	570	13	390
74	760	43	560	12	380
73	760	42	560	11	370
72	750	41	550	10	360
71	740	40	550	9	360
70	740	39	540	8	350
69	730	38	540	7	350
68	730	37	530	6	340
67	720	36	520	5	340
66	710	35	520	4	330
65	700	34	510	3	330
64	700	33	500	2	320
63	690	32	500	1	320
62	680	31	490	0	310
61	680	30	490	−1	310
60	670	29	480	−2	300
59	660	28	480	−3	300
58	660	27	470	−4	290
57	650	26	470	−5	280
56	640	25	460	−6	280
55	640	24	450	−7	270

54	630	23	450	−8	270
53	620	22	440	−9	260
52	620	21	440	−10	260
51	610	20	430		
50	600	19	420		

This chart shows you that your score doesn't plummet with every question you can't answer confidently. You can do very well on this test without knowing or answering everything. The key to doing well on the SAT II Chemistry is to follow a strategy that ensures you will see and answer all the questions you can answer, while intelligently guessing on those slightly fuzzier questions.

For example, on an 80 question test, you could score:

- 800 if you answered 79 right and left 1 blank
- 750 if you answered 73 right, 4 wrong, and left 3 blank
- 700 if you answered 67 right, 8 wrong, and left 5 blank
- 650 if you answered 60 right, 12 wrong, and left 8 blank
- 600 if you answered 54 right, 16 wrong, and left 10 blank

We'll talk more about these strategies in the next chapter.

Strategies for Taking the SAT II Chemistry Test

Chapter Contents

A machine, not a person, will score your SAT II test. The tabulating machine sees only the filled-in ovals on your answer sheet and doesn't care how you came to those answers—it cares only whether your answers are correct. A lucky guess counts in your favor just as much as an answer you give confidently. By the same token, if you accidentally fill in (B) where you meant (C), you won't get any credit for having known what the answer was. Think of the multiple-choice test as a message to you from the ETS: "We score your answers, and not any of the work behind them." So give them right answers—as many as possible, using whatever means possible.

We'll start by discussing some general principles for test taking that you can use for this test as well as any other test you take, then we'll move on to strategies that apply directly to the SAT II Chemistry test.

The Strategies

Most of these "strategies" are common sense, and many of them you already know. The funny thing about high-pressure situations, though, is that common sense often goes out the window. If you review anything in the minutes before taking the test, review these strategies. Of course, that doesn't mean you should skip this section now. It's full of very useful hints, some of which might be new to you.

General Hint 1: Be Calm

The best way to do poorly on a test is to psych yourself out. If your mind starts thrashing about wildly, it will have a hard time settling on the right answers. There are a number of preventative measures you can take, beginning weeks or even months before you take the test. Buying this book was a good start: It's reassuring to see all the information you'll need to ace the test in a compact, manageable form. But there are a number of other things you ought to keep in mind:

- **Study in advance.** If you've studied at regular intervals leading up to the test rather than cramming the night before, the information will sit more easily in your mind.
- **Be well rested.** Get a good night's sleep on the two nights leading up to the test. If you're frazzled or wired, you're going to have a harder time buckling down and concentrating when it really counts.
- **Come up for air.** Don't assume that the best way to take an hour-long test is to spend the full hour nose to nose with the test questions. If it feels natural for you to take breathers, don't be afraid to do so. Lift your head occasionally, look about you, and take a deep breath—you may return to the test with a clearer mind.

General Hint 2: Grid Your Answers Carefully

No kidding. People make mistakes while entering their answers onto the grid and it can cost them big-time. This slipup occurs most frequently if you skip a question. If you left question 43 blank and then unthinkingly put the answer to question 44 into row 43, you could be starting a long, painful chain of wrong answers. Don't do it.

You can avoid this by filling in your answer sheet five questions at a time rather than one at a time, but if you feel that's too complicated, just be careful to check the number of the answer sheet against the question number each time.

General Hint 3: Pace Yourself

At the very least, aim to *look* at every question on the test. You can't afford to lose points because you didn't even get to a question you could have easily answered correctly. While you can spend an average of 42 seconds on each question, you'll probably breeze through some in 10 seconds and dwell on others for two minutes. Knowing how to pace yourself is a critical skill:

- **Don't dwell on any one question for too long.** If you've spent a couple of minutes laboring over the question, you might just want to circle it and move on. If you feel the answer is on the tip of your tongue, it might come more easily if you revisit it later. Not only is it demoralizing to spend five minutes on a single question, it also eats up precious time in which you might have answered a number of easier questions.

- **Nail the easy questions.** As we said in the previous chapter, the questions will generally get progressively harder as you go through the test. Nonetheless, some tough ones will be thrown in right at the start, and hopefully you'll be finding ones that seem like a cinch right up until the end. Remember: you get as many points for correctly answering an easy question as a difficult one.

- **Skip the unfamiliar.** If you encounter a question you can't make heads or tails of, just circle it and move on. Don't work too hard trying to sort out what's going on. If you have time at the end, you can come back to it and see if you can make an educated guess. Your first priority should be to get all the easy questions, and your second priority should be to get through the questions you can solve with some work. Unfamiliar material should be at the bottom of your list of priorities.

General Hint 4: Set a Target Score

You can make the job of pacing yourself much easier if you go into the test knowing how many questions you have to answer correctly to earn the score you want. What score do you want to get? Ideally, your answer should be an 800, but be realistic: Consider how much you know about chemistry and how well you generally do on these types of tests. You should also do a little research—talk to the admissions offices of the colleges you might want to attend, look in college guidebooks, or talk to your guidance counselor. Find out the average score of a student admitted to the schools of your choice, and set your target score above it. Then take a look at the chart we showed you before. You can score

- 800 if you answered 80 right and left 5 blank
- 750 if you answered 75 right, 4 wrong, and left 6 blank
- 700 if you answered 62 right, 8 wrong, and left 15 blank
- 650 if you answered 56 right, 20 wrong, and left 9 blank
- 600 if you answered 48 right, 24 wrong, and left 13 blank

Suppose the average score on the SAT II Chemistry test for the school you're interested in is 650. Set your target at about 700. To get that score, you need to get 62 questions right, while giving yourself room to get eight wrong and leave 15 blank. As long as you have some idea of how many questions you need to answer, bearing in mind that you'll proba-bly get some questions wrong, you can pace yourself accordingly. Taking practice tests is the best way to work on your pacing. See how many questions you can leave blank and still get the score you want, and you'll have a better sense of what to aim at on the big day.

If you find yourself effortlessly hitting your target score when you take the practice tests, don't just pat yourself on the back. Set a higher target score and start gunning for that one. The purpose of buying this book and studying for the test is to improve your score as much as possible, so be sure to push your limits.

General Hint 5: Know What You're Being Asked

You can't know the answer until you know the question. This might sound painfully obvi-ous, but many a point has been lost by the careless student who seizes an answer choice hastily before properly understanding the question. Take the following example:

Three cylinders labeled A, B, C, are all at the same temperature. The volumes of the containers are 2.0 L, 4.0 L, and 6.0 L, respectively. Cylinder A contains 0.679 grams of neon gas at a pressure of 120 mmHg, cylinder B contains 2.45 grams of nitrogen gas at a pressure of 210 mmHg, and cylinder C is completely empty at the start. If the contents of A and B were completely transferred to C (assuming ideal conditions), what would the pressure become in cylinder C?

(A)   0.25 atm
(B)   180 mmHg
(C)   330 mmHg
(D)   675 mmHg
(E)   1980 mmHg

This is a fairly difficult question, but perhaps more importantly, the question is long and complicated looking. By the time the hasty student finishes reading it, he or she might have forgotten the beginning of the question and decided to simply add the pressures together and choose an incorrect answer, **C**.

To avoid situations like this, take a moment to truly *understand* the question before answering it. Read the question and then vocalize to yourself what the question is asking and what the pertinent information they give you is. Then go ahead and answer the ques-tion or solve the problem before you even look at the answer choices. This will help ensure that you aren't seduced by any of the incorrect answer choices listed. By the way, the cor-rect answer to this question is **B**.

General Hint 6: Know How to Guess

ETS doesn't take off $\frac{1}{4}$ of a point for each wrong answer to punish you for guessing—they do it so you won't get a reward for guessing blindly. Suppose that without even glancing at any of the questions, you just randomly entered responses in the first 20 spaces on your answer sheet. Because you have a 20% chance of guessing correctly on any given question, odds are you would guess right for four questions and wrong for 16 questions. Your raw score for those 20 questions would then be

$$(4 \times 1) - (16 \times \frac{1}{4}) = 0$$

As you can see, you'd be no better or worse off blindly guessing than if you'd left those 20 spaces blank.

Now suppose that in each of the first 20 questions you are able to eliminate just one possible answer choice, so that you guess with a 25% chance of being right. Odds are, you'd get five questions right and 15 questions wrong, giving you a raw score of

$$(5 \times 1) - (15 \times \frac{1}{4}) = 1.25$$

All of a sudden, you're over a point up. It isn't much, but every little bit helps. Here's a list of your priorities when you come to each question on this test.

First priority:	Answer the question correctly.
Second priority:	If you don't know the answer, try to eliminate answer choices and then guess.
Third priority:	If you can't eliminate any answer choices, circle the question and move on to the next one. You might have time to come back to it when you've finished the other questions.

The lesson to be learned here is that blind guessing doesn't help, but educated guessing does. If you can eliminate even one of the five possible answer choices, *you must guess.* We'll discuss how to eliminate answer choices on certain special kinds of questions in Chemistry Hint 5.

Guessing as Partial Credit

Some students feel that guessing is similar to cheating—that guessing correctly means getting credit where none is due. But instead of looking at guessing as an attempt to gain undeserved points, you should see it as a form of partial credit. For example, suppose you're stumped on the question above that asks about total pressure after different gases are mixed into a new container. And suppose you're pretty sure that the answer isn't simply adding the pressures given, even though you know Dalton's law of partial pressures. You do know many gas laws but are a little unsure as to how to answer this question. You do know that the pressure will be less or at least close to the other two pressures because you have some knowledge of Boyle's law. Don't you deserve something for that extra knowledge? Well, you do get something: when you look at this question, you can throw out answer choices **C** and **E**, which leaves you with a one-in-three chance of getting the question right if you guess. Your extra knowledge gives you better odds of getting this question right, exactly as extra knowledge should.

SAT II Chemistry Test-Taking Strategies

All the strategies discussed above can be applied equally to the SAT II Chemistry test and the SAT II Modern Hebrew test. That's why they're called "general hints." However, as you may have noticed in the past, there are a number of dissimilarities between the study of chemistry and the study of modern Hebrew. And because chemistry is unlike modern Hebrew, and even unlike English and biology, a number of strategies apply uniquely to the SAT II Chemistry exam. Some of these strategies will help you out in chemistry generally, while some are suited to the unique idiosyncrasies of the SAT II format.

Chemistry Hint 1: Know Those Formulas!

As you know, you aren't allowed to bring a calculator into the SAT II test, nor are you allowed to bring in a sheet of paper with useful information on it. That means that if you haven't memorized formulas like Boyle's law and the ideal gas equation, you're going to lose points.

This doesn't mean you have to do a lot of rote memorization. In fact, it's more important to truly understand the principles of chemistry than it is for you to memorize equations. You'll find that as the principles of chemistry become second nature to you, the equations that express these principles will become increasingly intuitive. Knowing your chemistry will help guide you to the right conclusions.

A lot of people feel burdened coming into an exam with lots of formulas and equations in their head. It's like your mind is "full," and there's no room for the problem solving at hand. If you have trouble remembering formulas, you might want to look them over carefully in the minutes before the test and then, before you even look at the first question, write down the formulas you have a hard time remembering on the back of the question booklet. That way you can refer back to them without any painful effort of recollection.

Chemistry Hint 2: Estimate

This hint goes hand in hand with one of the general hints above: Know What You're Being Asked. Don't dive blindly into five possible answer choices until you've already taken your best stab at coming up with the answer yourself. Obviously, estimation is only useful in questions involving calculation: you can't "estimate" which law of thermodynamics states that the world tends toward increasing disorder. In questions involving a calculation, though, it may save you from foolish errors if you, for example, have a sense of the order of magnitude you're looking at. If you're being asked to calculate the pH of a slightly acidic solution, you can be pretty confident that the answer won't be pH = 0.50, which would be too small, or pH = 14.00, which would be too big. You know that the correct answer must lie somewhere between 2 and 6. Estimation is a good way to eliminate some wrong answers when you're making an educated guess.

Chemistry Hint 3: Put It on Paper

Don't be afraid to write and draw compulsively. The first thing you should do once you've made sure you understand the question is to make your own notes about what you're dealing with. Sketch molecules when dealing with a bonding question, or electron configurations for periodic trend questions, or whatever else may be appropriate. Not only will a visual representation relieve some of the pressure on your beleaguered mind, it may also help the solution jump right off the page at you.

Don't forget to write down important information! Writing down all of the information may lead you to a correct answer even if you don't really understand the question. Suppose the question asks for the volume of a gas produced in a certain reaction. Write a balanced equation, plug in values, fiddle around a little, and see if you can come up with an answer that looks right. Chances are, it will be.

Chemistry Hint 4: Answers Are Not Convoluted

Remember, on the SAT II Chemistry test you're not allowed to use a calculator, and you're only given, on average, 42 seconds to answer each question. If you're working on a problem and you find yourself writing out lines and lines of conversions as you try to figure out the answer, you're probably not on the right track. These questions are designed in such a way that if you understand what you're being asked, you will need at most a couple of simple calculations to get the right answer.

Chemistry Hint 5: Eliminate Wrong Answers

In the general hints above, Know How to Guess, we explained the virtues of eliminating answers you know to be wrong and taking a guess. For most questions, there will be at least one or two answer choices you can eliminate. There are also certain styles of question that lend themselves to particular process-of-elimination methods.

Classification Questions

The weakness of classification questions is that the same five answer choices apply to several questions. Invariably, some of these answer choices will be tempting for some questions but not for others.

Questions 1–3 relate to the following molecules:

(A)   Sugar
(B)   Ammonia
(C)   Hydrochloric acid
(D)   Carbon dioxide
(E)   Acetic acid

1.   An organic solid with a low melting point

2.   Acts as a weak base when bubbled into pure water

3.   Would be the best choice of the above to neutralize excess NaOH

For instance, if you're pretty sure that ammonia, hydrochloric acid, and acetic acid are not organic solids, just from your general knowledge of chemistry, then you can eliminate **B**, **C**, and **E**. This helps you narrow the answer choices down to two, and if you have to guess, you have a 50-50 chance of choosing the correct answer.

Another point that may help you guess in a pinch is that you'll rarely find the same answer choice being correct for two different questions. True, the directions for classification questions explicitly state that an answer choice "may be used once, more than once, or not at all," but on the whole, the ETS people shy away from the "more than once" possibility. This is by no means a sure bet, but if you're trying to eliminate answers, you might want to eliminate those choices that you've already used on other questions in the same set.

If you're wondering, the answers to the above questions are 1 **A**, 2 **B**, and 3 **C**.

"EXCEPT"-Type Questions

"EXCEPT" questions are five-choice multiple-choice questions that contain a bunch of right answers and one wrong answer. The questions always contain an all-caps EXCEPT, LEAST, or some other similar word. Even if you aren't sure of the answer, you should be able to identify one or two of the answer choices as being true statements and eliminate them.

Most compounds containing primarily ionic bonds are characterized by all of the following EXCEPT:

(A)   High melting points
(B)   Exist mainly in the gaseous state of matter
(C)   An attraction between positive and negative ions
(D)   Usually composed of a metal and nonmetal or polyatomic ion
(E)   Most dissolve readily in water

Perhaps you're not sure which of the five answer choices is wrong. But you should be able to identify that choice **C** or **D** might be correct because of the word *ion* in the statement. See, you've already eliminated two possible answers and can make a pretty good guess from there.

If you're interested, the answer is **B**: ionic compounds usually exist as crystalline solids, not gases, at room temperature.

"I, II, and III" Questions

As we discussed earlier, I, II, and III questions are multiple-choice questions that provide you with three possible answers, and the five answer choices list different combinations of those three.

A student performed an experiment to determine the heat of neutralization of a strong acid with a strong base. Which of the following statements are true of this type of experiment?

        I.   The reaction is exothermic.
        II.   Energy for this reaction cannot be directly measured.
        III.   The specific heat must be calculated for the acid.

(A)   I only
(B)   II only
(C)   I and II only
(D)   II and III only
(E)   I, II, and III

There's an upside and a downside to questions of this type. Suppose, for example, that you know that in experiments involving heat of neutralization for acids and bases, you need to know the specific heat—and you suspect that you need the specific heat for the acid. This means that you can eliminate **A, B**, and **C** and significantly increase your chance of guessing the right answer. As long as you're not afraid to guess—and remember that you should never be afraid to guess if you've eliminated an answer—these questions shouldn't be too daunting. By the way, the answer is **E**.

Strategies

The Structure
of Matter

F or this subject review, we'll start where you would usually start in a chemistry class: with a study of the atom and atomic theory.

Atomic Structure—What We Know Today

Elements and Atoms

An **atom** is the smallest particle of an element that retains the chemical properties of that element, and an **element** is defined as a substance that can't be broken down or separated into simpler substances through a chemical reaction. Elements contain just one type of atom, and each different element contains a different type of atom. Take the element sulfur (S). A pile of sulfur (a yellow, powdery or crystallized substance) sitting on a table represents a single element—sulfur—and this pile of sulfur is made up of only one type of atom—sulfur atoms.

Each atom, regardless of its identity, is made up of three types of subatomic particles. **Protons**, which are positively charged and situated at the center of the atom (also known as the atomic **nucleus**); **neutrons**, which are electrically neutral (meaning that they have no charge) and are also in the nucleus of the atom; and **electrons**, which are negatively charged and are situated outside the nucleus. The majority of the mass of an atom is contained in its nucleus: while electrons are about the same size as protons and neutrons, an electron has 1/837th the mass of protons or neutrons. You should also be aware that the nucleus of an atom is much, much smaller and more dense than the space occupied by an atom's electrons—if an atom were the size of a football field, the nucleus would be the size of a flea on the 50-yard line!

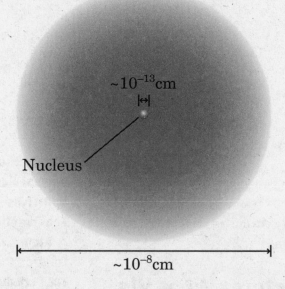

$\sim 10^{-13}$cm

Nucleus

$\sim 10^{-8}$cm

The number of protons an atom possesses is what gives the atom its identity—all atoms of a particular element have the same number of protons in their nuclei. For example, all of the sulfur atoms in the pile of sulfur we looked at above have 16 protons in their nucleus. If they had one more proton in their nucleus, they would have a different identity—they'd be chlorine (Cl) atoms, and with one less, they'd be phosphorus (P) atoms.

Atoms of a given element can, however, differ in the number of neutrons they contain, and atoms of the same element that have different numbers of neutrons are known as **isotopes**. Most elements have at least two isotopes that occur naturally, although a few have just one. Now take a look at how atoms are usually symbolized:

Mass number (Z) =
protons + neutrons

$^{12}_{6}$C ← Element symbol

Atomic number
(A) = protons only

This represents a carbon atom that has 6 protons and 6 neutrons. In this notation, the **atomic number (A)**, which is the number of protons the atom contains, is indicated by the subscript, and the **mass number (Z)**, which is the number of the atom's protons plus the

Example • 29

number of its neutrons, is indicated by the superscript. Some relatively common isotopes of carbon can contain 5, 7, or 8 neutrons, so although their atomic numbers would all be 6, their mass numbers, respectively, would be 11 (6 + 5), 13 (6 + 7), and 14 (6 + 8). Isotopes can also be written as carbon-14, carbon-15, carbon-16, etc., or C-14, C-15, C-16, where the number represents the mass number of the atom.

The last thing you should know about the basic structure of an atom is that atoms have the same number of protons and electrons, and since protons are positively charged and electrons are negatively charged, *neutral atoms have no net electrical charge.*

Example

The atomic number of a certain element is 11, and its atomic mass number is 23. How many protons and neutrons does this atom have, and what is its chemical symbol?

Explanation

If the atomic number is 11, this element is sodium and its symbol is Na. If the atomic mass number is 23, the number of neutrons is equal to 23 − 11 = 12.

Atoms and the Periodic Table

The day of the SAT II Chemistry exam, you will be given a periodic table to use while answering the questions. However, this periodic table will most likely be much simpler than the ones you use in class or have seen in your chemistry text. It will give you only two pieces of information for each element: the element's atomic number and the element's atomic weight, which is written below the element's symbol in each box. The **atomic weight** of an element represents its average atomic mass based on the relative abundance of various isotopes of that element in nature. So, when we say that the atomic weight of carbon is 12.0107, we mean that the average weights of all of the isotopes of carbon that exist in nature, whether the carbon is carbon-11, -12, -13, or -14, is 12.0107.

But what does it mean to say that the isotopes "weigh" 12.0107? 12.0107 what? Certainly not grams, or the isotopes would be a lot bigger than they are. Atomic weights have the unit amu, or **atomic mass unit**, and one atomic mass unit is equal to 1.66054×10^{-24} g.

Nuclear Reactions

All of the processes discussed in this section are examples of *nuclear* reactions, which are different from ordinary chemical reactions. Ordinary chemical reactions involve the exchange and sharing of electrons, while nuclear reactions involve alterations in the very core of an atom; that dense nucleus made up of protons and neutrons.

Structure of Matter

Radioactivity

You will need to be familiar with several types of nuclear reactions and terms related to them to be fully prepared for the SAT II Chemistry test, and in this section we'll review everything you'll need to know. The first concept we discuss is radioactivity. Strictly speaking, **radioactivity** is the spontaneous disintegration of an unstable atomic nucleus and the subsequent emission of radiation. But what makes atoms radioactive to begin with, and what makes them undergo radioactive decay? It turns out that there is a stable ratio of protons to neutrons for each element; for the first 20 elements on the periodic table (hydrogen through calcium), this ratio is 1 proton to 1 neutron, for example. Protons and neutrons in excess of this stable number can be emitted radioactively. Below we have listed examples of the important types of radioactive decay.

Alpha decay occurs when the nucleus emits an alpha particle. Alpha particles have a positive charge and are equivalent in size to a helium nucleus, and so they are symbolized as $_2^4He$. Alpha particles are the largest radioactive particle emitted. This type of radioactivity results in a decrease in the atomic number by 2 and a decrease in the atomic mass by 4. The equation below shows uranium-234 undergoing alpha decay:

$$_{92}^{234}U \rightarrow {}_2^4He + {}_{90}^{230}Th$$

Beta decay occurs when the nucleus emits a beta particle. Beta particles have a negative charge and are much smaller than alpha particles. They're equivalent to high-speed electrons and are symbolized by $_{-1}^0\beta$ or $_{-1}^0e$. This type of radioactivity causes an increase in the atomic number by 1 but no change in mass number. The equation below represents uranium-233 undergoing beta decay.

$$_{92}^{233}U \rightarrow {}_{-1}^0\beta + {}_{93}^{233}Np$$

How does a nucleus, which is composed of only protons and neutrons, eject an electron? A neutron is composed of a proton and an electron fused together. In beta emission, the electron is emitted from the nucleus, while the proton part remains behind, thus increasing the atomic number by 1.

Example

Complete the balanced equation by determining the missing term.

$$_{33}^{80}As \rightarrow {}_{-1}^0\beta + ?$$

Explanation

Remember, the sum of the atomic numbers and the mass numbers must be equal on both sides of the equation. We are looking for a component that has mass number of 80 and an atomic number of 34 (34 protons). Using this information and the periodic table, we can

Example • 31

identity the element produced by this beta decay as Se, or selenium. The missing term is $^{80}_{34}$Se. And the completed equation is:

$$^{80}_{33}\text{As} \rightarrow {}^{0}_{-1}\beta + {}^{80}_{34}\text{Se}$$

Gamma decay consists of the emission of pure electromagnetic energy; no particles are emitted during this process, and it is symbolized by equation; $^{0}_{0}\gamma$. After beta, positron, or alpha decay, the nucleus is left in a high-energy state, and at this point it will often emit gamma rays, which allows it to relax to its lower-energy ground state. Since gamma rays do not affect charge or mass, they are often not included in nuclear equations.

 Positron emission occurs when an atom becomes more stable by emitting a **positron** $^{0}_{1}e$, which is the same size and mass as an electron but has a positive charge. This process converts a proton into a neutron; the positron is emitted and the neutron remains behind in the nucleus, decreasing the atomic number by 1.

$$p \rightarrow {}^{1}_{-0}n + {}^{0}_{1}e$$

Often the emission of an alpha or a beta particle creates another radioactive species, which undergoes further radiation/emission in a cascade called a **radioactive series**. Notice that in the course of all of these types of radioactive decay, neither protons nor neutrons are either created or destroyed: this is due to what's known as the **law of conservation of matter**, which states that mass is neither created nor destroyed. So when you see radioactivity equations on the SAT II Chemistry test, one of the most important things to remember is that the sum of the mass numbers and the sum of the atomic numbers must both be equal on both sides of the equation.

Example

Write the equation for the alpha decay of radium-221. Write the equation for the beta decay of sulfur-35.

Explanation

The radium-221 atom has atomic number (A) = 88 and mass number (Z) = 221. When an alpha particle is emitted, the atomic number is reduced by 2 and the mass number is reduced by 4. The atomic number of the resulting atom is 86, so the element created as a result of this radioactive decay is radon-217.

$$^{221}_{88}\text{Ra} \rightarrow {}^{4}_{2}\alpha + {}^{217}_{86}\text{Rn}$$

The sulfur-35 atom has an atomic number of 16 and a mass number of 35. When it undergoes beta decay, the atomic number is increased by 1 and the mass number remains the same. The atomic number of the atom created is 17, so the atom is chlorine-35.

$$^{35}_{16}\text{S} \rightarrow {}^{0}_{-1}e + {}^{35}_{17}\text{Cl}$$

Fission and Fusion

There are two main types of nuclear reactions: fusion and fission. In **fusion** reactions, two light nuclei are combined to form a heavier, more stable nucleus. In **fission** reactions, a heavy nucleus is split into two nuclei with smaller mass numbers. Both processes involve the exchange of huge amounts of energy: about a million times more energy than that associated with ordinary chemical reactions. In either case, if the new particles contain more stable nuclei, vast quantities of energy are released.

Nuclear power plants rely on fission to create vast quantities of energy. For example, U-235 nuclides can be bombarded with neutrons, and the result is *lots* of energy, three neutrons, and two stable nuclei (Kr-92 and Ba-141). The three neutrons formed can collide with other U-235 atoms, setting off a chain reaction and releasing tons of energy.

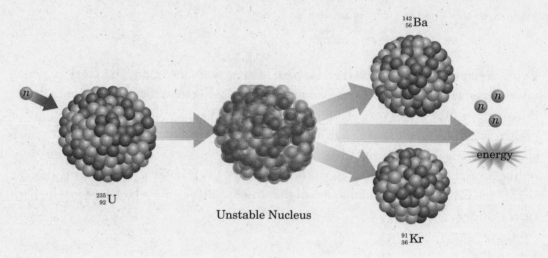

Example

Is the following process an example of fission or fusion?

$$^{235}_{92}U + {}^{1}_{0}n \rightarrow {}^{146}_{57}La + {}^{87}_{35}Ba + 3{}^{1}_{0}n$$

Explanation

This is an example of fission. Fission occurs when a large nucleus is bombarded by a small particle, such as a neutron. The result is two smaller nuclei and additional neutrons, and a chain reaction process begins.

Half-Lives

In discussions of radioactivity, the *half-life* of an isotope refers to the time it takes for one-half of the sample to decay. If we start with 100 g of a radioactive substance whose half-life

Example • 33

is 15 days, after 15 days 50 g of the substance will remain. After 3Q days, 25 g will remain, and after 45 days, 12.5 g remains, and so on.

Example

A radioactive substance has a half-life of 20 minutes. If we begin with a 500 g sample, how much of the original sample remains after two hours?

Explanation

The easiest way to attack these questions is to start with the original amount of the sample, then draw arrows representing each half-life. Two hours is 120 minutes, so that's six half-lives. At the end of the stated time period, 7.8 g remains.

$$500 \text{ g} \rightarrow 250 \text{ g} \rightarrow 125 \text{ g} \rightarrow 62.5 \text{ g} \rightarrow 31.25 \text{ g} \rightarrow 15.625 \text{ g} \rightarrow 7.8125 \text{ g}$$

The Quantum Mechanical Model of the Atom

Energy Is Quantized

After Max Planck determined that energy is released and absorbed by atoms in certain fixed amounts known as **quanta**, Albert Einstein took his work a step further, determining that radiant energy is also quantized—he called the discrete energy packets **photons**. Einstein's theory was that electromagnetic radiation (light, for example) has characteristics of both a wave and a stream of particles.

Light as:

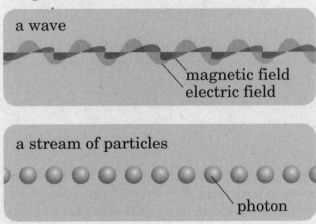

a wave

magnetic field
electric field

a stream of particles

photon

The Bohr Model of the Atom

In 1913, Niels Bohr used what had recently been discovered about energy to propose his planetary model of the atom. In the Bohr model, the neutrons and protons are contained in a small, dense nucleus, which the electrons orbit in defined spherical orbits. He referred to these orbits as "shells" or "energy levels" and designated each by an integer: 1, 2, 3, etc. An electron occupying the first energy level was thought to be closer to the nucleus and have lower energy than one that was in a numerically higher energy level. Bohr theorized that energy in the form of photons must be absorbed in order for an electron to move from a lower energy level to a higher one, and is emitted when an electron travels from a higher energy level to a lower one. In the Bohr model, the lowest energy state available for an electron is the **ground state**, and all higher-energy states are **excited states**.

Orbitals and Quantum Numbers

In the 1920s, Werner Heisenberg put forth his **uncertainty principle**, which states that, at any one time, it is impossible to calculate both the momentum and the location of an electron in an atom; it is only possible to calculate the **probability** of finding an electron within a given space. This meant that electrons, instead of traveling in defined orbits or hard, spherical "shells," as Bohr proposed, travel in diffuse clouds around the nucleus.

When we say "orbital," the image below is what we picture in our minds.

To describe the location of electrons, we use **quantum numbers**. Quantum numbers are basically used to describe certain aspects of the locations of electrons. For example, the quantum numbers n, l, and m_l describe the position of the electron with respect to the nucleus, the shape of the orbital, and its special orientation, while the quantum number m_s describes the direction of the electron's spin within a given orbital.

Below are the four quantum numbers, showing how they are depicted and what aspects of electrons they describe.

Principal quantum number (n)	Has positive values of 1, 2, 3, etc. As n increases, the orbital becomes larger—this means that the electron has a higher energy level and is less tightly bound to the nucleus.
Second quantum number or azimuthal quantum number (l)	Has values from 0 to $n - 1$. This defines the shape of the orbital, and the value of l is designated by the letters s, p, d, and f, which correspond to values for l of 0, 1, 2, and 3. In other words, if the value of l is 0, it is expressed as s; if $l = 1 = p$, $l = 2 = d$, and $l = 3 = f$.
Magnetic quantum number (m_l)	Determines the orientation of the orbital in space relative to the other orbitals in the atom. This quantum number has values from $-l$ through 0 to $+l$.
Spin quantum number (m_s)	Specifies the value for the spin and is either +1/2 or −1/2. No more than two electrons can occupy any one orbital. In order for two electrons to occupy the same orbital, they must have opposite spins.

Orbitals that have the same principal quantum number, n, are part of the same **electron shell**. For example, orbitals that have $n = 2$ are said to be in the second shell. When orbitals have the same n and l, they are in the same **subshell**; so orbitals that have $n = 2$ and $l = 3$ are said to be $2f$ orbitals, in the $2f$ subshell.

Finally, you should keep in mind that according to the **Pauli exclusion principle**, *no two electrons in an atom can have the same set of four quantum numbers*. This means no atomic orbital can contain more than *two* electrons, and if the orbital does contain two electrons, they must be of opposite spin.

Electron Configurations

Now let's discuss how to determine the electron configuration for an atom—in other words, how electrons are arranged in an atom. The first and most important rule to remember when attempting to determine how electrons will be arranged in the atom is **Hund's rule**, which states that the most stable arrangement of electrons is that which allows the maximum number of unpaired electrons. This arrangement minimizes electron-electron repulsions. Here's an analogy. In large families with several children, it is a luxury for each child to have his or her own room. There is far less fussing and fighting if siblings are not forced to share living quarters: the entire household experiences a lower-intensity, less-frazzled energy state. Likewise, electrons will go into available orbitals singly before beginning to pair up. All the single–occupant electrons of orbitals have parallel spins, are designated with an upward-pointing arrow, and have a magnetic spin quantum number of +1/2.

As we mentioned earlier, each principal energy level, n, has n sublevels. This means the first has one sublevel, the second has two, the third has three, etc. The sublevels are named s, p, d, and f.

Energy level principal quantum number, n	Number of sublevels	Names of sublevels
1	1	s
2	2	s, p
3	3	s, p, d
4	4	s, p, d, f

At each additional sublevel, the number of available orbitals is increased by two: $s = 1$, $p = 3$, $d = 5$, $f = 7$, and as we stated above, each orbital can hold only two electrons, which must be of opposite spin. So s holds 2, p holds 6 (2 electrons times the number of orbitals, which for the p sublevel is equal to 3), d holds 10, and f holds 14.

Sublevel	s	p	d	f
Number of orbitals	1	3	5	7
Maximum number of electrons	2	6	10	14
Quantum number, l	0	1	2	3

We can use the periodic table to make this task easier.

Example • 37

Notice there are only two elements in the first **period** (the first row of the periodic table); their electrons are in the first principal energy level: $n = 1$. The second period (row) contains a total of eight elements, which all have two sublevels: s and p; s sublevels contain two electrons when full, while p sublevels contain six electrons when full (because p sublevels each contain three orbitals).

The third period looks a lot like the second because of electron-electron interference. It takes less energy for an electron to be placed in $4s$ than in $3d$, so $4s$ fills before $3d$. Notice that the middle of the periodic table contains a square of 10 columns: these are the elements in which the d orbitals are being filled (these elements are called the transition metals). Now look at the two rows of 14 elements at the bottom of the table. In these rare earth elements, the f orbitals are being filled.

One final note about electron configurations. You can use the periodic table to quickly determine the valence electron configuration of each element. The **valence electrons** are the outermost electrons in an atom—the ones that are involved in bonding. The day of the test, as soon as you get your periodic table (which comes in the test booklet), label the rows as shown in the art above. The number at the top of each of the rows (i.e., 1A, 2A, etc.) will tell you how many valence electrons each element in that particular row has, which will be very helpful in determining Lewis dot structures. More on this later.

Example

Using the periodic table, determine the electron configuration for sulfur.

Explanation

First locate sulfur in the periodic table; it is in the third period, in the p block of elements. Count from left to right in the p block, and you determine that sulfur's valence electrons have an ending configuration of $3p^4$, which means everything up to that sublevel is also full, so its electron configuration is $1s^2 2s^2 2p^6 3s^2 3p^4$. You can check your answer—the neutral sulfur atom has 16 protons, and 16 electrons. Add up the number of electrons in your answer: $2 + 2 + 6 + 2 + 4 = 16$.

Another way of expressing this and other electron configurations is to use the symbol for the noble gas preceding the element in question, which assumes its electron configuration, and add on the additional orbitals. So sulfur, our example above, can be written [Ne] $3s^2 3p^4$.

Orbital Notation

Orbital notation is basically just another way of expressing the electron configuration of an atom. It is very useful in determining quantum numbers as well as electron pairing. The

Structure of Matter

orbital notation for sulfur would be represented as follows:

Notice that electrons 5, 6, and 7 went into their own orbitals before electrons 8, 9, and 10 entered, forcing pairings in the 2p sublevel; the same thing happens in the 3p level.

Now we can determine the set of quantum numbers. First, $n = 3$, since the valence electron (the outermost electron) is a 3p electron. Next, we know that p sublevels have an l value of 1. We know that m_l can have a value between l and $-l$, and to get the m_l quantum number, we go back to the orbital notation for the valence electron and focus on the 3p sublevel alone. It looks like this:

Simply number the blanks with a zero assigned to the center blank, with negative numbers to the left and positive to the right of the zero. The last electron was number 16 and "landed" in the first blank as a down arrow, which means its $m_l = -1$ and $m_s = -1/2$, since the electron is the second to be placed in the orbital and therefore must have a negative spin.

So, when determining m_l, just make a number line underneath the sublevel, with zero in the middle, negative numbers to the left, and positive numbers to the right. Make as many blanks as there are orbitals for a given sublevel. For assigning m_s, the first electron placed in an orbital (the up arrow) gets the $+1/2$ and the second one (the down arrow) gets the $-1/2$.

Example

Which element has this set of quantum numbers: $n = 5$, $l = 1$, $m_l = -1$, and $m_s = -1/2$?

Explanation

First, think about the electron configuration: $n = 5$ and $l = 1$, so it must be a 5p electron. The m_s quantum number corresponds to this orbital notation picture:

Be sure to number the blanks and realize that the $-1/2$ means it is a pairing electron! The element has a configuration of $5p^4$; so it must be tellurium.

Example • 39

Example

Complete the following table:

Element	Valence electron configuration	Valence orbital notation	Set of quantum numbers
		[Ar] ↑ (0, 4s)	
	[Ar] $3d^6$		
		1s ↑↓ 2s ↑↓ 2p (−1, 0, +1) ↑ ↑ ↑	
			5, 1, 0, +1/2
	$4p^5$		
			6, 0, 0, −1/2

Answer: element	Valence electron configuration	Valence orbital notation	Set of quantum numbers (n, l, m_l, m_s)
K	[Ar] $4s^1$	[Ar] ↑ (0, 4s)	4, 0, 0, +1/2
Fe	[Ar] $4s^2 3d^6$	[Ar] 4s ↑ (0); 3d (−2,−1,0,+1,+2) ↑↓ ↑ ↑ ↑ ↑	3, 2, −2, −1/2
N	$1s^2 2s^2 2p^3$	1s ↑↓ 2s ↑↓ 2p (−1,0,+1) ↑ ↑ ↑	2, 1, 1, +1/2
Sn	[Kr] $5s^2 4d^{10} 5p^2$	[Kr] 5s ↑↓; 4d ↑↓ ↑↓ ↑↓ ↑↓ ↑↓; 5p (−1,0,+1) ↑ ↑ ☐	5, 1, 0, +1/2
Br	[Ar] $4s^2 3d^{10} 4p^5$	[Ar] 4s ↑↓; 3d ↑↓ ↑↓ ↑↓ ↑↓ ↑↓; 4p (−1,0,+1) ↑↓ ↑↓ ↑	4, 1, 0, −1/2
Ba	[Xe] $6s^2$	[Xe] ↑↓ (0, 6s)	6, 0, 0, −1/2

The Periodic Table and Periodic Properties

We just saw how the periodic table can help us quickly determine electron configurations and quantum numbers. As you'll see in this section, this is possible because of the special arrangement of elements in the periodic table. There will almost definitely be at least one question about trends in the periodic table on the SAT Chemistry test, so be sure to read this section closely.

The Anatomy of the Periodic Table

As you are probably well aware, in the periodic table, elements are arranged in order of increasing atomic number. The 18 vertical columns of the table are called **groups** or **families**, while the seven horizontal rows are called **periods** and correspond to the seven principal quantum energy levels, $n = 1$ through $n = 7$.

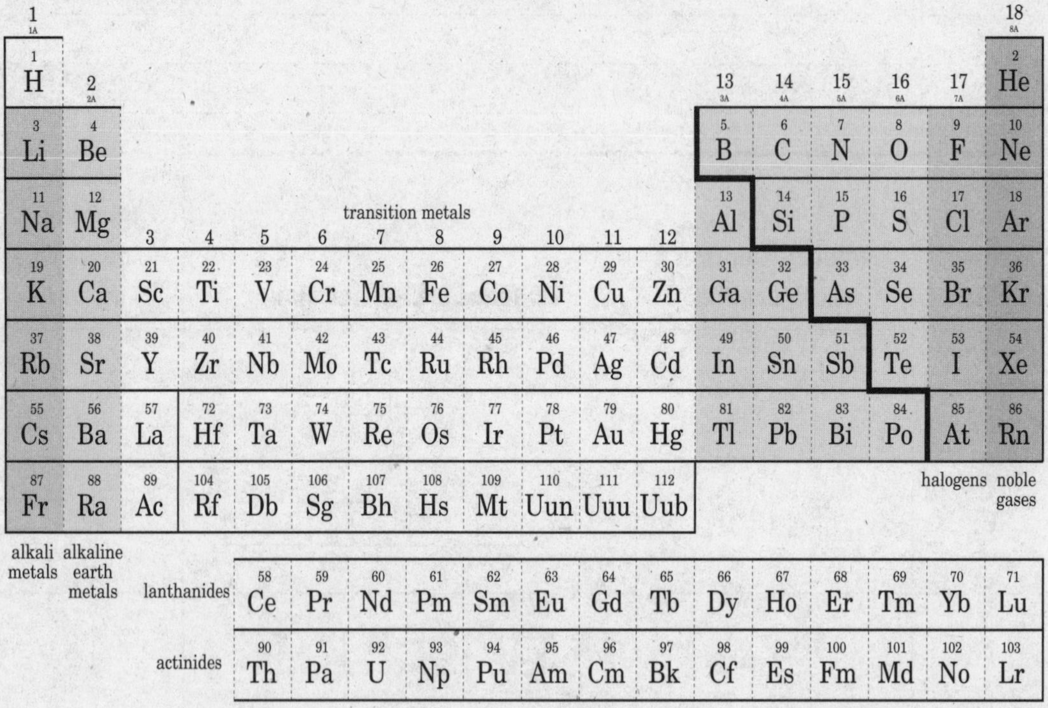

On the right side of the periodic table is a dividing line resembling a staircase. To the left of the staircase lie the metals, and to the right of the staircase lie the nonmetals. Many of the elements that touch the staircase are called metalloids, and these exhibit both metallic and non-metallic properties. Study the diagram below and memorize the names of the different types of elements, because you will definitely see questions about these groupings on the test!

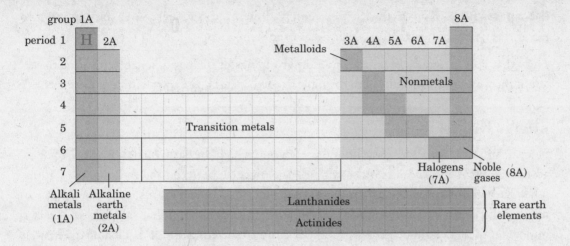

Metals are malleable, ductile, and have luster; most of the elements on the periodic table are metals. They oxidize (rust and tarnish) readily and form *positive* ions (cations). They are excellent conductors of both heat and electricity. The metals can be broken down into several groups.

Transition metals (also called the transition elements) are known for their ability to refract light as a result of their unpaired electrons. They also have several possible oxidation states. Ionic solutions of these metals are usually colored, so these metals are often used in pigments. The actinides and lanthanides are collectively called the **rare earth elements** and are filling the *f* orbitals. They are rarely found in nature. Uranium is the last naturally occurring element; the rest are man-made.

Nonmetals lie to the right of the staircase and do not conduct electricity well because they do not have free electrons. All the elemental gases are included in the nonmetals. Notice that hydrogen is placed with the metals because it has only one valence electron, but it is a nonmetal.

Here are some specific families you should know about, within the three main groups (metals, nonmetals, and metalloids):

Alkali metals (1A)—The most reactive metal family, these must be stored under oil because they react violently with water! They dissolve and create an alkaline, or basic, solution, hence their name.

Alkaline earth metals (2A)—These also are reactive metals, but they don't explode in water; pastes of these are used in batteries.

Halogens (7A)—Known as the "salt formers," they are used in modern lighting and always exist as diatomic molecules in their elemental form.

Structure of Matter

Noble gases (8A)—Known for their extremely slow reactivity, these were once thought to never react; neon, one of the noble gases, is used to make bright signs.

Now that you're familiar with the different groupings of the periodic table, it's time to talk about the ways we can use the periodic table to predict certain characteristics of elements.

Atomic Radius

Since in an atom there is no clear boundary beyond which the electron never strays, the way atomic radius is measured is by calculating the distance between the two nuclei of atoms when they are involved in a chemical bond. If the two bonded atoms are of the same element, you can divide the distance by 2 to get the atom's radius. That said, one of the two important things you'll need to know about atomic radii for the SAT II Chemistry exam is that **atomic radii decrease ($\downarrow$) moving across a period from left to right**. But why? It seems as though the more protons you add, the more space the atom should take up, but this is not the case. The reason for this lies in the basic concept that opposite charges attract each other and like charges repel each other. As you increase the number of protons in the nucleus of the atom, you increase the **effective nuclear charge** of the atom (Z_{eff}), and the nucleus pulls more strongly on the entire electron cloud. This makes the atomic radius decrease in size. The second thing you'll need to know is that **atomic radii increase moving down a group or family**. This is easier to understand if you refer to the Bohr model. As you move down the table, the value of n increases as we add another shell. Remember that the principal quantum number, n, determines the size of the atom. As we move down a family, the attractive force of the nucleus dissipates as the electrons spend more time farther from the nucleus.

One more thing about atomic size. As you know, when an atom loses an electron, a **cation**, or positive ion, is formed. When we compare the neutral atomic radius to the cationic radius, we see that the cationic radius is smaller. Why? The protons in the nucleus hold the remaining electrons more strongly. As you might expect, for negatively charged ions, or **anions**, the nuclear attractive force decreases (and there is enhanced electron-electron repulsion), so the electrons are less tightly held by the nucleus. The result is that the anion has a larger radius than the neutral atom.

The SAT II Chemistry test might ask you to compare the sizes of two atoms that are **isoelectronic**, meaning that they have the same number of electrons. In this case, you would then consider the number of protons the two atoms possess.

Example

Which ion is larger, F^- or O^{2-}?

Explanation

Since these two atoms are isoelectronic and in the same period, the atom with more protons in its nucleus will hold its electrons more tightly and be smaller. Fluoride will be smaller since it has more protons (9, compared to oxide's 8).

Ionization Energy (IE)

The **ionization energy** of an atom is the energy required to remove an electron from the atom in the gas phase. Although removing the first electron from an atom requires energy, the removal of each subsequent electron requires even more energy. This means that the second IE is usually greater than the first, the third IE is greater than the second, and so on. The reason it becomes more difficult to remove additional electrons is that they're closer to the nucleus and thus held more strongly by the positive charge of the protons.

Ionization energies differ significantly, depending on the shell from which the electron is taken. For instance, it takes less energy to remove a *p* electron than an *s* electron, even less energy to extract a *d* electron, and the least energy to extract an *f* electron. As you can probably guess, this is because *s* electrons are held closer to the nucleus, while *f* electrons are far from the nucleus and less tightly held. You'll need to remember two important facts about ionization energy for the test. The first is that *ionization energy increases as we move across a period*.

The reason for this, as is the case with periodic trends in atomic radii, is that as the nucleus becomes more positive, the effective nuclear charge increases its pull on the electrons and it becomes more difficult to remove an electron.

The second thing you'll need to remember is that *ionization energy decreases as you move down a group or family*. The increased distance between electrons and the nucleus and increased shielding by a full principal energy level means that it requires less energy to remove an electron. **Shielding** occurs when the inner electrons in an atom shield the outer electrons from the full charge of the nucleus. Keep in mind that this phenomenon is only important as you move down the periodic table! Here are the values for the first ionization energies for some elements:

1A	2A		3A	4A	5A	6A	7A	8A
H 13.60								He 24.59
Li 5.39	Be 9.32		B 8.30	C 11.26	N 14.53	O 13.62	F 17.42	Ne 21.57
Na 5.14	Mg 7.65		Al 5.99	Si 8.15	P 10.49	S 10.36	Cl 12.97	Ar 15.76
K 4.34	Ca 6.11		Ga 6.00	Ge 7.90	As 9.81	Se 9.75	Br 11.81	Kr 14.00
Rb 4.18	Sr 5.70		In 5.76	Sn 7.34	Sb 8.64	Te 9.01	I 10.45	Xe 12.13
Cs 3.89	Ba 5.21		Tl 6.11	Pb 7.42	Bi 7.29	Po 8.42	At —	Rn 10.75

Structure of Matter

There are some important exceptions to the above two ionization energy trends in the periodic table, so make sure you study these closely:

- When electron pairing first occurs within an orbital, electron-electron repulsions increase, so that removing an electron takes less energy (it's easier); thus the IE drops at this time. For example, less energy is required to remove an electron from oxygen's valence *in spite of an increasing* Z_{eff} because oxygen's p^4 electron is the first to pair within the orbital. The repulsion created lowers the amount of energy required to remove either electron.
- There is also a drop in ionization energy from s^2 to p^1 — also *in spite of an increasing* Z_{eff}. This drop is due to the fact that you are removing a p electron rather than an s electron. The p electrons are less tightly held *because* they do not penetrate the electron cloud toward the nucleus as well as an s electron does.

Example

Which of the following elements has the highest ionization energy: K, Ca, Ga, As, or Se?

Explanation

The answer is arsenic, or As. Since IE increases as we move across a period, you may have chosen Se. However, there is a drop in IE in spite of increasing Z_{eff} due to the increased electron-electron repulsion in the family that contains oxygen, since they are np^4.

Electron Affinity

An atom's **electron affinity** is the amount of energy released when an electron is added to the atom in its gaseous state—when an electron is added to an atom, the atom forms a negative ion. Most often, energy is *released* as an electron is added to an atom, and the greater the attraction between the atom and the electron added, the more negative the atom's electron affinity.

For the SAT II Chemistry test, remember that *electron affinity becomes more negative as we move across a period*. This means that it's easier to add an electron to elements, the farther to the right you travel on the periodic table. Why? Again, this is because the higher Z_{eff} increases the nuclear attraction for the incoming electron. Important exceptions to this rule are the noble gases: He, Ne, Ar, Kr, and Xe. They have electron affinities that are positive (meaning very low), because if they were to accept another electron, that electron would have to go into a new, higher-energy subshell, and this is energetically unfavorable.

Electron affinities do not change very much as you go down a group. This is because the lower electron-nucleus attraction that's seen as we go down a group is pretty evenly counterbalanced by a simultaneous lowering in electron-electron repulsion. Remember that there is no clear trend for electron affinity as you go down a group on the periodic table—this fact could come up in a synthesis of knowledge question!

Electronegativity

Electronegativity is a measure of the attraction an atom has for electrons when it is involved in a chemical bond. Elements that have high ionization energy and high electron affinity will also have high electronegativity since their nuclei strongly attract electrons. Electronegativity increases from left to right as we move across a period and decreases as we move down any group or family.

By now, these trends should make sense. You know that ionization energies tend to decrease with increasing atomic number in a group, although there isn't a significant change in electron affinity, so it makes sense that atoms' attraction for electrons in a bond would also increase as their Z_{eff} increased. We will discuss the concept of electronegativity further in the next section, when we discuss chemical bonding.

Here's a summary of the trends we discussed in this section. Make sure to memorize them!

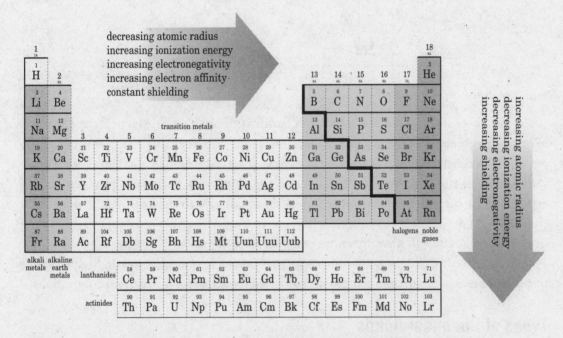

Chemical Bonding and Molecular Structure

What Are Chemical Bonds, and Why Do They Form?

A **chemical bond** is the result of an attraction between atoms or ions. The types of bonds that a molecule contains will determine its physical properties, such as melting point, hardness, electrical and thermal conductivity, and solubility. How do chemical bonds occur? As we mentioned before, only the outermost, or **valence**, electrons of an atom are involved in chemical bonds. Let's begin our discussion by looking at the simplest element, hydrogen. When two hydrogen atoms approach each other, electron-electron repulsion and proton-proton repulsion both act to try to keep the atoms apart. However, proton-electron attraction can counterbalance this, pulling the two hydrogen atoms together so that a **bond** is formed. Look at the energy diagram below for the formation of an H–H bond.

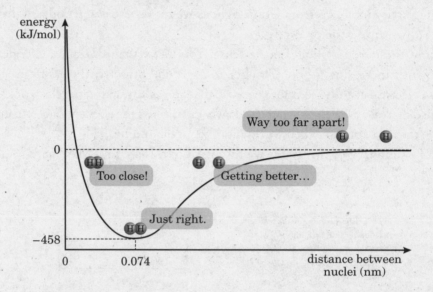

As you'll see throughout our discussion, atoms will often gain, lose, or share electrons in order to possess the same number of electrons as the noble gas that's nearest them on the periodic table. All of the noble gases have eight valence electrons (s^2p^6) and are very chemically stable, so this phenomenon is known as the **octet rule**. There are, however, certain exceptions to the octet rule. One group of exceptions is atoms with fewer than eight electrons—hydrogen (H) has just one electron. In BeH_2, there are only four valence electrons around Be: Beryllium contributes two electrons and each hydrogen contributes one. The second exception to the octet rule is seen in elements in periods 4 and higher. Atoms of these elements can be surrounded by more than four valence pairs in certain compounds.

Types of Chemical Bonds

You'll need to be familiar with three types of chemical bonds for the SAT II Chemistry exam: ionic bonds, covalent bonds, and metallic bonds.

Ionic bonds are the result of an electrostatic attraction between ions that have opposite charges; in other words, cations and anions. Ionic bonds usually form between metals and nonmetals; elements that participate in ionic bonds are often from opposite ends of the periodic table and have an electronegativity difference greater than 1.67. Ionic bonds are very strong, so compounds that contain these types of bonds have high melting points and exist in a solid state under standard conditions. Finally, remember that in an ionic bond, an electron is actually *transferred* from the less electronegative atom to the more electronegative element. One example of a molecule that contains an ionic bond is table salt, NaCl.

Covalent bonds form when electrons are *shared* between atoms rather than transferred from one atom to another. However, this sharing rarely occurs equally because of course no two atoms have the same electronegativity value. (The obvious exception is in a bond between two atoms of the same element.) We say that covalent bonds are **nonpolar** if the electronegativity difference between the two atoms involved falls between 0 and 0.4. We say they are **polar** if the electronegativity difference falls between 0.4 and 1.67. In both nonpolar and polar covalent bonds, the element with the higher electronegativity attracts the electron pair more strongly. The two bonds in a molecule of carbon dioxide, CO_2, are covalent bonds.

Covalent bonds can be single, double, or triple. If only one pair of electrons is shared, a **single bond** is formed. This single bond is a **sigma bond (σ)**, in which the electron density is concentrated along the line that represents the bond joining the two atoms.

However, double and triple bonds occur frequently (especially among carbon, nitrogen, oxygen, phosphorus, and sulfur atoms) and come about when atoms can achieve a complete octet by sharing more than one pair of electrons between them. If two electron pairs are shared between the two atoms, a **double bond** forms, where one of the bonds is a sigma bond, and the other is a **pi bond (π)**. A pi bond is a bond in which the electron density is concentrated above and below the line that represents the bond joining the two atoms. If three electron pairs are shared between the two nuclei, a **triple bond** forms. In a triple bond, the first bond to form is a single, sigma bond and the next two to form are both pi.

Multiple bonds increase electron density between two nuclei: they decrease nuclear repulsion while enhancing the nucleus-to-electron density attractions. The nuclei move closer together, which means that double bonds are shorter than single bonds and triple bonds are shortest of all.

Metallic bonds exist only in metals, such as aluminum, gold, copper, and iron. In metals, each atom is bonded to several other metal atoms, and their electrons are free to move throughout the metal structure. This special situation is responsible for the unique properties of metals, such as their high conductivity.

Drawing Lewis Structures

Here are some rules to follow when drawing Lewis structures—you should follow these simple steps for every Lewis structure you draw, and soon enough you'll find that you've memorized them. While you will not specifically be asked to draw Lewis structures on the test, you will be asked to predict molecular shapes, and in order to do this you need to be able to draw the Lewis structure—so memorize these rules! To predict arrangement of atoms within the molecule

1. Find the total number of valence electrons by adding up group numbers of the elements. For anions, add the appropriate number of electrons, and for cations, subtract the appropriate number of electrons. Divide by 2 to get the number of electron pairs.

2. Determine which is the central atom—in situations where the central atom has a group of other atoms bonded to it, the central atom is usually written first. For example, in CCl_4, the carbon atom is the central atom. You should also note that the central atom is usually less electronegative than the ones that surround it, so you can use this fact to determine which is the central atom in cases that seem more ambiguous.

3. Place one pair of electrons between each pair of bonded atoms and subtract the number of electrons used for each bond (2) from your total.

4. Place lone pairs about each terminal atom (except H, which can only have two electrons) to satisfy the octet rule. Leftover pairs should be assigned to the central atom. If the central atom is from the third or higher period, it can accommodate more than four electron pairs since it has d orbitals in which to place them.

5. If the central atom is not yet surrounded by four electron pairs, convert one or more terminal atom lone pairs to double bonds. Remember that not all elements form double bonds: only C, N, O, P, and S!

Example

Which one of the following molecules contains a triple bond: PF_3, NF_3, C_2H_2, H_2CO, or HOF?

Explanation

The answer is C_2H_2, which is also known as ethyne. When drawing this structure, remember the rules. Find the total number of valence electrons in the molecule by adding the group numbers of its constituent atoms. So for C_2H_2, this would mean C = 4 × 2 (since there are two carbons) = 8. Add to this the group number of H, which is 1, times 2 because there are two hydrogens = a total of 10 valence electrons. Next, the carbons are clearly acting as the central atoms since hydrogen can only have two electrons and thus can't form more than one bond. So your molecule looks like this: H—C—C—H. So far you've used up six electrons in three bonds. Hydrogen can't support any more electrons, though: both H's have their maximum number! So your first thought might be to add the remaining electrons to the central carbons—but there is no way of spreading out the remaining four

Example • 49

electrons to satisfy the octets of both carbon atoms except to draw a triple bond between the two carbons.

For practice, try drawing the structures of the other four compounds listed.

Example

How many sigma (σ) bonds and how many pi (π) bonds does the molecule ethene, C_2H_4, contain?

Explanation

First draw the Lewis structure for this compound, and you'll see that it contains one double bond (between the two carbons) and four single bonds. Each single bond is a sigma bond, and the double bond is made up of one sigma bond and one pi bond, so there are five sigma bonds and one pi bond.

$$
\begin{array}{c}
\text{H} \qquad\qquad \text{H} \\
\diagdown \qquad \diagup \\
\text{C}=\text{C} \\
\diagup \qquad \diagdown \\
\text{H} \qquad\qquad \text{H}
\end{array}
$$

Exceptions to Regular Lewis Structures—Resonance Structures

Sometimes you'll come across a structure that can't be determined by following the Lewis dot structure rules. For example, ozone (O_3) contains two bonds of equal bond length, which seems to indicate that there are an equal number of bonding pairs on each side of the central O atom. But try drawing the Lewis structure for ozone, and this is what you get:

$$:\ddot{O} - \ddot{O} = \ddot{O}$$

We have drawn the molecule with one double bond and one single bond, but since we know that the bond lengths in the molecule are equal, ozone can't have one double and one single bond—the double bond would be much shorter than the single one. Think about it again, though—we could also draw the structure as below, with the double bond on the other side:

$$\ddot{O} = \ddot{O} - \ddot{O}:$$

Together, our two drawings of ozone are resonance structures for the molecule. **Resonance structures** are two or more Lewis structures that describe a molecule: their composite represents a true structure for the molecule. We use the double-directional arrows to indicate resonance and also bracket the structures or simply draw a single, composite picture.

Resonance structures for ozone: Composite:

$$\left[:\ddot{O} - \ddot{O} = \ddot{O}: \right] \longleftrightarrow \left[:\ddot{O} = \ddot{O} - \ddot{O}: \right] \qquad\qquad \left[:\ddot{O} \text{---} \ddot{O} \text{---} \ddot{O}: \atop _{-\frac{1}{2}} \phantom{\ddot{O}} _{-\frac{1}{2}} \right]$$

Structure of Matter

Let's look at another example of resonance, in the carbonate ion CO_3^{2-}:

Resonance structures for carbonate ion: Composite:

Notice that resonance structures differ only in electron pair positions, not atom positions!

Example

Draw the Lewis structures for the following molecules: HF, N_2, NH_3, CH_4, CF_4, and NO^+.

Explanation

		valence electrons	single bonds	remaining electrons	final Lewis structure	number of electrons
a.	HF	$1 + 7 = 8$	H—F	6	H—F̈:	H: 2 F: 8
b.	N_2	$5 + 5 = 10$	N—N	8	:N≡N:	N: 8 N: 8
c.	NH_3	$5 + 3(1) = 8$	H—N—H | H	2	H—N̈—H | H	H: 2 N: 8
d.	CH_4	$4 + 4(1) = 8$	H | H—C—H | H	0	H | H—C—H | H	H: 2 C: 8
e.	CF_4	$4 + 4(7) = 32$	F | F—C—F | F	24	:F̈: | :F̈—C—F̈: | :F̈:	F: 8 C: 8
f.	NO^+	$5 + 6 - 1 = 10$	N—O	8	$[:N≡O:]^+$	N: 8 O: 8

Structure of Matter

Molecular Shape

While Lewis dot structures can tell us how the atoms in molecules are bonded to each other, they don't tell us the shape of the molecule. In this section, we'll discuss the methods for predicting molecular shape. The most important thing to remember when attempting to predict the shape of a molecule based on its chemical formula and the basic premises of the **VSPER model** is that the molecule will assume the shape that most minimizes electron pair repulsions. In attempting to minimize electron pair repulsions, two types of electron sets must be considered: electrons can exist in **bonding pairs**, which are involved in creating a single or multiple covalent bond, or **nonbonding pairs**, which are pairs of electrons that are not involved in a bond, but are localized to a single atom.

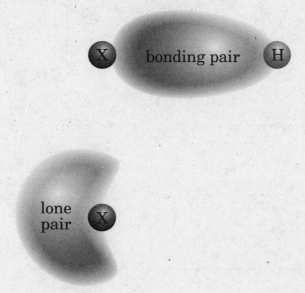

The VSPER Model—Determining Molecular Shape

Total number of single bonds, double bonds, and lone pairs on the central atom	Structural pair geometry	Shape
2	Linear	linear
3	Trigonal planar	trigonal planar
4	Tetrahedral	tetrahedral
5	Trigonal bipyramidal	trigonal bipyramidal
6	Octahedral	octahedral

The above table represents a single atom with all of the electrons that would be associated with it as a result of the bonds it forms with other atoms plus its lone electron pairs. However, since atoms in a molecule can never be considered alone, the shape of the actual molecule might be different from what you'd predict based on its structural pair geometry. You use the structural pair geometry to determine the molecular geometry by following these steps:

1. Draw the Lewis dot structure for the molecule and count the total number of single bonds, multiple bonds, and unpaired electrons.
2. Determine the structural pair geometry for the molecule by arranging the electron pairs so that the repulsions are minimized (based on the table).
3. Use the table above to determine the molecular geometry.

The table below shows all of the commonly occurring molecular geometries that are found for molecules with four or fewer bonding domains around their central atom.

	Electron-Domain Geometry	Bonding Domains	Nonbonding Domains	Molecular Geometry	Example
2	linear	2	0	linear	$\ddot{O} = C = \ddot{O}$
3	trigonal planar	3	0	trigonal planar	$\ddot{F}$ — B — $\ddot{F}$ $\ddot{F}$
		2	1	bent	$\left[\ddot{O} \cdot \overset{\ddot{N}}{} \cdot \ddot{O} \right]^-$

	Electron-Domain Geometry	Bonding Domains	Nonbonding Domains	Molecular Geometry	Example
4	tetrahedral	4	0	tetrahedral	H $-$ C with H's
		3	1	trigonal pyramidal	N with H's
		2	2	bent	O with H's

As you can see from the table, atoms that have normal valence—meaning atoms that have no more than four structural electron pairs and obey the octet rule (and have no lone pairs)—are tetrahedral. For instance, look at methane, which is CH_4:

Ammonia (NH_3), which has three sigma bonds and a lone pair, however, is trigonal pyramidal:

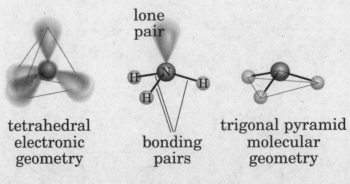

tetrahedral electronic geometry   lone pair bonding pairs   trigonal pyramid molecular geometry

Structure of Matter

Water (H_2O) has two lone pairs and its molecular geometry is "bent," which is also called V shaped:

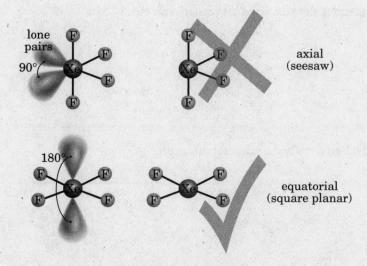

tetrahedral electronic geometry

lone pair

lone pair

bonding pairs

bent or V-shaped molecular geometry

So as you can see, lone pairs have more repulsive force than do shared electron pairs, and thus they force the shared pairs to squeeze more closely together.

tetrahedron   109.5°

trigonal pyramid   107°

bent or V-shaped   104.5°

As a final note, you may remember that we mentioned before that only elements with a principal energy level of 3 or higher can expand their valence and violate the octet rule. This is because *d* electrons are necessary to make possible bonding to a fifth or sixth atom. In XeF_4, there are two lone pairs and four shared pairs surrounding Xe, and two possible arrangements exist:

lone pairs   90°

axial (seesaw)

180°

equatorial (square planar)

In the axial arrangement, shared pairs are situated "top and bottom." In the equatorial arrangement, shared pairs surround Xe. The equatorial arrangement is more stable since the lone pairs are 180° apart and this minimizes their repulsion. In both molecular arrangements, the electronic geometry is octahedral, with 90° angles. The top figure has a molecular geometry known as "seesaw," while the bottom figure has a molecular geometry that is more stable, known as square planar.

Example

Draw the dot formula for SeF_4 and determine the hybridization at Se.

Explanation

First determine the number of valence electrons this molecule has: SeF_4 has 6 + 4(7) = 34 valence electrons, which is equal to 17 pairs of electrons.

$$\ddot{\underset{\cdot\cdot}{F}}-\overset{\cdot\cdot}{Se}-\ddot{\underset{\cdot\cdot}{F}}$$

Selenium is surrounded by four fluorines and a lone pair of electrons. That's five sites of electron density, which translates into sp^3d hybridization. Se is from the fourth period, so it may have an expanded octet.

So, to recap, focus on the number of binding "sites" or areas of concentrated electron density:

Two areas of electron density: linear, planar molecule

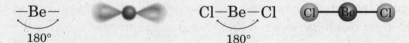

Three areas of electron density: trigonal planar molecule

Four areas of electron density: tetrahedral molecule

Five areas of electron density: trigonal bipyramidal molecule

Six areas of electron density: octahedral molecule

Molecular Polarity

In chemical bonds, polarity refers to an uneven distribution of electron pairs between the two bonded atoms—in this case, one of the atoms is slightly more negative than the other. But molecules can be polar too, and when they are polar, they are called dipoles. **Dipoles** are molecules that have a slightly positive charge on one end and a slightly negative charge on the other. Look at the water molecule. The two lone electron pairs on the oxygen atom establish a negative pole on this bent molecule, while the bound hydrogen atoms constitute a positive pole. In fact, this polarity of water accounts for most of water's unique physical properties. However, molecules can also contain polar bonds and not be polar. Carbon dioxide is a perfect example. Both of the C—O bonds in carbon dioxide are polar, but they're oriented such that they cancel each other out, and the molecule itself is not polar.

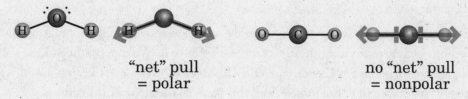

"net" pull
= polar

no "net" pull
= nonpolar

Valence Bond Theory

Another topic that you'll need to be familiar with for the SAT II Chemistry test is that of valence bond theory. By now, you are aware that two atoms will form a bond when there is orbital overlap between them, and a maximum of two electrons can be present in the overlapping orbitals.

Structure of Matter

Since the pair of electrons is attracted to both atomic nuclei, a bond is formed, and as the extent of overlap increases, the strength of the bond increases. The electronic energy drops as the atoms approach each other, but it begins to increase again when they become too close. This means there is an optimum distance, the observed bond distance, at which the total energy is at a minimum.

Let's delve a little more deeply into sigma bonds now and describe them in more detail. As you know, sigma (σ) bonds are single bonds. They result from the overlap of two s orbitals, an s and a p orbital, or two head-to-head p orbitals. The electron density of a sigma bond is greatest *along the axis* of the bond. Maximum overlap forms the strongest-possible sigma bond, and the two atoms will arrange themselves to give the greatest-possible orbital overlap. This is tricky with p orbitals since they are directional along the x, y, and z axes.

Hybrid orbitals result from a blending of atomic orbitals (in other words, s and p orbitals) to create orbitals that have energy that's in between the energy of the lone orbitals. Look at the methane molecule, for example: all four of the C—H bonds are 109.5° apart, while nonbonded p orbitals are only 90° apart.

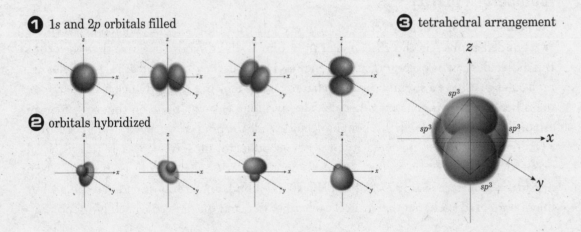

❶ 1s and 2p orbitals filled

❷ orbitals hybridized

❸ tetrahedral arrangement

The orbitals shown at the left of the figure are for a nonbonded carbon atom, but once the carbon atom begins to bond with other atoms (in this case hydrogen), the atomic orbitals hybridize, and this changes their shape considerably. Notice how the first set of figures form the sp^3 atomic orbital, the hybrid, and this leads to further hybridization.

Ammonia also has sp^3 hybridization, even though it has a lone pair.

Multiple Bonding

Now let's look more closely at pi bonds. As we mentioned earlier in this chapter, pi (π) bonds result from the sideways overlap of p orbitals, and pi orbitals are defined by the region above and below an imaginary line connecting the nuclei of the two atoms. Keep in mind that pi bonds never occur unless a sigma bond has formed first, and they may form only if unhybridized p orbitals remain on the bonded atoms. Also, they occur when sp or sp^2 hybridization is present on central atom but *not sp^3* hybridization.

Below, we show the formation of a set of sp^2 orbitals. This molecule would contain a double bond, like ethene. Notice again how the first set of figures form the sp^2 atomic orbital, the hybrid, and the last figure shows full hybridization:

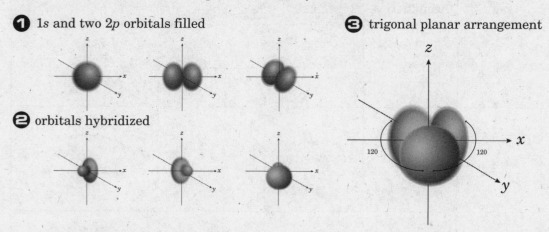

❶ $1s$ and two $2p$ orbitals filled

❷ orbitals hybridized

❸ trigonal planar arrangement

The set of p orbitals that are unhybridized are not shown in this depiction:

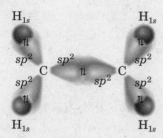

A different view, which doesn't show the hydrogens and centers on the C atoms, shows the unhybridized p orbitals that create the sideways overlap that's necessary to create the double pi bond:

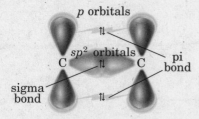

Here's how it looks with all the pieces put together:

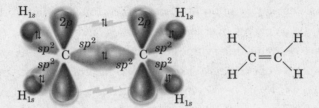

Here is a table summarizing hybridization and structure:

effective pairs	hybridization	geometry		
2	sp	linear		
3	sp^2	trigonal planar		
4	sp^3	tetrahedral		
5	dsp^3	trigonal bipyramidal		
6	d^2sp^3	octahedral		

Practice Questions

1. An element consists of three isotopes in the following relative abundance:

   30.00% = 40.00 amu
   50.00% = 41.00 amu
   20.00% = 42.00 amu

   What is the atomic mass of this element?

   (A) 40.90
   (B) 41.00
   (C) 41.90
   (D) 42.20
   (E) 42.90

2. The total number of electrons that can be accommodated in the fourth principal energy level is _____.

   (A) 2
   (B) 8
   (C) 18
   (D) 32
   (E) 50

3. If the set of quantum numbers $n = 3$, $l = 1$, $m_l = 0$, $m_s = \pm 1/2$ represents the last electron to be added to complete the ground state electron configuration of an element, which one of the following could be the symbol for the element?

   (A) Na
   (B) Si
   (C) Th
   (D) V
   (E) Zn

4. Which element has the following electron configuration?
   $1s^2 2s^2 2p^6 3s^2 3p^6 4s^2 3d^4$

   (A) Cr
   (B) Mn
   (C) Mo
   (D) S
   (E) Se

5. Complete the balanced equation
   $$^{14}_{6}C \rightarrow {}^{10}_{4}Be + ?$$
   The missing term is

   (A) $^{0}_{-1}\beta$
   (B) $^{0}_{1}\beta$
   (C) $^{4}_{2}He$
   (D) $^{0}_{0}\gamma$
   (E) $^{1}_{0}n$

6. Oxygen-15 has a half-life of 9.98 minutes. How much of a 20.0 g sample of oxygen-15 remains after 60.0 minutes?

(A)   0.156 g
(B)   0.312 g
(C)   0.625 g
(D)   1.25 g
(E)   2.50 g

7. Which of the following atoms would have the largest second ionization energy?

(A)   Mg
(B)   Cl
(C)   S
(D)   Ca
(E)   Na

Remember this type of question from Part I of the book?

| 8. | Hydrogen has a lower ionization energy than does helium. | BECAUSE | Hydrogen bonds with halogens to form polar covalent bonds. |

9. Order the elements S, Cl, and F in terms of increasing atomic radii.

(A)   S, Cl, F
(B)   Cl, F, S
(C)   F, S, Cl
(D)   F, Cl, S
(E)   S, F, Cl

| 10. | The second ionization energy of B is higher than that of Be. | BECAUSE | The second electron to be removed from B and Be comes from the same principal energy level. |
| 11. | Oxygen has a smaller first ionization energy than fluorine. | BECAUSE | Oxygen has a higher Z_{eff} value than does fluorine. |

12. Removing an electron from sodium is an _____ process and removing an electron from fluorine is an _____ process.

(A)   Endothermic, exothermic
(B)   Exothermic, endothermic
(C)   Endothermic, endothermic
(D)   Exothermic, exothermic
(E)   More information is needed

13. Which numbered response lists all the molecules below that exhibit resonance and none that do not?

     I. AsF_5
     II. HNO_3
     III. SO_2

(A)   I only
(B)   II only
(C)   II and III
(D)   III and IV
(E)   I, II, and III

14. The sulfur hexafluoride molecule is nonpolar and contains no lone (unshared) electron pairs on the sulfur atom. Which answer choice lists all of the bond angles contained in sulfur hexafluoride?

(A)   120°
(B)   180°
(C)   90° and 180°
(D)   90°, 120°, and 180°
(E)   109.5°

15.	Molecules that contain a polar bond are not necessarily polar compounds.	BECAUSE	If polar bonds in a molecule are symmetrically arranged, then their polarities will cancel and they will be nonpolar.
16.	The NH_3 molecule is more polar than the NF_3 molecule.	BECAUSE	Fluorine atoms are larger than hydrogen atoms.

17. Which one of the following molecules is octahedral?

(A) $BeCl_2$
(B) SeF_6
(C) BF_3
(D) PF_5
(E) CF_4

18. Which molecule is incorrectly matched with the molecular geometry?

    <u>Molecule</u>   <u>Molecular geometry</u>

(A) SF_6 octahedral
(B) CH_4 tetrahedral
(C) SO_3 trigonal planar
(D) $SeCl_4$ tetrahedral
(E) PH_3 trigonal pyramidal

Explanations

1. **A**

There are two ways to get this answer, the hard way and the easy way. To solve this problem the hard way, first multiply the percent abundance by the atomic mass of a given isotope and then add the products together. You'll see that the hard way actually isn't very hard:

30.00% = 40.00 amu: 30% is 3 × 10%, right? So if 10% of 40 is 4, then 3 × 4 = 30% of 40, which is equal to 12 amu.

50.00% = 41.00 amu, and 50% is ½ of 41, which is 20.5 amu.

20.00% = 42.00 amu, and 20% = 2 × 10%, so 10% of 42 = 4.2, and 20% = 2 × 4.2, which is 8.4 amu.

Now add those three numbers together to get your answer: 12 + 20.5 + 8.4 = 40.9 amu. But the easy way to get the answer is to guesstimate: 50% of the element exists as the 41.00 amu isotope. Now, 30% of the remaining element is the 40.00 amu isotope, and only 20% of the element exists as the 42.00 isotope. Therefore you can estimate that the average of these three amounts should be *less* than 41 since there is more of the lighter isotope. The only answer choice that's less than 41 is **A**.

2. **D**

The fourth principal energy level has four sublevels: s, p, d, and f. If the sublevel is completely filled, then $s = 2$ electrons, $p = 6$ electrons, $d = 10$ electrons, and $f = 14$ electrons; thus $2 + 6 + 10 + 14 = 32$ total electrons for a full fourth principal energy level.

3. **B**

The set of quantum numbers given was $n = 3$, $l = 1$, $m_l = 0$, $m_s = \pm 1/2$. If $n = 3$, this means that it's a third energy level electron; if $l = 1$, then it's a p-sublevel electron; if $m_l = 0$, then it's in the middle position of the set of three p orbitals. The only tricky thing is that $m_s = +$ or $-1/2$. This means it's either a p^2 or a p^5 electron. However, if it were p^5, then one of the answer choices would be argon (a noble gas), but it isn't listed, so it must be the p^2, which makes silicon the correct answer.

4. **A**

The configuration given is $1s^2 2s^2 2p^6 3s^2 3p^6 3d^4 4s^2$. The $3d^4$ is the important part—it means the element we desire is in the first row of the d-block elements and is the fourth element in that block, so it is Cr, or chromium.

5. C

The mass number and atomic number must be equal on both sides of the equation in order for the equation to be properly balanced. We are looking for a component that has a mass number of 4 and an atomic number of 2: helium. This is an example of alpha decay, and the answer is **C**, $_2^4$He.

The complete equation is:

$$_6^{14}C \rightarrow {}_2^4He + {}_4^{10}Be$$

6. B

This problem is easily solved without a calculator, especially if you've been practicing your math skills. The half-life is given as 9.98 minutes, which is mighty close to 10 minutes. The total time is given as 60.0 minutes, so the sample undergoes six half-lives. Start with this mass and keep cutting it in half; each 10-minute half-life should be represented with an arrow, and you can even put numbers under each arrow if you want, in order to keep track.

$20.0 \rightarrow 10.0 \rightarrow 5.0 \rightarrow 2.5 \rightarrow 1.25 \rightarrow 0.625 \rightarrow 0.3125$, which is **B**.

7. E

This question asks about the *second* ionization energy. Remember that the second ionization energy of any element is always larger than its first ionization energy. The second ionization energy is *significantly* larger if the second electron comes from a completed sublevel or principal energy level. Na's first electron removed is $3s^1$, while the second to be removed comes from $2p^6$. There is a *huge* increase in the amount of energy needed to remove that second electron because of the change in principal energy levels.

8. T, T

(Do *not* fill in **CE**, for "correct explanation.") Remember this type of question? We told you about it in the first part of the book. Here we go: statement I is true: hydrogen has a lower IE than helium. The electron removed in each case is from the $1s$ sublevel, so Z_{eff} becomes very important: H has a Z_{eff} of 1, while He has a Z_{eff} of 2. He attracts its electrons with more force; thus it requires more energy to remove them. Statement II is also true: The halogens are highly electronegative and form polar bonds with hydrogen. However, is statement II the correct explanation for why statement I is true? No, so you would not fill in the **CE** bubble.

9. E

Remember, atomic radii *decrease* moving across a period from left to right. This is because protons are added to the nucleus and these protons attract the electrons more strongly, pulling them in tighter and decreasing the atomic radius. Atomic radius *increases* moving down a group or family, however, because the value of *n* increases as you add another shell, the electrons spend more time away from the nucleus, dissipating the attraction between nuclear protons and themselves. Since fluorine and chlorine are both in the same group but chlorine is below fluorine, we know that chlorine is bigger than fluorine. Sulfur is to the left of both chlorine and fluorine, so it must be the smallest of all. Arranged in order of increasing size, they are S, F, Cl, or answer **E**.

10. **T, T**

(Do not fill in **CE**.) In general, the ionization energy increases with increasing Z_{eff}, and the same is true for second ionization energies. B has a higher Z_{eff} than does Be, and since the second ionization energy would be needed to remove protons from the same principal energy level, B's higher Z_{eff} means that its second ionization energy would be higher than that of Be.

11. **F, F**

(Do not fill in **CE**.) While oxygen has a lower first ionization energy than *nitrogen* due to the p^4 anomaly, as you pass oxygen (going from left to right across the period), the trend of increasing ionization energy continues; the increased Z_{eff} results in subsequent elements in the period (such as fluorine) having a higher ionization energy than oxygen. Oxygen does not have a higher Z_{eff} than that of fluorine, so the second statement is also false, and you would not fill in the **CE** oval.

12. **C**

It simply requires the input of energy to remove an electron from any type of atom. This is because energy must be put into the system in order to overcome the favorable attraction between the electron and the positively charged atomic nucleus. A reaction that must consume energy in order to proceed is known as endothermic, while a reaction that gives off energy is exothermic; both of these reactions are endothermic, and the answer is **C**.

13. **C**

Draw each structure using the rules for drawing Lewis dot structures. Remember that resonance structures refer to two or more Lewis structures that are equally good descriptions of a molecule. So, you're looking for structures in which you found yourself placing one double bond arbitrarily between a pair of atoms that, elsewhere in the molecule, share only a single pair of atoms. You should also be looking for a combination of single and multiple bonds occurring between the central atom and a member of C, N, O, P, or S.

I

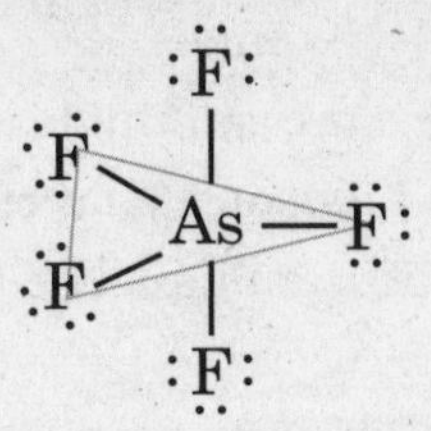

II

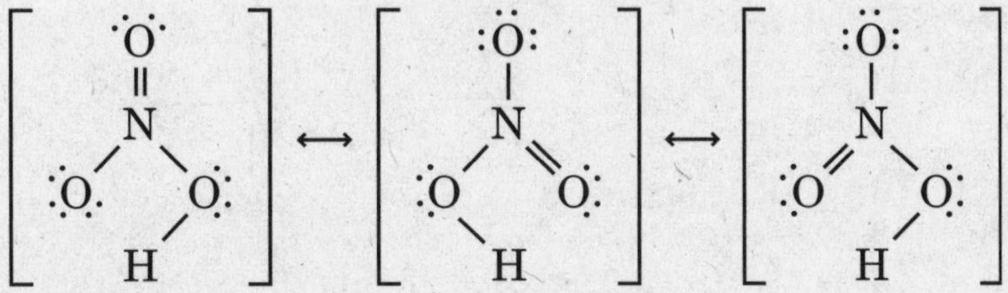

III

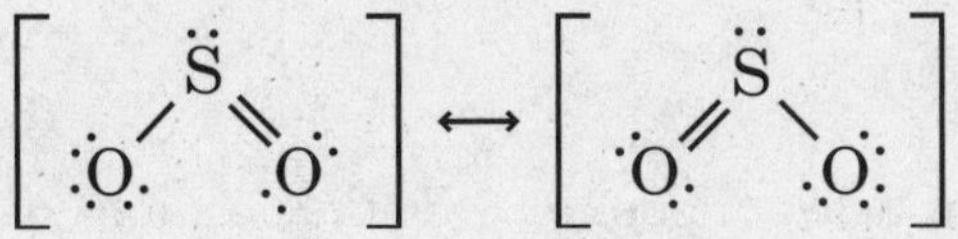

14. C

SF_6 has six bonding sites as seen by its Lewis structure, drawn below. It is octahedral. The four equatorial sites have F—S—F bond angles of 90°, while the two axial sites have F—S—F bond angles of 180°, so as you can see, choice **C** is the best answer.

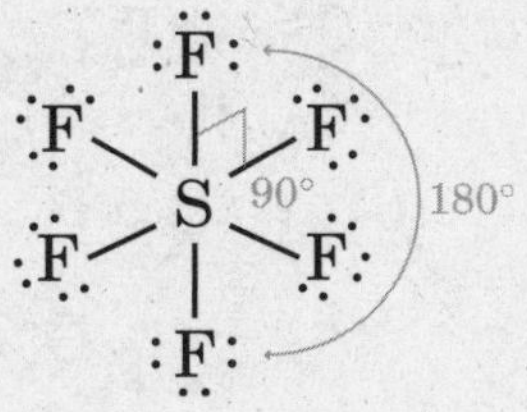

15. T, T, CE

The first statement is true: not all molecules that contain a polar bond are themselves polar. And the second statement correctly explains why this is so: in order for a molecule to be polar, it must contain at least one polar bond or unshared pair of electrons that are *not* arranged symmetrically so as to cancel each other out. If they are arranged so that they do cancel each other out, the molecule will be nonpolar.

16. T, T

(Do not fill in **CE**.) While fluorine is indeed bigger than hydrogen, this is not the reason NH_3 is more polar than NF_3. The true reason for this is that the three N—F bonds are more polar than the N—H bonds: the difference between the electronegativities of N and H are greater than that between N and F, so in NH_3, the nitrogen attracts electrons much more strongly than do the hydrogens, and a significant dipole moment is created.

17. **B**

An octahedral geometry is produced from six bonding sites, sp^3d^2 hybridization, and an expanded octet. You know it cannot be $BeCl_2$, BF_3, or CF_4 since neither Be, B, nor C is from the third period or higher. SeF_6 and PF_5 are both possibilities. The Lewis structures for the remaining choices appear below:

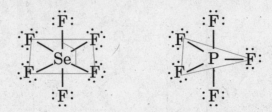

You can see that PF_5 has five bonding sites and is thus trigonal bipyramidal. SeF_6 has six bonding sites and is octahedral.

18. **D**

All of the Lewis structures appear below. Focus *only* on the positions of the nuclei—you can't see the lone pairs, but they determine the molecular shape by their repulsions.

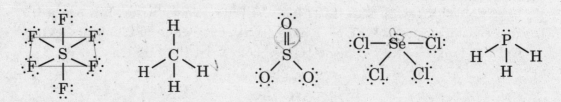

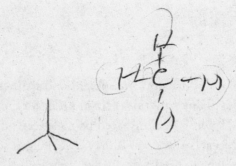

The States of Matter

Now that you know a bit about chemical bonding, let's talk about the different forms that groups of molecules can take. In other words, let's talk about the states of matter. The states of matter that you'll need to know for the SAT II Chemistry test are solid, liquid, and gas.

You might wonder why there are different states of matter at all. After all, molecules only bond together in one way, right? The answer lies in the type of intramolecular and intermolecular forces that exist both within and between molecules of substances.

Chapter Contents

solid

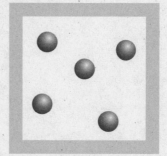
liquid   gas

Intra- and Intermolecular Forces

Whether a particular group of bonded molecules takes the form of a solid, liquid, or gas depends not only on the bonds that exist within each individual molecule, but also on the presence and type of bonds between molecules. Hark back to the different types of bonds we reviewed in the last chapter: ionic, covalent, and metallic. Of these, ionic bonds tend to be the strongest, and this means that substances that contain ionic bonds are solids at room temperature. Substances that are primarily made up of covalent bonds, which are weaker, can be solid or liquid, and their state will depend on the presence and type of **intermolecular** forces.

The two main types of intermolecular forces that exist between molecules are dipole-dipole forces (including hydrogen bonds) and London dispersion forces.

Dipole-Dipole Forces

Dipole-dipole attractions take place when two or more neutral, polar molecules are oriented such that their positive (+) and negative (−) ends are close to each other.

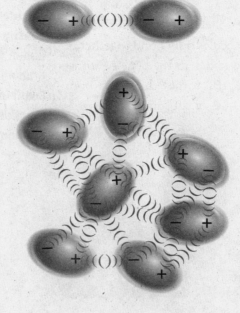

Because of the attraction between unlike charges, this is a fairly strong type of intermolecular force, and molecules held together by dipole-dipole forces tend to be in the solid or liquid state. Also, for molecules that are about the same size and weight, the strength of the dipole-dipole forces increases as the degree of polarity increases. In other words, the more polar a molecule is, the stronger the dipole-dipole forces it will form with itself and other molecules.

One very important and unique case of the dipole-dipole attraction is known as **hydrogen bonding**. Hydrogen bonds are not true bonds: they're just strong attractive forces between the hydrogen on one molecule and a highly electronegative atom on a nearby molecule.

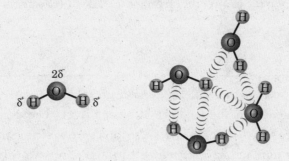

Hydrogen bonds most commonly form between hydrogen atoms and fluorine, oxygen, or nitrogen. This type of intermolecular force is responsible for water's unique characteristics, such as its high specific heat and boiling point temperature—but more about that later.

London Dispersion Forces—Weak Intermolecular Forces

London forces are relatively weak forces of attraction that exist between nonpolar molecules and noble gas atoms, like argon (a noble gas) and octane (a hydrocarbon; C_8H_{18}). These types of attractive forces are caused by a phenomenon known as **instantaneous dipole formation**. In this process, electron distribution in the individual molecules suddenly becomes asymmetrical, and the newly formed dipoles are now attracted to one another.

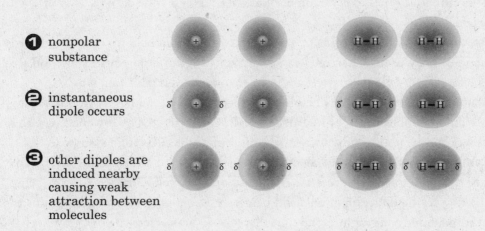

❶ nonpolar substance

❷ instantaneous dipole occurs

❸ other dipoles are induced nearby causing weak attraction between molecules

The States of Matter

The ease with which the electron cloud of an atom can be distorted to become asymmetrical is called the molecule's **polarizability**. Think of this as a probability issue. The greater the number of electrons an electron has, the farther they will be from the nucleus, and the greater the chance for them to shift positions within the molecule. This means that larger nonpolar molecules tend to have stronger London dispersion forces. This is evident when you look at the diatomic elements in group 7, the halogens. All of these diatomic elements are nonpolar, covalently bonded molecules. Now, going down the group, fluorine and chlorine are gases, bromine is a liquid, and iodine is a solid! For nonpolar molecules, the farther you go down the group, the stronger the London dispersion forces.

Solids

As we mentioned above, the molecules that make up solids are generally held together by ionic or strong covalent bonding, and the attractive forces between the atoms, ions, or molecules in solids are very strong. In fact, these forces are so strong that particles in a solid are held in fixed positions and have very little freedom of movement. Solids have definite shapes and definite volumes and are not compressible to any extent. There are a few types of solids that you should be familiar with for the SAT II Chemistry test, and we've listed them below. However, we will start by saying that there are two main categories of solids—crystalline solids and amorphous solids. **Crystalline solids** are those in which the atoms, ions, or molecules that make up the solid exist in a regular, well-defined arrangement. The smallest repeating pattern of crystalline solids is known as the **unit cell**, and unit cells are like bricks in a wall—they are all identical and repeating. The other main type of solids are called the amorphous solids. **Amorphous solids** do not have much order in their structures. Though their molecules are close together and have little freedom to move, they are not arranged in a regular order as are those in crystalline solids. Common examples of this type of solid are glass and plastics.

There are four types of crystalline solids, all of which you should be familiar with for the exam.

Ionic solids—Made up of positive and negative ions and held together by electrostatic attractions. They're characterized by very high melting points and brittleness and are poor conductors in the solid state. An example of an ionic solid is table salt, NaCl.

Molecular solids—Made up of atoms or molecules held together by London dispersion forces, dipole-dipole forces, or hydrogen bonds. Characterized by low melting points and flexibility and are poor conductors. An example of a molecular solid is sucrose.

Covalent-network (also called atomic) solids—Made up of atoms connected by covalent bonds; the intermolecular forces are covalent bonds as well. Characterized as being very hard with very high melting points and being poor conductors. Examples of this type of solid are diamond and graphite, and the fullerenes. As you can see below, graphite has only 2-D hexagonal structure and therefore is not hard like diamond. The sheets of graphite are held together by only weak London forces!

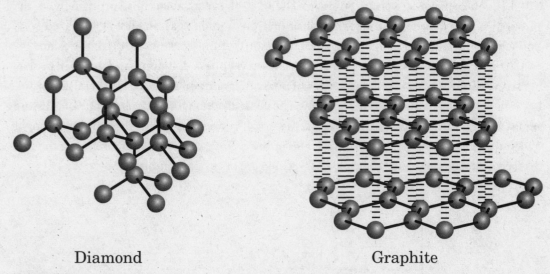

Diamond   Graphite

Metallic solids—Made up of metal atoms that are held together by metallic bonds. Characterized by high melting points, can range from soft and malleable to very hard, and are good conductors of electricity.

Liquids

Liquids are generally made up of molecules that contain covalent bonds and have strong intermolecular attractive forces. The atoms and molecules that make up liquids have more freedom of movement than do those in solids. Also, liquids have no definite shape but do have a definite volume, and they are not easily compressible. We will discuss liquids in more detail in the section on solutions in this chapter.

Gases

Gases generally consist of atoms and molecules that are covalently bonded, and their intermolecular forces are very weak. The molecules of a gas are highly separated, so we say that gases are mostly empty space. A gas has no definite shape—it will take the shape of the container that holds it, and gases are easily compressible.

Phase Changes

In order for a substance to move between the states of matter; for example, to turn from a solid into a liquid, which is called **fusion**, or from a gas to a liquid (**vaporization**), energy must be gained or lost. The **heat of fusion** (symbolized H_{fus}) of a substance is the amount of energy that must be put into the substance for it to melt. For example, the heat of fusion of water is 6.01 kJ/mol, or in other terms, 80 cal/g. The **heat of vaporization**, not surprisingly, is the amount of energy needed to cause the transition from liquid to gas, and it is symbolized H_{vap}. You will not be required to memorize heat of fusion or vaporization values for the exam.

Changes in the states of matter are often shown on phase diagrams, and you will probably see at least one of two different types of phase diagrams on the SAT II Chemistry exam. Let's start with the phase diagram for water. The **phase diagram** for water is a graph of pressure versus temperature. Each of the lines on the graph represents an equilibrium position, at which the substance is present in two states at once. For example, anywhere along the line that separates ice and water, melting and freezing are occurring simultaneously.

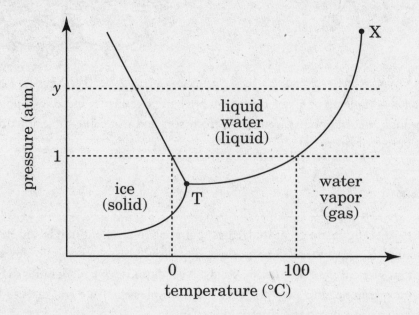

The intersection of all three lines is known as the **triple point** (represented by a dot and a T on the figure). At this point, all three phases of matter are in equilibrium with each other. Point X represents the **critical point**, and at the critical point and beyond, the substance is forever in the vapor phase.

This diagram allows us to explain strange phenomena, such as why water boils at a lower temperature at higher altitudes, for example. At higher altitudes, the air pressure is lower, and this means that water can reach the boiling point at a lower temperature. Interestingly enough, water would boil at room temperature if the pressure was low enough!

One final note: If we put a liquid into a closed container, the evaporation of the liquid will cause an initial increase in the total pressure of the system, and then the pressure of the system will become a constant. The value of this final pressure is unique to each liquid and is known as the liquid's **vapor pressure**. Water has a relatively low vapor pressure because it takes a lot of energy to break the hydrogen bonds so that molecules enter the gas phase. Water and other liquids that have low vapor pressures are said to be **nonvolatile**. Substances

Example • 75

like rubbing alcohol and gasoline, which have relatively high vapor pressures, are said to be **volatile**.

Example

What happens to water when the pressure remains constant at 1 atm but the temperature changes from –10°C to 75°C?

Explanation

Looking at the phase change diagram for water and following the dashed line at 1 atm, you can see that water would begin as a solid (ice) and melt at 0°C. All of the water would be in liquid form by the time the temperature reached 75°C.

The second type of phase change graph you might see on the SAT II Chemistry exam is called a **heating curve**. This is a graph of the change in temperature of a substance as energy is added in the form of heat. The pressure of the system is assumed to be held constant, at normal pressure (1 atm). As you can see from the graph below, at normal pressure water freezes at 0°C and boils at 100°C.

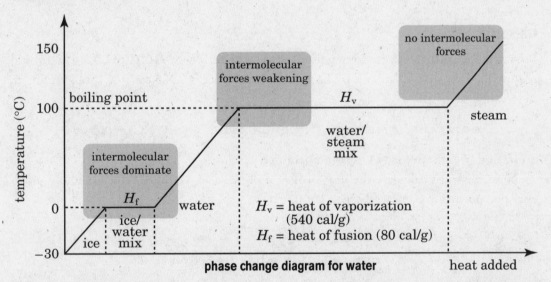

phase change diagram for water

The plateaus on this diagram represent the points where water is being converted from one phase to another; at these stages the temperature remains constant since all the heat energy added is being used to break the attractions between the water molecules.

Specific Heat

On the SAT II Chemistry test, you might see a diagram that looks something like this one, and you might come across a question that asks you to calculate the amount of energy needed to take a particular substance through a phase change. This would be one of the

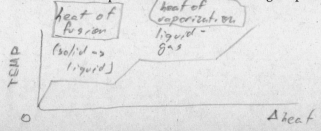

The States of Matter

$C_{ice} = .485\, cal/g\, °C$

most difficult questions on the exam, but you might see something like it, or at least part of it. If you were asked to do this, you would need to use the following equation:

$$\text{energy (in calories)} = mC_p\Delta T$$

where m = the mass of the substance (in grams)

C_p = the specific heat of the substance (in cal/g °C)

ΔT = the change in temperature of the substance (in either Kelvins or °C, but make sure all your units are compatible!)

As you can see, this requires that you know the specific heat of the substance. A substance's **specific heat** refers to the heat required to raise the temperature of 1 g of a substance by 1°C. You will not be required to remember any specific heat values for the exam.

Work through the example below to get a feel for how to use this equation.

Example

If you had a 10.0 g piece of ice at −10°C, under constant pressure of 1 atm, how much energy would be needed to melt this ice and raise the temperature to 25.0°C?

Explanation

First, the temperature of the ice would need to be raised from −10°C to 0°C. This would require the following calculation. The specific heat for ice is 0.485 cal/g °C. Substituting in the formula

$$\text{energy} = mC_p\Delta T; \text{energy} = (10.0\text{ g})(0.485\text{ cal/g °C})(10.0°C) = 48.5\text{ cal}$$

So 48.5 calories are needed to raise temperature.

Next, we must calculate the heat of fusion of this ice: we must determine how much energy is needed to completely melt the 10 g of it.

$$\text{energy} = mH_{fus}$$

$$\text{energy} = (10.0\text{ g})(80\text{ cal/g}) = 800\text{ cal}$$

So 800 cal of energy are needed to completely melt this sample of ice.

Next, we need to see how much energy would be needed to raise the temperature of water from 0°C to 25°C. The specific heat for liquid water is 1.00 cal/g °C. So again use

$$\text{energy} = mC_p\Delta T \text{ to get energy} = (10.0\text{ g})(1.00\text{ cal/g °C})(25.0°C) = 250\text{ cal}$$

Finally, add together all of the energies to get the total: 48.5 + 800 + 250 = about 1100 calories are needed to convert the ice to water at these given temperatures.

The States of Matter

The Gas Laws

Ideal Gases

You will definitely see some questions on gases and the laws that govern them on the SAT II Chemistry exam. All of the gas laws rely on some basic assumptions that are made about gases, and together they constitute what it means for a gas to be in an **ideal state**. In an ideal state

1. All gas particles are in constant, random motion.
2. All collisions between gas particles are perfectly elastic (meaning that the kinetic energy of the system is conserved).
3. The volume of the gas molecules in a gas is negligible.
4. Gases have no intermolecular attractive or repulsive forces.
5. The average kinetic energy of the gas is directly proportional to its Kelvin temperature and is the same for all gases at a specified temperature.

Only four measurable properties are used to describe a gas: its quantity, temperature, volume, and pressure. The quantity (amount) of the gas is usually expressed in moles (n). The temperature, T, of gases must always be converted to the Kelvin temperature scale (the absolute temperature scale). The volume, V, of a gas is usually given in liters. Finally, the pressure, P, of a gas is usually expressed in atmospheres. Gases are often discussed in terms of **standard temperature and pressure (STP)**, which means 273K (or 0°C) and 1 atm.

Example

Which of the following statements is not true of ideal gases?

1. The volume occupied by gas particles is only significant at very low pressures.
2. Gas molecules occupy an insignificant volume compared to the volume of the container that holds them.
3. The particles of a gas move in random straight line paths until a collision occurs.
4. The collisions that occur between gas particles are considered elastic.
5. At a given temperature, all gas molecules within a sample possess the same average kinetic energy.

Explanation

In this example, choice 1 is incorrect. Choices 2, 3, 4, and 5 all describe an ideal gas. Choice 1 makes an incorrect assumption: it begins with a true statement about volume not being very significant but then turns around and gives the incorrect scenario—if the pressure is low, then gas particles undergo very few collisions, so the volume is insignificant. The volume only becomes significant if gas particles collide often, increasing the chances that intermolecular forces will hold them together.

Measuring the Pressure of a Gas

Gas pressure is a gauge of the number and force of collisions between gas particles and the walls of the container that holds them. The SI unit for pressure is the pascal **(Pa)**, but other pressure terms include **atmospheres (atms), millimeters of mercury (mmHg)**, and **torr**. The following is a list of all of the standard pressure in every unit for pressure. Memorize these for the exam so you can convert units where necessary:

760 mmHg
760 torr
1.00 atm
101,325 Pa
101.325 kPa

The piece of lab equipment specifically designed to measure the pressure of gases is known as the barometer. A **barometer** uses the height of a column of mercury to measure gas pressure in millimeters of mercury or torr (1 mmHg = 1 torr). The mercury is pushed up the tube from the dish until the pressure at the bottom of the tube (due to the mass of the mercury) is balanced by the atmospheric pressure.

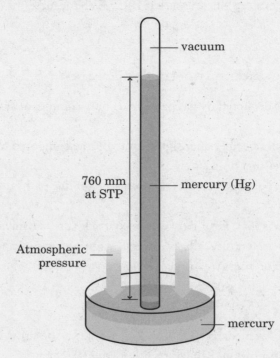

When using a barometer, you calculate gas pressure with the following equation:

Gas pressure = atmospheric pressure – *h* (height of the mercury)

The **open-tube manometer** is another device that can be used to measure pressure. The open-tube manometer is used to measure the pressure of a gas in a container.

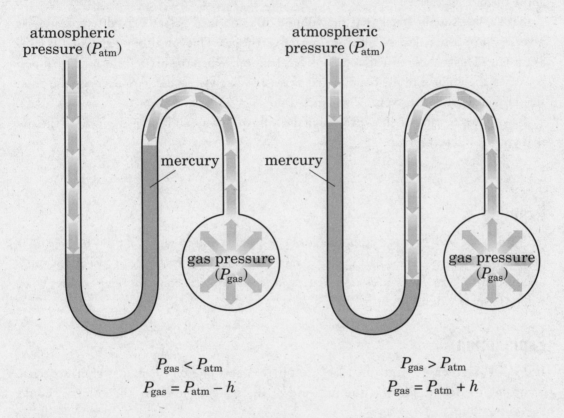

atmospheric pressure (P_{atm})

atmospheric pressure (P_{atm})

mercury

mercury

gas pressure (P_{gas})

gas pressure (P_{gas})

$P_{gas} < P_{atm}$
$P_{gas} = P_{atm} - h$

$P_{gas} > P_{atm}$
$P_{gas} = P_{atm} + h$

The pressure of the gas is given by *h* (the difference in mercury levels) in units of torr or mmHg. Atmospheric pressure pushes on the mercury from one direction, and the gas in the container pushes from the other direction. In a manometer, since the gas in the bulb is pushing more than the atmospheric pressure, you add the atmospheric pressure to the height difference:

gas pressure = atmospheric pressure + *h*

There is one other possibility for a manometer question that could appear on the SAT II Chemistry test: they could ask you about a **closed-tube manometer**. Closed-tube manometers look similar to regular manometers except that the end that's open to the atmospheric pressure in a regular manometer is sealed and contains a vacuum. In these systems, the difference in mercury levels (in mmHg) is equal to the pressure in torr.

The States of Matter

Boyle's Law

This is the first of the five-odd gas laws you'll need to know for the SAT II Chemistry test. Study these laws closely because you are sure to see a question or two that asks you to apply them.

Boyle's law simply states that the volume of a confined gas at a fixed temperature is inversely proportional to the pressure exerted on the gas. This can also be expressed as $PV =$ a constant. This makes sense if you think of a balloon. When the pressure around a balloon increases, the volume of the balloon decreases, and likewise, when you decrease the pressure around a balloon, its volume will increase.

Boyle's law to can also be expressed in the following way, and this is the form of the law that you should memorize:

$$P_1 V_1 = P_2 V_2$$

Example

Sulfur dioxide (SO_2) gas is a component of car exhaust and power plant discharge, and it plays a major role in the formation of acid rain. Consider a 3.0 L sample of gaseous SO_2 at a pressure of 1.0 atm. If the pressure is changed to 1.5 atm at a constant temperature, what will be the new volume of the gas?

Explanation

If $P_1 V_1 = P_2 V_2$, then $(1.0 \text{ atm}) (3.0 \text{ L}) = (1.5 \text{ atm}) (V_2)$, so $V_2 = 2.0$ L. This answer makes sense according to Boyle's law—as the pressure of the system increases, the volume should decrease.

Charles's Law

Charles's law states that if a given quantity of gas is held at a constant pressure, its volume is directly proportional to the absolute temperature. Think of it this way. As the temperature of the gas increases, the gas molecules will begin to move around more quickly and hit the walls of their container with more force—thus the volume will increase. Keep in mind that you must use only the *Kelvin* temperature scale when working with temperature in all gas law formulas! Here's the expression of Charles's law that you should memorize:

$$\frac{V_1}{T_1} = \frac{V_2}{T_2}$$

Try using Charles's law to solve the following problem.

Example • 81

Example

A sample of gas at 15°C and 1 atm has a volume of 2.50 L. What volume will this gas occupy at 30°C and 1 atm?

Explanation

The pressure remains the same, while the volume and temperature change—this is the hallmark of a Charles's law question.

$$\text{So,} \frac{V_1}{T_1} = \frac{V_2}{T_2}, \text{then 2.50 L/288K} = V_2/303\text{K, and } V_2 = 2.63 \text{ L}$$

This makes sense—the temperature is increasing slightly, so the volume should increase slightly. Be careful of questions like this—it's tempting to just use the Celsius temperature, but you must first convert to Kelvin temperature (by adding 273) to get the correct relationships!

Avogadro's Law

The volume of a gas at a given temperature and pressure is directly proportional to the quantity of the gas. Avogadro's hypothesis comes directly from this relationship, and you should definitely remember the following statement (which is an extrapolation of the above idea) for the SAT II Chemistry test: *Equal volumes of gases under the same conditions of temperature and pressure contain equal numbers of molecules.* Avogadro's law, which is derived from this basic idea, says that the volume of a gas maintained at constant temperature and pressure is directly proportional to the number of moles of the gas, or

$$V = \text{constant} \times n \text{ (where } n \text{ is the number of moles of the gas)}$$

The Ideal Gas Law

The ideal gas law is the most important gas law for you to know: it combines all of the laws you learned about in this chapter thus far, under a set of standard conditions. The four conditions used to describe a gas—pressure, volume, temperature, and number of moles (quantity)—are all related, along with R, the universal gas law constant, in the following formula:

$$PV = nRT$$

where P = pressure (atm), V = volume (L), n = number of moles (mol), R = 0.08206 L · atm/mol · K, and T = temperature (K).

Now try an example using the ideal gas law equation.

$PV = nRT$

Example

A 16.0 g sample of methane gas, CH_4, the gas used in chemistry lab, has a volume of 5.0 L at 27°C. Calculate the pressure.

$5L = 1(.082)(300)$ $S = 24.$

Explanation

Looking at all the information given, you have a mass, a volume, and a temperature, and you need to find the pressure of the system. As always, start by checking your units. You must first convert 16.0 g of CH_4 into moles: 16.0 g CH_4 × 1 mol CH_4/16.0 g CH_4 = 1 mol of methane. The volume is in the correct units, but you must convert the temperature into Kelvins: 27 + 273 = 300K. Now you're ready to plug these numbers into the ideal gas law equation:

$$PV = nRT$$

$(P)(5.0\ L) = (1.0\ mol)(0.0821\ \underline{L \cdot atm/mol \cdot K})(300K)$, so $P = 4.9$ atm

Don't let the math scare you. Remember that your test will be all multiple choice. You may be asked for proper setup, or at least you will have answers to choose from, and you won't have to do these lengthy calculations without a calculator. These examples are only meant to give you practice using the gas law equations.

Density of Gases

Since gases are mostly empty space, the densities of gases are reported in g/L, *not* g/mL as found for solids and liquids. As you're probably aware, density is equal to mass per unit of volume. To calculate the density of a gas at standard temperature and pressure, you take the molecular formula weight of the gas (grams per mole—from the periodic table) and divide that by the **standard molar volume for a gas**, which is **22.4 L per mole**:

$$\text{Density} = \frac{FW}{22.4}$$

where the formula weight (*FW*) is in g/mol, and the standard molar volume is 22.4 L/mol. Now try using this in a problem.

Example

What is the density of helium gas at STP?

Explanation

If the density of the gas is equal to $\frac{FW}{22.4}$, then $d = 4.00$ g/mol ÷ 22.4 L/mol, so the density = 0.179 g/L.

If conditions are not standard, we can use this expanded version of the ideal gas equation:

$$d = \frac{M}{V} = \frac{P(FW)}{RT}$$

Another really handy rearrangement of the ideal gas equation can be used to find the molecular weight of an unknown gas $MW = \frac{dRT}{P}$. You'll get a chance to practice using these in the problems at the end of the chapter. However, there is no need to memorize these last equations since they are all rearrangements of the ideal gas law. Okay, two more important laws and then we're finished with our discussion of gases, and we move on to solutions.

Dalton's Law of Partial Pressures

Dalton's law states that the pressure of a mixture of gases is the sum of the pressures that each of the individual gases would exert if it were alone:

$$P_{total} = P_1 + P_2 + \ldots P_n$$

Graham's Law of Diffusion and Effusion

Graham's law states that the rates of effusion of two gases are inversely proportional to the square roots of their molar masses at the same temperature and pressure:

$$\frac{\text{Rate of effusion of gas 1}}{\text{Rate of effusion of gas 2}} = \sqrt{\frac{FW_2}{FW_1}}$$

Effusion is the term used to describe the passage of a gas through a tiny orifice into an evacuated chamber, as shown in the figure below.

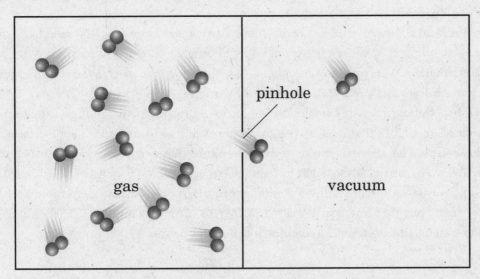

The **rate of effusion** measures the **speed** at which the gas travels through the tiny hole into a vacuum. Another term to remember for the test is diffusion. **Diffusion** is the term used to describe the spread of a gas throughout a space or throughout a second substance.

Solutions

This section will focus on what you need to know about solutions, solution concentrations, and colligative properties in order to be successful on the SAT II Chemistry test. This material is closely tied in with the material from the first half of this chapter and "The Structure of Matter."

Properties of Solutions

A **solution** is a homogenous mixture of two or more substances that exist in a single phase. There are two main parts to any solution. The **solute** is the component of a solution that is dissolved in the solvent; it is usually present in a smaller amount than the solvent. The **solvent** is the component into which the solute is dissolved, and it is usually present in greater concentration. For example, in a solution of salt water, salt is the solute and water is the solvent. In solutions where water is the solvent, the solution is referred to as an *aqueous* solution.

A solution does not have to involve liquids. For instance, air is a solution that consists of nitrogen, oxygen, carbon dioxide, and other trace gases, and solder is a solution of lead and tin. The general rule of thumb for solutions is the idea that *like dissolves like*. Polar, ionic substances are soluble in polar solvents, while nonpolar solutes are soluble in nonpolar solvents. For example, alcohol and water, which are both polar, can form a solution and iodine and carbon tetrachloride, which are both nonpolar, make a solution. However, iodine will not readily dissolve in polar water.

In a solution, the particles are really small—anywhere from 0 to 100 nm. They never settle on standing, they cannot be separated by filtering, and light will pass through a solution unchanged. One type of mixture that is not a solution is known as the colloid. In a **colloid**, particles are between 100 and 1000 nm in size—still too small for our eyes to distinguish, but particles this small will not settle. As is the case in solutions, the particles cannot be filtered, but they do scatter light. Some examples of colloids include gelatin, fog, smoke, and shaving cream. Another type of mixture that is not considered a solution is known as a suspension. **Suspensions** have much larger particles: usually over 1000 nm. Particles in a suspension will settle on standing, can often be separated by a filter, and may scatter light, but they are usually not transparent. Some examples of suspensions are muddy water, paint, and some medicines, like Pepto-Bismol.

The Solution Process

In order for a solute to be dissolved in a solvent, the attractive forces between the solute and solvent particles must be great enough to overcome the attractive forces within the pure solvent and pure solute. The solute and the solvent molecules in a solution are expanded compared to their position within the pure substances.

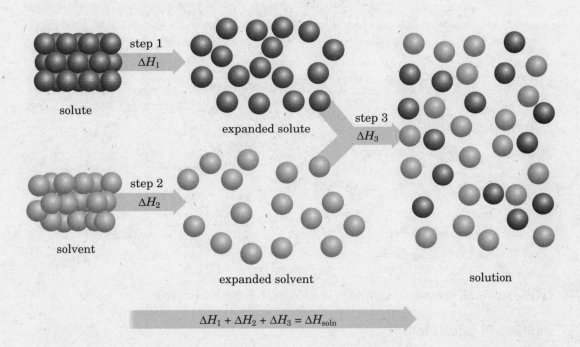

$$\Delta H_1 + \Delta H_2 + \Delta H_3 = \Delta H_{soln}$$

The process of expansion, for both the solute and solvent, involves a change in the energy of the system: this process can be either exothermic or endothermic. After dissolving, the solute is said to be fully **solvated** (usually by dipole-dipole or ion-dipole forces), and when the solvent is water, the solute is said to be **hydrated**. The separation of the solute particles from one another prior to dissolving is an endothermic process for both solvent and solute (steps 1 and 2), but when the solute and solvent combine with each other, this is an exothermic process (step 3). If the energy released in step 3 is greater than the energy absorbed in steps 1 and 2, the solution forms and is stable.

The term **solubility** refers to the maximum amount of material that will dissolve in a given amount of solvent at a given temperature to produce a stable solution. By looking at the plot of solubilities below, you can see that most solids increase in solubility with an increase in temperature.

The States of Matter

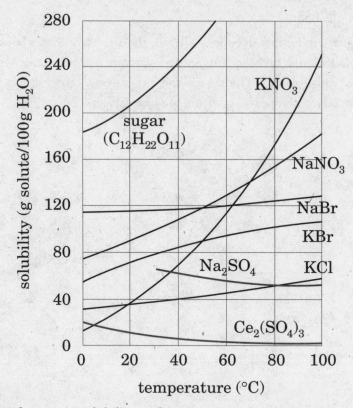

Gases, however, *decrease* in solubility with an increase in temperature.

Degrees of Saturation

When referring to solutions, there are three degrees of saturation—unsaturated, saturated, and supersaturated. If a solution is **unsaturated**, the solvent is capable of dissolving more solute. When the solution is **saturated**, the solvent has dissolved the maximum amount of solute that it can at the given temperature. At this point we say that the solution is in a state of **dynamic equilibrium**—the processes of dissolving and precipitation are happening at the same rate. A **supersaturated** solution is one in which the solvent contains more solute than it can theoretically hold at a given temperature. Supersaturated solutions are often formed by heating a solution and dissolving more solute, then cooling the solution down slowly. These solutions are unstable and crystallize readily.

Concentration Terms

Solutions are often referred to as being concentrated or dilute. These two terms are very general. While **concentrated** indicates that there is a lot of solute dissolved in the solvent (perhaps the solution is near to being saturated) and **dilute** indicates that a small amount of solute is dissolved in the solvent, we often need to be exact with quantities in chemistry. The units of concentration that you should be familiar with for the SAT II exam are reviewed below.

Example • 87

Molarity (*M*)

$$M = \frac{\text{moles of solute}}{\text{liters of solution}}$$

The **molarity** of a solution is a measure of the number of moles of solute per liter of solution. This is the most common concentration unit used in chemistry. For instance, you might see an expression that looks like this:

$$[NaCl] = 0.75$$

which means that 0.75 mole of NaCl is dissolved per 1.00 L of solution. The brackets around the number indicate that the concentration is expressed in terms of molarity. Let's now run through how you calculate the molarity of a solution.

Example

Calculate the molarity of a solution prepared by dissolving 20.0 g of solid NaOH in enough water to make 100 mL of solution.

Explanation

Convert grams to moles:

$$\frac{20.0 \text{ g NaOH}}{40.0 \text{ g/mol NaOH}} = 0.500 \text{ mol NaOH}$$

Then convert mL to liters:

$$\frac{100 \text{ mL}}{1000 \text{ mL/L}} = 0.100 \text{ L solution}$$

Then divide:

$$\frac{0.500 \text{ mol}}{0.100 \text{ L}} = 5.00 \text{ } M \text{ NaOH}$$

Dilution

Dilution is the process of taking a more concentrated solution and adding water to make it less concentrated. The more concentrated solution before the dilution is performed is known as the *stock* solution. You can relate the concentration of the stock solution to the concentration of the diluted solution using the equation below:

$$M_1 V_1 = M_2 V_2$$

where *M* is molarity and *V* is the volume, in liters, of the solution. Try the following example using this equation.

The States of Matter

Example

What volume of 6.0 M sulfuric acid (H_2SO_4) must be used to prepare 2.0 L of a 0.10 M H_2SO_4 solution?

Explanation

Just plug the numbers into the formula! Be careful to read closely.

$$M_1V_1 = M_2V_2$$

$$(6.0\ M)(V_1) = (0.10\ M)(2.0\ L)$$

$$V_1 = 0.033\ L$$

or 33 mL should be measured out and then diluted by adding enough water to make 2.00 L total volume.

Mass Percent (Weight Percent)

The mass percent of a solution is another way of expressing its concentration. Mass percent is found by dividing the mass of the solute by the mass of the solution and multiplying by 100; so a solution of NaOH that is 28% NaOH by mass contains 28 g of NaOH for each 100 g of solution. Here's the equation:

$$\text{Mass percent} = \frac{\text{grams of solute}}{\text{g of solute} + \text{g of solvent}} \times 100$$

Now try a problem involving the equation:

Example

A solution is prepared by mixing 5.00 g ethanol (C_2H_5OH) with 100.0 g water. Calculate the mass percent of ethanol in this solution.

Explanation

Plugging the values we were given into the mass percent equation, we get:

$$\% = \frac{5.00\ g}{100\ g + 5.00\ g} \times 100 = 4.76\%\ \text{ethanol}$$

Molality (*m*)

$$m = \frac{\text{moles of solute}}{\text{kilograms of solvent}}$$

The **molality** of a solution is a measure of the number of moles of solute per kilogram of solvent. Whereas the *molarity* of a solution is dependent on the volume of the solution, the *molality* is dependent on the mass of the solvent in the solution. Do not get these con-

Example • 89

fused, and when you see either term on the SAT II Chemistry test, double-check to make sure which one they're talking about—the words look similar, too! Try an example:

Example

A solution is prepared by mixing 80.0 g of sodium hydroxide (NaOH) with 500.0 g of water. Calculate the molality of this solution.

Explanation

Convert grams of solute to moles:

$$\frac{80.0 \text{ g NaOH}}{40.0 \text{ g/mol NaOH}} = 2.00 \text{ mol}$$

Convert grams of solvent to kg:

$$\frac{500.0 \text{ g}}{1000 \text{ g/kg}} = 500 \text{ kg}$$

Divide:

$$\frac{2.00 \text{ mol NaOH}}{0.500} = 4.00 \text{ m}$$

Electrolytes

Certain solutions are capable of conducting an electric current and these solutions are referred to as **electrolytes**. Generally speaking, we say that there are three classes of electrolytes (solutions that conduct a current): acids, bases, and salts.

- **Strong electrolytes** consist of solutes that dissociate completely in solution. Strong acids, strong bases, and soluble salts are in this category. (We will discuss acids and bases in chapter 6.)
- **Nonelectrolytes** are substances that are predominantly covalently bonded, generally will not produce ions in solution, and therefore are considered nonconductors.
- **Weak electrolytes** consist of solutes that dissociate only a little in solution. Weak acids, weak bases, and slightly soluble salts are in this category.

The greater the degree of dissociation of the solute, the greater the conductivity of the solution. Consider two acid solutions that have the same concentration—hydrochloric acid and acetic acid. Hydrochloric acid ionizes completely, while only about 2% of the acetic acid molecules ionize. If a conductivity apparatus were used to test the two solutions, HCl would conduct an electric current to a much greater degree because there is more available charge in solution. Below is a figure showing the ionization of barium chloride; as you can see, the Ba^+ and Cl^- ions are floating free in solution, and this makes barium chloride an electrolyte.

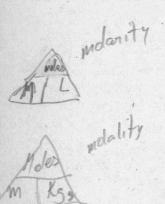

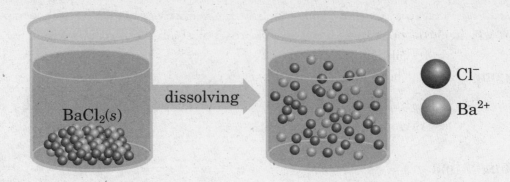

dissolving

BaCl$_2$(s)

Cl$^-$

Ba^{2+}

molarity

moles / M / L

molality

Moles / m / Kg

Colligative Properties

Properties of solutions that depend on the number of solute particles present per solvent molecule are called **colligative properties**. The concentration of solute in a solution can affect various physical properties of the solvent including its freezing point, boiling point, and vapor pressure. For the SAT II you will only need to be familiar with the first two.

Freezing Point Depression

The freezing point of a substance is defined as the temperature at which the vapor pressure of the solid and the liquid states of that substance are equal. If the vapor pressure of the liquid is lowered, the freezing point decreases.

Why is a solution's freezing point depressed below that of a pure solvent? The answer lies in the fact that molecules cluster in order to freeze. They must be attracted to one another and have a spot in which to cluster; if they act as a solvent, solute molecules get in the way and prevent them from clustering tightly together. The more ions in solution, the greater the effect on the freezing point. We can calculate the effect of these solute particles by using the following formula:

$$\Delta T_f = K_f \times m_{\text{solute}} \times i$$

where

ΔT_f = the change in freezing point

K_f = molal freezing point depression constant for the substance (for water = 1.86°C/m)

m = molality of the solution

i = number of ions in solution (this is equal to 1 for covalent compounds and is equal to the number of ions in solution for ionic compounds)

Density H$_2$O

= 1g/ml

Boiling Point Elevation

As you learned earlier in this chapter, the boiling point of a substance is the temperature at which the vapor pressure equals atmospheric pressure. Because vapor pressure is lowered by the addition of a nonvolatile solute, the boiling point is increased. Why? Since the solute

$$m = \frac{moles\ of\ solute}{Kg\ solvent}$$

The States of Matter

Example • 91

particles get in the way of the solvent particles trying to escape the substance as they move around faster, it will take more energy for the vapor pressure to reach atmospheric pressure, and thus the boiling point increases. We can calculate the change in boiling point in a way that's similar to how we calculate the change in freezing point:

$$\Delta T_b = K_b \times m_{solute} \times i$$

where

K_b = molal boiling point elevation constant (for water = 0.51°C/m)

Now try a problem that deals with freezing point depression and boiling point elevation.

Example

Calculate the freezing point and boiling point of a solution of 100 g of ethylene glycol ($C_2H_6O_2$) in 900 g of water.

Explanation

Calculate molality:

$$100 \text{ g ethylene glycol } \times \frac{1 \text{ mol ethylene glycol}}{62.0 \text{ g ethylene glycol}}$$

$$m = \frac{1.61 \text{ mol}}{0.900 \text{ kg}} = 1.79 \ m$$

Freezing point depression = $(m)(K_f)(i)$
$T_f = (1.79)(1.86)(1) = 3.33°C$
Freezing point = 0°C – 3.33°C = –3.33°C

Boiling point elevation = $(m)(K_m)(i)$
$T_b = (1.79)(0.51)(1) = 0.91°C$
Boiling point = 100°C + 0.91°C = 100.91°C

Practice Questions

1.	Ice, unlike most substances, is denser than water in the liquid phase.	BECAUSE	In water, hydrogen bonds can form between the positively charged H atom on one water molecule and the slightly negatively charged O atom on a nearby water molecule.

2. Which of the following gases would be the densest at standard temperature and pressure?

(A)   Helium
(B)   Argon
(C)   Carbon dioxide
(D)   Xenon
(E)   Nitrogen

3. In the laboratory, a sample of hydrogen is collected by water displacement. The sample of hydrogen has a volume of 25 mL at 24.0°C and a barometric pressure for the day of 758 mmHg. What is the pressure of the dry gas at this temperature? (The vapor pressure of water at 24.0°C is 22.4 mmHg.)

(A)   455 mmHg
(B)   470 mmHg
(C)   736 mmHg
(D)   758 mmHg
(E)   780 mmHg

4. Calculate the approximate amount of heat necessary to raise the temperature of 50.0 grams of liquid water from 10.0°C to 30.0°C. (The specific heat of water liquid is 4.18 J/g°C.)

(A)   20 J
(B)   80 J
(C)   100 J
(D)   200 J
(E)   4,180 J

Refer to the phase diagram below to answer question 5.

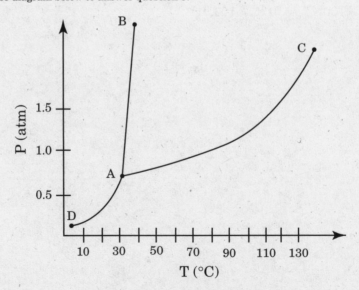

5. Using the sketch of the phase diagram for water given above, determine which of the following statements is incorrect:

(A)   The triple point is point *A*. This is the point at which all three phases are in equilibrium with one another.

(B)   The line *AB* is the line representing the solid-liquid equilibrium line. Anywhere along this line the substance could melt or freeze.

(C)   The slope of line *AB* is negative. This slope indicates that the solid is much denser than the liquid.

(D)   Line *AD* represents the phase changes of sublimation and deposition.

(E)   Line *AC* represents where the substance would condense and vaporize.

| 6. | Most ionic solids have high melting points. | BECAUSE | Ionic solids are made up of positive and negative ions held together by electrostatic attractions. |

7. Which of the following best illustrates a graph of pressure versus volume for a gas at constant temperature?

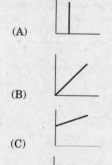

(A)

(B)

(C)

(D)

(E)

8. Which of the following solutions would probably have the highest boiling point?

(A)   0.100 *m* KOH
(B)   0.100 *m* Na_2SO_4
(C)   0.100 *m* $C_6H_{12}O_6$
(D)   0.200 *m* $CaCl_2$
(E)   0.200 *m* CH_3CH_2OH

9. Which of the following must be measured in order to calculate the molality of a solution?

      I.   Mass of the solute
      II.   Mass of the solvent
      III.   Total volume of the solution

(A)   I only
(B)   I and III only
(C)   II and III only
(D)   I and II only
(E)   I, II, and III

10. The molarity of a solution that is composed of 80.00 g of sodium hydroxide dissolved in 2.0 L of solution is

(A)   1.0 M
(B)   2.0 M
(C)   4.0 M
(D)   40.0 M
(E)   160.0 M

11. Which of the following substances would dissociate completely when placed into excess amounts of distilled water?

(A) C_2H_5OH
(B) $HC_2H_3O_2$
(C) $LiNO_3$
(D) $Mg(OH)_2$
(E)   All of these will dissociate completely in water

12.	The solubility of carbon dioxide in a soft drink decreases with a decrease in pressure.	BECAUSE	The solubility of a gas generally increases with an increase in temperature.

13. The molarity of a solution obtained when 50.0 mL of 6.0 M HCl is diluted to a final volume of 300.0 mL is

(A)   0.01 M
(B)   0.10 M
(C)   0.20 M
(D)   0.30 M
(E)   1.0 M

14. Which of the following solutes and solvents would be expected to form stable solutions?

	Solute	Solvent
I.	ethanol	water
II.	salt	water
III.	oil	vinegar
IV.	oil	gasoline

(A)   I only
(B)   I and II only
(C)   III only
(D)   I, II, and III only
(E)   I, II, and IV only

Explanations

1. F, T

(Do not fill in **CE**.) The first statement is false—water is actually *less* dense in its solid, frozen form, which is not true of most liquids. This is due to the hydrogen bonds that form between water molecules in water's liquid state. When the temperature of water becomes low enough that water freezes, the molecules are locked into a regular, crystal lattice structure in which the molecules are actually farther apart from each other than they are when water is in its liquid state. The second statement is true, but since the first is false, there is no need to fill in the **CE** oval.

2. D

You'll need to use the periodic table you're given during the exam to answer this question since you'll have to find the masses of the gases. Remember that the density of a gas is measured in grams per liter and that you will calculate the volume using the standard for gases at STP: 22.4 L per mole. Finally, remember that the heavier the molecule, the more dense the gas. **A** Helium is only 4 g/mol, **B** argon is 40 g/mol, **C** carbon dioxide is 44 g/mol, **D** xenon is 131 g/mol, and **E** nitrogen (N_2) is diatomic, so this means it has a mass of 28 g/mol. The best choice is **D**, xenon.

3. C

This question appears to be very involved, so you might be tempted to use the ideal gas equation; however, the question only asks for the pressure of the dry gas. You're given atmospheric pressure and water vapor pressure at the defined temperature, so all you need to do is subtract the water vapor from the atmospheric pressure: 758 mmHg – 22.4 mmHg = 735.6 mmHg; this matches **C**. Since you will not have a calculator, round numbers off: 760 – 20 = 740. The closest answer choice is **C**.

4. E

In this problem, the phase does not change; liquid water increases in temperature by 20.0°C. This will take energy—to calculate the energy, use the equation $q = mC_p\Delta T$. You have all the information that you need: $Q = (50.0 \text{ g})(4.184 \text{ J/g°C})(20.0°C)$. Again, make the math easy: approximate that $20 \times 50 = 1000$, then multiply by 4 to get 4000 J—the only answer choice that's close is choice **E**.

5. C

A is the triple point, so this statement is true. **B** is the line that separates the solid and the liquid, so this is also a true statement. **C** is the answer. The slope of this line is not negative; it is positive. The second half of the statement is true: when there is a positive slope, the solid is more dense than the liquid. **D** is where the solid and vapor phase meet, so this statement is also true—sublimation and deposition are the changes of state associated with solids and gases. Finally, **E** is also a true statement—the line represents where the liquid meets the vapor, and so these changes of state could take place.

6.   **T, T**

(Fill in **CE**.) The first statement is true: most ionic solids are characterized as having a high melting point. Ionic solids are also hard and brittle, with poor thermal and electrical conduction. The second statement is also true—ionic solids consist of positive and negative ions held together by electrostatic attractions, and you should fill in **CE** because the second statement is the reason for the first statement's being true.

7.   **E**

To answer this question, you must think about the relationship between pressure and volume. Boyle's law states that if the pressure is increased, the volume will decrease if all other factors are held constant. This type of relationship is an inverse relationship, and choice **E** is the only graph that shows an inverse relationship.

8.   **D**

The boiling point of a solution depends on the solution's concentration in molality and the number of ions that exist in solution. First eliminate any answer choices that contain organic compounds, since carbon compounds are covalently bonded and do not disassociate into ions in solution; in this way you can eliminates choices **C** and **E**. Choice **A** would produce two ions in solution, choice **B** would produce three ions in solution, and choice **D** would produce three ions in solution. Now you must choose between **B** and **D**. Since the molality is greater in **D** and **D** produces the same number of ions, it would have the highest boiling point.

9.   **D**

This question requires that you know the definition of molality: molality is the number of moles of solute per kilogram of solvent. Since moles are not directly measured, instead the mass of the solute, (I), would be the component measured in the laboratory. The mass of the solvent can be expressed in kilograms of solvent, or (II). The total volume, (III), is not needed to calculate molality—just molarity, so look for an answer that contains both (I) and (II); the answer is **D**.

10.   **A**

This question asks you to calculate the molarity, which is the moles of solute per liter of solution. 80.0 grams of NaOH can be converted to moles by dividing 80 by 40 (the molecular weight of NaOH), and this gives you 2 moles. Now divide 2 by 2 to get 1.0 M, which is answer choice **A**.

11. **C**

This question in essence asks which of the answer choices is a strong electrolyte. Strong electrolytes are strong acids, strong bases, and soluble salts. Let's go through the answer choices. Choice **A** is not a strong electrolyte—it's an alcohol. Choice **B** is acetic acid, an organic acid, and is only a weak electrolyte. Choice **C** is a soluble salt; all nitrates are soluble and thus dissociate in solution. This is the correct answer. Choice **D** is ionically bonded but is not a strong base. In group 2A, only barium, strontium, and calcium hydroxides are considered to be strong. $Mg(OH)_2$ is a chalky white liquid often taken as a laxative.

12. **T, F**

(Do not fill in **CE**.) Statement I is true—when the pressure of a system is decreased, the solubility of a gas decreases; as you probably know from experience, when you open a soda bottle, the pressure of the system decreases significantly, and gas bubbles rise to the top and escape. Statement II says that heating a gas in a solution will make the gas more soluble; this is not true. Since this statement is false, you would not fill in the **CE** oval.

13. **E**

This is a dilution problem, so use the formula you learned in this chapter to solve it: $M_1V_1 = M_2V_2$. The problem gave you the following values to plug in: $(6.0 \ M)(50.0 \ \text{mL}) = (M)(300.0 \ \text{mL})$. Do the math, and you get 300 divided by 300 = 1.0 M. This is answer choice **E**.

14. **E**

When you see a problem that looks like this, inspect each pairing one at a time. Here keep in mind that "like dissolves like," so polar substances will be soluble in polar and ionic substances, and nonpolar substances will be soluble in nonpolar substances. Look at (I): ethanol is a polar substance due to the hydroxyl group, and water is also polar, so these two substances should make a stable solution. (II) Salt is ionically bonded and water is polar, so these two should also make a stable solution. (III) Oil is nonpolar, and vinegar (acetic acid) is polar because of its carboxylic acid group, so these two substances should not mix well. (IV) Oil and gasoline are both nonpolar, so these two substances should make a stable solution. Look for the answer choice that contains I, II, and IV; choice **E** is the match.

The States of Matter

Reaction Types

Now that you are familiar with atoms and molecules and how they make up the solids, liquids, and gases we see around us, let's discuss what happens when two molecules meet: namely, chemical reactions. A **chemical reaction** is defined as a process by which one or more substances are changed into one or more new substances. Chemical reactions are usually portrayed in this way:

$$\text{reactant} \rightarrow \text{product}$$

The $\rightarrow$ is read as "yields" or "produces." You will often see the states of matter in parentheses as subscripts after the chemical formulas of the reactants and products. The symbols for the states of matter and some other chemical reaction symbols you should be familiar with are given in the table below.

Symbol	Meaning
$\rightarrow$	"Yields" or "produces"
$+$	"Reacts with" or "and"
(g)	Gaseous state
(l)	Liquid state
(s)	Solid state
(aq)	Aqueous state (dissolved in water)
number subscript	Represents the number of atoms of the element it's to the right of

Symbol	Meaning
number coefficient	How many molecules or moles of the substance are reacting
$\xrightarrow{Pt}$	A substance named above the arrow represents a catalyst in the reaction
↑	A gas is produced
↓	A precipitate is formed
kJ or J	Energy term (kilojoules or joules)
⇔	Reversible equation; equilibrium
$\xrightarrow{\Delta}$	A delta above the reaction arrow indicates that heat is added to the reaction

Balancing Chemical Equations

You may remember that the law of conservation of mass says that matter is neither created nor destroyed during a chemical reaction. This means that all chemical reactions must be balanced—the number of atoms, moles, and ultimately the total mass must be conserved during a chemical process. Here are the rules to follow when balancing equations:

1. Determine the correct formulas for all the reactants and products in the reaction.
2. Begin balancing with the most complicated-looking group. A polyatomic ion that appears unchanged on both sides of the equation can be counted as a single unit.
3. Save the elemental (single elements) reactant and products for last, *especially* if it is hydrogen or oxygen. Keep your eye out for diatomic molecules such as oxygen, hydrogen, and the halogens.
4. If you get stuck, double the most complicated-looking group and try again.
5. Finally, make sure that all coefficients are in the lowest-possible ratio.
6. Know when to quit! None of the reactions you will encounter will be that difficult. If the coefficients are getting wild, double-check what you've done since you may have a simple mistake.

When balancing reactions, keep your hands off the subscripts! Use only coefficients to balance chemical equations. Now let's try an example. When you solve it yourself, make sure to follow the steps!

Example

Write the balanced equation for the reaction between chlorine and sodium bromide, which produces bromine and sodium chloride.

Reaction Types

Explanation

First write the chemical formulas—be on the lookout for the diatomic elements (such as Cl_2):

$$Cl_2 + NaBr \rightarrow Br_2 + NaCl$$

Next, find the reagent with the scariest subscripts. In this case, start with Cl_2. You need a coefficient of 2 in front of NaCl, which then requires a coefficient of 2 in front of NaBr. The balanced equation becomes

$$Cl_2 + 2NaBr \rightarrow Br_2 + 2NaCl$$

Finally, count up everything to make sure you balanced the equation correctly. You have two chlorine atoms, two sodium atoms, and two bromines on the reactants side and two bromines, two sodiums, and two chlorines on the products side. You're done.

Example

Write the balanced equation for the reaction between aluminum sulfate and calcium chloride, which produces aluminum chloride and calcium sulfate.

Explanation

Write the chemical formulas on their correct sides:

$$Al_2(SO_4)_3 + CaCl_2 \rightarrow AlCl_3 + CaSO_4$$

In this reaction, the aluminum sulfate looks the most complicated, so start there. Look at what happens with sulfate—since it remains sulfate on the right side of the reaction, treat it as a unit. You have three on the left side and only one on the right side, so place a coefficient of 3 in front of calcium sulfate. Now deal with the aluminum. You have three on the left and one on the right, so place a coefficient of 2 in front of aluminum chloride. Last, you must place a coefficient of 3 in front of calcium chloride.

$$Al_2(SO_4)_3 + 3CaCl_2 \rightarrow 2AlCl_3 + 3CaSO_4$$

Count the atoms on both sides of the reaction and you'll see that you're done.

Types of Chemical Reactions

It is important that you know the basic types of chemical reactions for the SAT II Chemistry test since the test often refers to reactions as being of one type or another. Here's a list of the different types of reactions, with examples of each type included.

Synthesis reaction: This is a reaction in which two or more elements or compounds combine to form a single product. This type of reaction follows the general equation

$$A + B \rightarrow C$$

Reaction Types

where A and B may be either elements or compounds.

Here are some examples:

$$2Na_{(s)} + Cl_{2(g)} \rightarrow 2NaCl_{(s)}$$

$$MgO_{(s)} + H_2O_{(l)} \rightarrow Mg(OH)_{2(aq)}$$

$$SO_{2(g)} + H_2O_{(l)} \rightarrow H_2SO_{3(aq)}$$

Decomposition reaction: In this type of reaction, a single reactant, a compound, breaks into two or more parts. Often these are the most difficult to predict. Here is the general equation:

$$AB \rightarrow A + B$$

where A and B may be either elements or compounds.

Here are some examples of decomposition reactions:

$$2H_2O_{(l)} \rightarrow 2H_{2(g)} + O_{2(g)}$$

$$H_2CO_{3(aq)} \rightarrow H_2O_{(l)} + CO_{2(g)}$$

$$CaCO_{3(s)} \rightarrow CaO_{(s)} + CO_{2(g)}$$

$$2KClO_{3(s)} \rightarrow 2KCl_{(s)} + 3O_{2(g)}$$

Single replacement or displacement reaction: In this type of reaction, a more active element replaces a less active element in a compound. Among the halogens, F_2 is the most active halogen, and the activity of the halogens decreases as you go down the group. For the metals, you will need to be given an activity series. General equation:

$$A + BC \rightarrow AC + B$$

where A is a metal.

Here is an example of a displacement reaction in which a metal is involved:

$$Cu_{(s)} + 2AgNO_{3(aq)} \rightarrow 2Ag_{(s)} + Cu(NO_3)_{2(aq)}$$

General equation:

$$A + BC \rightarrow BA + C$$

where A is a nonmetal.

Here is an example of a displacement reaction where a nonmetal is involved:

$$Cl_{2(g)} + 2NaI_{(aq)} \rightarrow 2NaCl_{(aq)} + I_{2(s)}$$

Double replacement or displacement reaction: In this type of reaction, two compounds react to form two new compounds. The formation of a molecular compound such as water, the formation of a gas, or the formation of a precipitate usually drives these reactions. Here's the general equation:

$$AB + CD \rightarrow AD + CB$$

And here are a couple of examples:

$$Pb(NO_3)_{2(aq)} + 2KI_{(aq)} \rightarrow 2KNO_{3(aq)} + PbI_{2(s)}$$

$$HCl_{(aq)} + NaOH_{(aq)} \rightarrow H_2O_{(l)} + NaCl_{(aq)}$$

Combustion reaction: In this type of reaction, often a hydrocarbon is burned in the presence of oxygen gas to form carbon dioxide (in a complete combustion) or carbon monoxide (in an incomplete combustion, due to a limited amount of oxygen). Here is the general equation in the presence of plenty of oxygen:

$$C_xH_y + O_{2(g)} \rightarrow CO_{2(g)} + H_2O_{(l\ or\ g)}$$

An example of this is seen when methane gas is burned in the presence of excess oxygen (Bunsen burner reaction):

$$CH_{4(g)} + 2O_{2(g)} \rightarrow CO_{2(g)} + 2H_2O_{(g)}$$

Here is the general equation for when a hydrocarbon is burned in an incomplete combustion (oxygen is in limited supply):

$$C_xH_y + O_{2(g)} \rightarrow CO_{(g)} + H_2O_{(l)}$$

Hydrolysis reaction: A reaction that involves water. Here is the general equation for a hydrolysis reaction:

$$X^-_{(aq)} + H_2O_{(l)} \Leftrightarrow HX_{(aq)} + OH^-_{(aq)}$$

Net Ionic Equations

Net ionic equations are equations that show only the soluble, strong electrolytes reacting (these are represented as ions) and omit the **spectator ions**, which go through the reaction unchanged. When you encounter net ionic equations on the SAT II Chemistry test, you'll need to remember the following solubility rules, so memorize them! Also keep in mind that net ionic equations, which are the bare bones of the chemical reaction, usually take place in aqueous environments. Here are those solubility rules:

1. Most alkali metal compounds *and* NH_4^+ compounds are **soluble**.

2. Cl^-, Br^-, I^- compounds are **soluble**, except when they contain Ag^+, Hg_2^{2+}, or Pb^{2+}.

3. F^- compounds are **soluble**, except when they contain group 2A metals.

4. NO_3^-, ClO_3^-, ClO_4^-, and CH_3COO^- compounds are **soluble**.

5. SO_4^{2-} compounds are **soluble**, except when they include Ca^{2+}, Sr^{2+}, Ba^{2+}, Ag^+, Pb^{2+}, or Hg_2^{2+}.

6. CO_3^{2-}, PO_4^{3-}, $C_2O_4^{2-}$, CrO_4^{2-}, S^{2-}, OH^-, and O^{2-} compounds are **insoluble**.

7. Group 2A metal oxides are classified as strong bases even though they are not very soluble.

The two solubility rules that you will use the most are numbers 1 and 4. You must memorize that all group 1A metal and ammonium compounds are soluble. As soon as you see a compound NH_4^+, Li, Na, K, Rb, Cs, or Fr, you should know that it's soluble. Also, all nitrates are soluble—look at the end of the compound. If it ends in NO_3^-, you know that it's soluble.

What's the big deal with solubility? Well, if the ion is soluble, it won't form a precipitate, and this means it doesn't react and should be left out of the net ionic equation. The key is first to write the compound's chemical formula and then determine if it's soluble. If it is soluble, then ionize it—if it isn't, don't ionize it; leave it as a molecule.

Here are some additional rules about common reaction types that you should be familiar with for the exam:

- If an insoluble precipitate or gas can be formed in a reaction, it probably will be.
- Oxides (except group 1A) are insoluble, and when reacted with water, they form either acids (nonmetal oxides) or bases (metal oxides).
- There are six strong acids that completely ionize: HCl, HBr, HI, HNO_3, H_2SO_4, $HClO_4$. All other acids are weak and are written together, as molecules.
- The strong bases that ionize are oxides and hydroxides of group 1A and 2A metals. All other oxides and hydroxides are considered weak and written together, as molecules.

Now try writing some net ionic equations, using the rules above.

Example

Write the net ionic equation for a mixture of solutions of silver nitrate and lithium bromide.

Explanation

$$Ag^+ + NO_3^- + Li^+ + Br^- \rightarrow$$

Reaction Types

Example • 105

This is a double replacement reaction. Both compounds are soluble, so everything ionizes. If anything is formed, it will come from recombining the "inside" two ions with the "outside" two ions to make $LiNO_3$ and AgBr. If either of them is *in*soluble, a precipitate will be formed, and the ions that react to form it will be in our net ionic equation; the other ions are spectators and should be omitted! As we said, the two possible products are lithium nitrate and silver bromide. Since halides are soluble *except* those containing silver, mercury, or lead, we have a precipitate of silver bromide, and our net ionic equation looks like this:

$$Ag^+ + Br^- \rightarrow AgBr\downarrow$$

Example

Hydrochloric acid and sodium hydroxide are mixed. Write the net ionic equation.

Explanation

This is a mixture of a strong acid and a strong base, so each ionizes completely.

$$H^+ + Cl^- + Na^+ + OH^- \rightarrow$$

The two possible compounds formed are sodium chloride, which is soluble, and water, which is molecular; thus water is the only product in our net ionic equation.

$$H^+ + OH^- \rightarrow H_2O$$

Example

Chlorine gas is bubbled into a solution of potassium iodide; write the net ionic equation.

Explanation

This one is a single replacement, so you need to consider the activity series. Since halogens are involved, you can determine their activity by using the periodic table: Cl is more active than I.

$$Cl_2 + K^+ + I^- \rightarrow$$

Remember that halogen is diatomic and that all potassium compounds are soluble. The resulting compound is also soluble, so K^+ is a spectator and is left out of the final equation.

$$Cl_2 + I^- \rightarrow I_2 + Cl^-$$

Reaction Types

The Chemistry of Acids and Bases

Acid-Base Theories

Let's start our discussion of acids and bases by defining some terms that are essential to the topics that follow.

Arrhenius acids and bases are:

acid—a substance that increases the concentration of protons (H^+) in water

base—a substance that increases the concentration of hydroxide ions in water (OH^-)

These definitions are limited to aqueous solutions.

Brønsted and Lowry acids and bases as:

acid—a substance that donates a proton to another substance

base—a substance that accepts a proton

These definitions can also apply to reactions that are not aqueous, so they are more accurate.

Lewis acids and bases are:

acid—a substance that accepts an electron pair

base—a substance that donates an electron pair

Here are some other terms that you'll need to be familiar with:

hydronium (H_3O^+)—H^+ riding "piggyback" on a water molecule; water is polar, and the positive charge of the naked proton is greatly attracted to one of the negative electron pairs on adjacent oxygen

monoprotic—describes acids that can donate one H^+

diprotic—describes acids that can donate two H^+ ions

polyprotic—describes acids that can donate more than one H^+ ion

amphiprotic—describes a substance that can act as either an acid or a base. This means it can either lose a proton or gain one. Water is amphiprotic: it can form either a hydroxide ion or a hydronium ion. Other examples of amphiprotic substances are HCO_3^-, HSO_4^-, HPO_4^{2-}

Reaction Types

Conjugate Acid-Base Pairs

Now that we've defined acids and bases, let's discuss how they work together in reactions. Look at the generic acid-base reaction below:

$$HX_{(aq)} + H_2O_{(l)} \Leftrightarrow X^-_{(aq)} + H_3O_{(aq)}$$

When the forward reaction occurs, HX donates a proton to water (so it acts as the base) to form hydronium. When the reverse reaction occurs, the hydronium ion acts as the acid, donating a proton to the X^-. Together, HX and X^- are said to be conjugate acid-base pairs. Conjugate acid-base pairs are compounds that differ by the presence of one proton, or H^+. All acids have a conjugate base, which is formed when their proton has been donated; likewise, all bases have a conjugate acid, formed after they have accepted a proton.

Example

Apply the appropriate acid-base theory to first identify the acid and base reacting and then identify the conjugate acid-base pairs in the examples below:

1. $HNO_3 + H_2O \rightarrow H_3O^+ + NO_3^-$
2. $NH_4^+ + H_2O \rightarrow H_3O^+ + NH_3$

Explanation

1. In this first reaction, we see that HNO_3 gives a proton to water, which then forms a hydronium ion. This makes HNO_3 the acid in the forward reaction, and water acts as the base. HNO_3's conjugate base is NO_3^-, and water's conjugate acid is the hydronium ion, or H_3O^+.

$$HNO_3 + H_2O \rightarrow H_3O^+ + NO_3^-$$
$$\quad A \qquad B \quad\; CA \qquad CB$$

2. Here NH_4^+ donates the proton to water, so in the forward reaction it acts as the acid, and water is still the base. NH_4^+'s conjugate base is NH_3, and water's conjugate acid is again the hydronium ion, H_3O^+.

$$NH_4^+ + H_2O \rightarrow H_3O^+ + NH_3$$
$$\quad A \qquad B \quad\; CA \qquad CB$$

Relative Strengths of Acids and Bases

Certain acids are stronger than other acids, and some bases are stronger than others. What this means is that some acids are better at donating a proton, and some bases are better proton acceptors. A **strong** acid or base dissociates or ionizes completely in aqueous solution. A **weak** acid or base does not completely ionize.

Strong Acids

There are six strong acids that you'll need to memorize for the SAT II Chemistry test:

- Hydrohalic acids: HCl, HBr, HI
- Nitric acid: HNO_3
- Sulfuric acid: H_2SO_4
- Perchloric acid: $HClO_4$

Let's take a closer look at how acids differ in strength by focusing on perchloric acid. In general, the greater the number of oxygen atoms in a polyatomic ion, the stronger the acid.

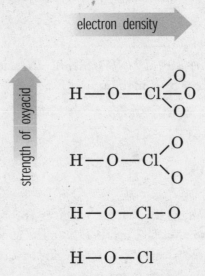

So $HClO_4$ is stronger than $HClO_3$, which is stronger than $HClO_2$, which is stronger than HClO. (Perchloric acid is the strongest among the six, but all the other oxyacids of chlorine are not considered strong acids.) Now think about why, as you take away oxygens, the strength of the acid decreases. The hydrogen (proton) to be removed is bonded to an oxygen atom. The oxygens are highly electronegative and are pulling the bonded pair of electrons *away* from the site where the hydrogen is bonded, thus making it easier to remove the H^+. As the number of oxygen decreases, the molecule becomes less polar, and the H^+ is harder to remove.

Strong Bases

There are fewer strong bases to memorize for the exam. These are hydroxides ($-OH$), oxides of 1A and 2A metals (except Mg and Be), H^-, and CH_3^-. Remember that the stronger the acid, the weaker its conjugate base, and the converse is also true. The figure below illustrates the relative strengths of some common conjugate acid-base pairs.

	ACID	BASE	
Strong — 100% ionized in H₂O	HCl	Cl⁻	**Negligible**
	H_2SO_4	HSO_4^-	
	HNO_3	NO_3^-	
	$H_3O^+(aq)$	H_2O	
Weak	HSO_4^-	SO_4^{2-}	**Weak**
	H_3PO_4	$H_2PO_4^-$	
	HF	F^-	
	$HC_2H_3O_2$	$C_2H_3O_2^-$	
	H_2CO_3	HCO_3^-	
	H_2S	HS^-	
	$H_2PO_4^-$	HPO_4^{2-}	
	NH_4^+	NH_3	
	HCO_3^-	CO_3^{2-}	
	HPO_4^{2-}	PO_4^{3-}	
	H_2O	OH^-	
Negligible	OH^-	O^{2-}	**Strong** — 100% protonated in H₂O
	H_2	H^-	
	CH_4	CH_3^-	

Acid strength increases →

Base strength increases →

The pH Scale

As you know, water can act as either a proton donor (in the form of the hydronium ion, H_3O^+) or a proton acceptor (as OH^-). In solution, a water molecule can even donate a proton to or accept a proton from another water molecule, and this process is called **autoionization**:

$$2H_2O \rightarrow H_3O^+ + OH^-$$

Since this reaction takes place in equilibrium, we can write an equilibrium expression, K_{eq}, for it:

$$K_{eq} = [H_3O^+][OH^-]$$

And since this expression refers specifically to the ionization of water, we can write the equilibrium expression as K_w. At 25°C, the value of K_w, which is known as the **ion-product constant**, is 1×10^{-14}. This means that the $[H_3O^+] = [OH^-]$ and each is equal to 1×10^{-7}. When the concentrations of H^+ and OH^- are equal in a solution, the solution is said to be neutral. In acidic solutions, the concentration of H^+ is higher than that of OH^-, and in basic solutions, the concentration of OH^- is greater than that of H^+.

Reaction Types

	$[H^+]$	pH	
	10^{-14}	14	1 M NaOH
	10^{-13}	13	
	10^{-12}	12	ammonia
basic	10^{-11}	11	
	10^{-10}	10	
	10^{-9}	9	
	10^{-8}	8	blood
neutral	10^{-7}	7	distilled water
	10^{-6}	6	milk
	10^{-5}	5	
	10^{-4}	4	
acidic	10^{-3}	3	vinegar lemon juice
	10^{-2}	2	stomach acid
	10^{-1}	1	
	1	0	1 M HCl

The **pH** of a solution is calculated as the negative logarithm in base 10 of the hydronium ion concentration—it is an expression of the molar concentration of H^+ ions in solution:

$$pH = -\log[H^+] \text{ or } -\log[H_3O^+]$$

A solution like the equilibrium expression for water, which is neutral at standard temperature, would have a pH of

$$pH = -\log[1 \times 10^{-7}] = -(-7.00) = 7.00$$

So as you can see, neutral solutions have a pH of 7. If the solution contains more hydronium ions than this neutral solution ($[H^+] > 1 \times 10^{-7}$), the pH will be less than 7.00, and the solution will be acidic; if the solution contains more hydroxide ions than this neutral solution ($[OH^-] > 1 \times 10^{-7}$), the pH will be greater than 7.00, and the solution will be basic.

Similarly, the pOH of a solution is calculated as the negative logarithm in base 10 of the hydroxide ion concentration:

$$pOH = -\log[OH^-]$$

Reaction Types

and pH and pOH are related to each other by the equation

$$pH + pOH = 14$$

Since you won't be allowed to have a calculator for the SAT II Chemistry test, you can use the following equation if you need to calculate the hydronium ion concentration of a solution:

$$[H_3O^+] = 10^{-pH}$$

Now try a problem: What is the pH of a solution at 25°C in which $[OH^-] = 1.0 \times 10^{-5} M$?

Explanation

The fact that this solution is at 25°C tells us that we should use the K_w relationships. If the $[OH^-] = 1.0 \times 10^{-5}$ M, then pOH = 5. You know that 1.0×10^{-5} is the same as plain old 10^{-5}. The log of 10^{-5} is −5 (simply use the exponent when a number, any number, is written as 10^{power}, so the "negative" of the log is equal to −(−5), or simply 5. Now, if the pOH is 5, then the pH is 9 since pH + pOH = 14.

Acid–Base Reactions: Neutralization Reactions

When a strong acid and a strong base solution are mixed, a neutralization reaction occurs, and the products do not have characteristics of either acids or bases. Instead, a neutral salt and water are formed. Look at the reaction below:

$$HCl_{(aq)} + NaOH_{(aq)} \rightarrow H_2O_{(l)} + NaCl_{(aq)}$$

The anion from the acid (Cl^-) reacts with the cation from the base (Na^+) to give a salt, and a **salt** is defined as any compound formed whose anion came from an acid and whose cation came from a base.

When a strong acid and a weak base are mixed, the resulting salt will be acidic; likewise, if a strong base and a weak acid are mixed, the resulting salt will be basic. If on the SAT II Chemistry test you are asked to determine if a salt formed in a particular reaction is neutral, acidic, or basic, first ask yourself, *Which acid reacted with which base to form this salt?* Next ask yourself, *Was the acid strong or weak?* and then, *Was the base strong or weak?* Consider K_2CO_3. K_2CO_3 is formed when the base, potassium hydroxide (which is strong since potassium is a 1A metal), reacts with the acid, H_2CO_3 (which is weak since it isn't one of our six strong acids). Since this is a combination of a strong base and a weak acid, the salt formed will be basic.

The good news is that for the SAT II Chemistry exam, you needn't worry about weak-weak combinations. Now try some problems on your own.

Example

Classify each of the salts listed below as acidic, basic, or neutral.

1. $Fe(NO_3)_3$
2. $MgSO_4$
3. $Ni(ClO_4)_2$

Explanation

1. $Fe(NO_3)_3$—This salt was formed from the reaction of a weak base, iron (III) hydroxide, with a strong acid, nitric acid. This means that the salt will be acidic.
2. $MgSO_4$—This salt was formed from the reaction of a strong base, magnesium hydroxide, with strong acid, sulfuric acid. This reaction results in a neutral salt.
3. $Ni(ClO_4)_2$—This salt was formed from the reaction of a weak base, nickel (II) hydroxide, with a strong acid, perchloric acid. This is an acidic salt.

Redox and Electrochemistry

Oxidation-reduction (redox) reactions are another important type of reaction that you will see questions about on the SAT II Chemistry test. The test writers will expect you to be able to identify elements that are oxidized and reduced, know their oxidation numbers, identify half-cells, and balance redox reactions. The following is a brief overview of the basics.

Oxidation-Reduction

Oxidation-reduction reactions involve the transfer of electrons between substances. They take place simultaneously, which makes sense because if one substance loses electrons, another must gain them. Many of the reactions we've encountered thus far fall into this category. For example, all single-replacement reactions are redox reactions. Before we go on, let's review some important terms you'll need to be familiar with.

Electrochemistry: The study of the interchange of chemical and electrical energy.

Oxidation: The loss of electrons. Since electrons are negative, this will appear as an increase in the charge (e.g., Zn loses two electrons; its charge goes from 0 to +2). Metals are oxidized.

Oxidizing agent (OA): The species that is reduced and thus causes oxidation.

Reduction: The gain of electrons. When an element gains electrons, the charge on the element appears to decrease, so we say it has a reduction of charge (e.g., Cl gains one electron and goes from an oxidation number of 0 to –1). Nonmetals are reduced.

Reducing agent (RA): The species that is oxidized and thus causes reduction.

Oxidation number: The assigned charge on an atom. You've been using these numbers to balance formulas.

Half-reaction: An equation that shows either oxidation or reduction alone.

Rules for Assigning Oxidation States

A reaction is considered a redox reaction if the oxidation numbers of the elements in the reaction change in the course of the reaction. We can determine which elements undergo a change in oxidation state by keeping track of the oxidation numbers as the reaction progresses. You can use the following rules to assign oxidation states to the components of oxidation-reduction reactions:

1. The oxidation state of an element is *zero*, including all elemental forms of the elements (e.g., N_2, P_4, S_8, O_3).
2. The oxidation state of a monatomic ion is the same as its charge.
3. In compounds, fluorine is always assigned an oxidation state of –1.
4. Oxygen is usually assigned an oxidation state of –2 in its covalent compounds. Exceptions to this rule include peroxides (compounds containing the O_2^{2-} group), where each oxygen is assigned an oxidation state of –1, as in hydrogen peroxide (H_2O_2).
5. Hydrogen is assigned an oxidation state of +1. Metal hydrides are an exception: in metal hydrides, H has an oxidation state of –1.
6. The sum of the oxidation states must be zero for an electrically neutral compound.
7. For a polyatomic ion, the sum of the oxidation states must equal the charge of the ion.

Now try applying these rules to a problem.

Example

Assign oxidation numbers to each element in the following:

1. H_2S
2. MgF_2
3. PO_4^{3-}

Explanation

1. The sum of the oxidation numbers in this compound must be zero since the compound has no net charge. H has an oxidation state of +1, and since there are two H atoms, +1 times 2 atoms = +2 total charge on H. The sulfur S must have a charge of –2 since there is only one atom of sulfur, and +2 – 2 = 0, which equals no charge.

2. F is assigned an oxidation state of –1 (according to rule 3), and there are two atoms of F, so this gives F a total charge of –2. Mg must have a +2 oxidation state since +2 – 2 = 0 and the compound is electrically neutral.

3. This time the net charge is equal to –3 (the charge of the polyatomic ion—according to rule 7). Oxygen is assigned a –2 oxidation state (rule 4). Multiply the oxidation number by its subscript: –2 × 4 = –8. Since there is only 1 phosphorus, just use those algebra skills: P + –8 = –3. Phosphorus must have a +5 charge.

Example

When powdered zinc metal is mixed with iodine crystals and a drop of water is added, the resulting reaction produces a great deal of energy. The mixture bursts into flames, and a purple smoke made up of I_2 vapor is produced from the excess iodine. The equation for the reaction is

$$Zn_{(s)} + I_{2(s)} \rightarrow ZnI_{2(s)} + energy$$

Identify the elements that are oxidized and reduced, and determine the oxidizing and reducing agents.

Explanation

1. Assign oxidation numbers to each species. Zn and I_2 are both assigned values of 0 (rule 1). For zinc iodide, I has an oxidation number of –1 (group 7A—most common charge), which means that for zinc, the oxidation number is +2.

2. Evaluate the changes that are taking place. Zn goes from 0 to +2 (electrons are lost and Zn is oxidized). The half-reaction would look like this:

$$Zn^0 \rightarrow Zn^{2+} + 2e^-$$

And I_2 goes from 0 to –1 (it gains electrons and so is reduced). This half-reaction would look like this:

$$I_2^0 + 2e^- \rightarrow 2I^-$$

3. Here, zinc metal is the reducing agent—it causes the reduction to take place by donating electrons—while iodine solid is the oxidizing agent; iodine solid accepts electrons.

Voltaic (or Galvanic) Cells

Redox reactions release energy, and this energy can be used to do work if the reactions take place in a voltaic cell. In a **voltaic cell** (sometimes called a galvanic cell), the transfer of electrons occurs through an external pathway instead of directly between the two elements. The figure below shows a typical voltaic cell (this one contains the redox reaction between zinc and copper):

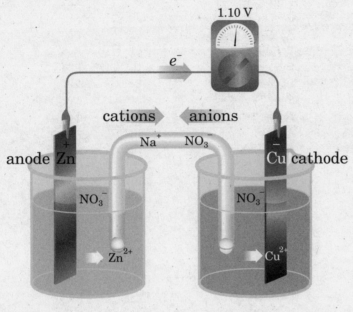

$$Zn(s) \rightarrow Zn^{2+}(aq) + 2e^- \qquad Cu^{2+}(aq) + 2e^- \rightarrow Cu(s)$$

As you can see, the **anode** is the electrode at which oxidation occurs; you can remember this if you remember the phrase "<u>an ox</u>" — "<u>oxidation occurs at the anode</u>." Reduction takes place at the **cathode**, and you can remember this with the phrase "<u>red cat</u>" — "<u>reduction occurs at the cathode</u>." An important component of the voltaic cell is the **salt bridge**, which is a device used to maintain electrical neutrality; it may be filled with agar, which contains a neutral salt, or be replaced with a porous cup. Remember that electron flow always occurs from anode to cathode, through the wire that connects the two half-cells, and a voltmeter is used to measure the cell potential in volts.

    Batteries are cells that are connected in series; the potentials add to give a total voltage. One common example is the lead storage battery (car battery), which has a Pb anode, a PbO_2 cathode, and H_2SO_4 electrolyte is their salt bridge.

Standard Reduction Potentials

The potential of a voltaic cell as a whole will depend on the half-cells that are involved. Each half-cell has a known potential, called its **standard reduction potential ($E°$)**. The cell potential is a measure of the difference between the two electrode potentials, and the potential at each electrode is calculated as the potential for *reduction* at the electrode. That's why they're standard reduction potentials, not standard oxidation potentials. Here is the chart:

STANDARD REDUCTION POTENTIALS IN AQUEOUS SOLUTION AT 25°C

Half-reaction			$E°$(V)
$F_2(g) + 2\,e^-$	→	$2\,F^-$	2.87
$Co^{3+} + e^-$	→	Co^{2+}	1.82
$Au^{3+} + 3\,e^-$	→	$Au(s)$	1.50
$Cl_2(g) + 2\,e^-$	→	$2\,Cl^-$	1.36
$O_2(g) + 4\,H^+ + 4\,e^-$	→	$2\,H_2O(l)$	1.23
$Br_2(l) + 2\,e^-$	→	$2\,Br^-$	1.07
$2\,Hg^{2+} + 2\,e^-$	→	Hg_2^{2+}	0.92
$Hg^{2+} + 2\,e^-$	→	$Hg(l)$	0.85
$Ag^+ + e^-$	→	$Ag(s)$	0.80
$Hg_2^{2+} + 2\,e^-$	→	$2\,Hg(l)$	0.79
$Fe^{3+} + e^-$	→	Fe^{2+}	0.77
$I_2(s) + 2\,e^-$	→	$2\,I^-$	0.53
$Cu^+ + e^-$	→	$Cu(s)$	0.52
$Cu^{2+} + 2\,e^-$	→	$Cu(s)$	0.34
$Cu^{2+} + e^-$	→	Cu^+	0.15
$Sn^{4+} + 2\,e^-$	→	Sn^{2+}	0.15
$S(s) + 2\,H^+ + 2\,e^-$	→	$H_2S(g)$	0.14
$2\,H^+ + 2\,e^-$	→	$H_2(g)$	0.00
$Pb^{2+} + 2\,e^-$	→	$Pb(s)$	−0.13
$Sn^{2+} + 2\,e^-$	→	$Sn(s)$	−0.14
$Ni^{2+} + 2\,e^-$	→	$Ni(s)$	−0.25
$Co^{2+} + 2\,e^-$	→	$Co(s)$	−0.28
$Tl^+ + e^-$	→	$Tl(s)$	−0.34
$Cd^{2+} + 2\,e^-$	→	$Cd(s)$	−0.40
$Cr^{3+} + e^-$	→	Cr^{2+}	−0.41
$Fe^{2+} + 2\,e^-$	→	$Fe(s)$	−0.44
$Cr^{3+} + 3\,e^-$	→	$Cr(s)$	−0.74
$Zn^{2+} + 2\,e^-$	→	$Zn(s)$	−0.76
$Mn^{2+} + 2\,e^-$	→	$Mn(s)$	−1.18
$Al^{3+} + 3\,e^-$	→	$Al(s)$	−1.66
$Be^{2+} + 2\,e^-$	→	$Be(s)$	−1.70
$Mg^{2+} + 2\,e^-$	→	$Mg(s)$	−2.37
$Na^+ + e^-$	→	$Na(s)$	−2.71
$Ca^{2+} + 2\,e^-$	→	$Ca(s)$	−2.87
$Sr^{2+} + 2\,e^-$	→	$Sr(s)$	−2.89
$Ba^{2+} + 2\,e^-$	→	$Ba(s)$	−2.90
$Rb^+ + e^-$	→	$Rb(s)$	−2.92
$K^+ + e^-$	→	$K(s)$	−2.92
$Cs^+ + e^-$	→	$Cs(s)$	−2.92
$Li^+ + e^-$	→	$Li(s)$	−3.05

On this reduction potential chart, the elements that have the *most positive* reduction potentials are easily reduced and would be good oxidizing agents (in general, the nonmetals), while the elements that have the least positive reduction potentials are easily oxidized and would be good reducing agents (in general, metals). Let's try a quick problem.

Example • 117

Example

Which of the following elements would be most easily oxidized: Ca, Cu, Fe, Li, or Au?

Explanation

Use the reduction potential chart: nonmetals are at the top and are most easily reduced. Metals are at the bottom and are most easily oxidized. Lithium is at the bottom of the chart—it's the most easily oxidized of all. So the order, from most easily oxidized to least easily oxidized, is Au, Fe, Cu, Ca, Li.

Example

Which one of the following would be the best oxidizing agent: Ba, Na, Cl, F, or Br?

Explanation

Using the reduction potential chart and the fact that oxidizing agents are the elements that are most easily reduced, we determine fluorine is the best oxidizing agent.

Electrolytic Cells

While voltaic cells harness the energy from redox reactions, electrolytic cells can be used to drive nonspontaneous redox reactions, which are also called **electrolysis reactions**. Electrolytic cells are used to produce pure forms of an element; for example, they're used to separate ores, in electroplating metals (such as applying gold to a less expensive metal), and to charge batteries (such as car batteries). These types of cells rely on a battery or any DC source—in other words, whereas the voltaic cell *is* a battery, the electrolytic cell *needs* a battery. Also unlike voltaic cells, which are made up of two containers, electrolytic cells have just one container. However, like in voltaic cells, in electrolytic cells electrons still flow from the anode to the cathode. An electrolytic cell is shown below.

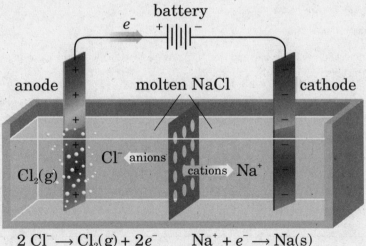

$$2\ Cl^- \longrightarrow Cl_2(g) + 2e^- \qquad Na^+ + e^- \longrightarrow Na(s)$$

Practice Questions

1. What is the sum of the coefficients of the following equation when it is balanced?

    $Al_2(SO_4)_3 + Ca(OH)_2 \rightarrow Al(OH)_3 + CaSO_4$

    (A)   5
    (B)   6
    (C)   7
    (D)   8
    (E)   9

2. Indium reacts with bromine to form $InBr_3$. In the balanced equation for this reaction, the coefficient of the indium (III) bromide is

    (A)   1
    (B)   2
    (C)   3
    (D)   4
    (E)   6

3. When the following equation is balanced, what is the sum of the coefficients?

    $Al_2(CO_3)_3 + Mg(OH)_2 \rightarrow Al(OH)_3 + MgCO_3$

    (A)   3
    (B)   4
    (C)   8
    (D)   9
    (E)   10

4. The balanced net ionic equation for the reaction of aluminum sulfate and sodium hydroxide contains which of the following terms?

    (A) $3Al^{3+}_{(aq)}$
    (B) $OH^-_{(aq)}$
    (C) $3OH^-_{(aq)}$
    (D) $2Al^{3+}_{(aq)}$
    (E) $2Al(OH)_{3(s)}$

5. When solutions of phosphoric acid and iron (III) nitrate react, which of the following terms will be present in the balanced molecular equation?

    (A) $HNO_{3(aq)}$
    (B) $3HNO_{3(aq)}$
    (C) $2FePO_{4(s)}$
    (D) $3FePO_{4(s)}$
    (E) $2HNO_{3(aq)}$

6.	The conjugate base of a weak acid is a strong base.	BECAUSE	Elements that are strong Brønsted-Lowry acids are not strong Brønsted-Lowry bases.

7. In solution, which of the following has the greatest $[H_3O^+]$?

(A)   HCN
(B) HNO_3
(C) H_2O
(D) OH^-
(E) CH_3OH

8. Which of the following is not true for a solution at 25°C that has a hydroxide concentration of 1.0×10^{-6} M?

(A) $K_w = 1 \times 10^{-14}$
(B)   The solution is acidic.
(C)   The solution is basic.
(D)   The $[H^+]$ is 1×10^{-8} M.
(E)   The pOH equals 6.0.

9. Which of the following would produce a basic aqueous solution?

(A) SO_2
(B)   KCl
(C) CO_2
(D) NH_4Cl
(E) Na_2O

10. Equimolar solutions of which of the following would produce the most acidic solution?

(A) H_3PO_4
(B)   HClO
(C) $HClO_2$
(D) $HClO_3$
(E) $HClO_4$

11. In which of the following substances would nitrogen have the highest oxidation number?

(A)   NO
(B) N_2O
(C) NO_2
(D) N_2O_4
(E) NO_3^-

12.	Voltaic cells harness the energy of redox reactions.	BECAUSE	In a voltaic cell, electron flow occurs through the salt bridge.
13.	Electrolytic cells require the input of energy.	BECAUSE	Electrolytic cells have just one container, while voltaic cells have two.

14. Which of the following half-cell reactions describes what is happening at the anode in the diagram?

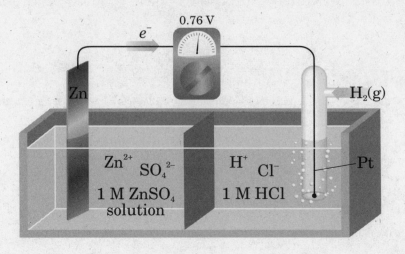

(A) $Zn \rightarrow Zn^{2+} + 2e^-$

(B) $H_2 \rightarrow 2H^+ + 2e^-$

(C) $2Cl^- \rightarrow Cl_2 + 2e^-$

(D) $SO_4^- \rightarrow S + 2O_2 + 6e^-$

(E) $2H^+ + 2e^- \rightarrow H_2$

15. Given the following chemical reaction for the formation of lithium oxide, which of the following statements is true?

$$4Li_{(s)} + O_{2(g)} \rightarrow 2Li_2O_{(s)}$$

(A)   Lithium metal is the oxidizing agent.

(B)   Oxygen gas is the reducing agent.

(C)   Lithium is oxidized.

(D)   Oxygen is oxidized.

(E)   Oxygen loses two electrons to become a −2 ion.

Explanations

1.   **E**

This equation has two polyatomic ions. If you recognize that right away, the question is not as difficult. Treat the polyatomic ions as one species. The balanced equation is

$$Al_2(SO_4)_3 + 3Ca(OH)_2 \rightarrow 2Al(OH)_3 + 3CaSO_4$$

The sum of the coefficients is then $1 + 3 + 2 + 3 = 9$.

2. B

Here you are basically given the correct chemical formula for the product. The balanced reaction is

$$2In + 3Br_2 \rightarrow 2InBr_3$$

The coefficient of the indium (III) bromide is 2.

3. D

The balanced equation is

$$Al_2(CO_3)_3 + 3Mg(OH)_2 \rightarrow 2Al(OH)_3 + 3MgCO_3$$

The sum of the coefficients is thus $1 + 3 + 2 + 3 = 9$.

4. C

You must know your solubility rules to get the correct answer. Aluminum sulfate is soluble, as is sodium hydroxide. The ions participating are Al^{3+}, SO_4^{2-}, Na^+, and OH^-. It is a double displacement, and the key is knowing that sodium sulfate is soluble, while aluminum hydroxide is written molecularly since it is a weak base. The balanced net ionic equation is

$$Al^{3+}_{(aq)} + 3OH^-_{(aq)} \rightarrow Al(OH)_{3(s)}$$

5. B

This is also a double displacement reaction. The balanced molecular equation is

$$H_3PO_4 + Fe(NO_3)_3 \rightarrow FePO_4 + 3HNO_3$$

6. T, T

(Fill in **CE**.) The first statement is true: the conjugate base of a weak acid is a strong base. Remember that conjugate acid-base pairs are acids and bases that differ only in the presence or absence of a proton. The second statement is also true: a strong Brønsted-Lowry acid will not be a strong Brønsted-Lowry base. It is an explanation for the first statement, so you would fill in the **CE** oval.

7. B

This question asks you to find the compound with the greatest $[H_3O^+]$, which means it's asking you to find the compound with the lowest pH or determine which one is the most acidic. As you look down the list, you can see only one compound that is on our list of the six strong acids, and that's choice **B**, HNO_3.

8. B

If the temperature is 25°C, then $K_w = 1.0 \times 10^{-14}$, so **A** is true. If the hydroxide concentration is equal to 1.0×10^{-6} M, then the pOH = 6, so **E** is true. (You know that 1.0×10^{-6} is the same as plain old 10^{-6}. The log of 10^{-6} is –6. Simply use the exponent when a number, any number, is written as 10^{power}, so the "negative" of the log is equal to –(–6) or simply 6.) Therefore the pH is equal to 14 – 6, which equals 8. If the pH = 8, then the solution is basic, so **C** is true. Furthermore, when the pH = 8, the $[H^+] = 1.0 \times 10^{-8}$, so **D** is true. Only **B** is not true.

9. E

Recall that aqueous solutions of oxides and hydroxides of 1A and 2A metals form strong bases. Now review what you learned about strong bases: the strong bases are hydroxides (—OH), and oxides of 1A and 2A metals (except Mg and Be), H^-, and CH_3^-.

10. E

Perchloric acid is the strongest acid in this list. Remember our discussion of how the increased number of oxygens makes the proton more likely to dissociate. Here's that list of strong acids again: the hydrohalic acids (HCl, HBr, HI), nitric acid (HNO_3), sulfuric acid (H_2SO_4), and perchloric acid ($HClO_4$).

11. E

In this problem, it is probably easiest to determine the charge on each nitrogen first. The oxygen in each case is –2. In choice **A**, NO, the nitrogen has a charge of +2. In choice **B**, N_2O, the charge on nitrogen is +1. In choice **C**, NO_2, and in choice **D**, N_2O_4, the nitrogen has a charge of +4. In choice **E**, NO_3^-, the nitrogen has a charge of +5.

12. T, F

(Do not fill in **CE**.) Statement I is a true statement: voltaic cells harness the energy released during redox reactions, and this energy is used to perform work. However, statement II is false. The flow of electrons from anode to cathode takes place through a wire, not the salt bridge. The salt bridge is present in order to retain electrical neutrality in the cells. Since the second statement is not an explanation or reason for the first statement, you would not fill in the **CE** oval.

13. T, T

(Do not fill in **CE**.) Look at the statements one at a time. The first statement is true—electrolytic cells require the input of energy. These cells are used to separate ores, to electroplate, and as car batteries. The second statement is also true: whereas voltaic cells have two containers, one at the anode and one at the cathode, electrolytic cells have just one (although they still have an anode and a cathode). Since the second statement is not an explanation for the first, you would not fill in the **CE** oval.

14. A

The anode and cathode are not labeled in the diagram, so you must first remember that electrons travel from the anode to the cathode—according to the arrow showing electron movement in the diagram, this means that the chamber on the left must be the anode. This narrows the answer choices down to **A** or **D** since these are the only two ions in the anode half-cell. Now, since oxidation occurs at the anode, the metal will lose electrons, and you can determine that choice **A** shows the appropriate half-reaction.

15. **C**

The first step to solving a problem like this is to assign charges to each element and then decide exactly what's happening before you look at the answer choices. On the reactants side, lithium and oxygen both are assigned charges of zero. In lithium oxide, Li has a +1 charge and O has a –2 charge. Li has been oxidized: it lost $2e^-$ and is the reducing agent. O has been reduced: it gained $2e^-$ and is the oxidizing agent. The only statement that matches is choice **C**.

Stoichiometry

Stoichiometry is a way of describing the quantitative relationships among elements in compounds and among substances as they undergo chemical changes. In plain English, if you have to calculate just about anything relating to moles or other chemical quantities, the calculations will involve stoichiometry.

Chapter Contents

The Mole

In the last chapter, we reviewed the process of balancing equations and based the rules for balancing equations on the principle that matter is neither created nor destroyed in the course of a chemical reaction. With this idea still in mind, let's begin our discussion of moles and formula weights.

When you look at the periodic table, you see that one of the pieces of data given for each element is its atomic weight. But what exactly is the atomic weight of a substance? It is the mass of one mole of a substance. In turn, one **mole** of a substance is equal to 6.02×10^{23} atoms or molecules of the substance (depending on what it is), and finally, the number 6.02×10^{23} is known as **Avogadro's number**. For example, carbon's atomic weight is roughly 12 amu; this means that 6.02×10^{23} carbon atoms, in a pile, weigh 12 grams.

In order to find the **formula weight** of a substance, you simply add up the atomic masses of all of the atoms in the molecular formula of a compound. But don't forget to multiply the atomic mass of each element by the subscript behind that element. Formula weights have the units amu, or atomic mass units; for example, the formula weight of water, H_2O, is about 18 amu. (O = 16 amu plus 2 times H = 1 amu = 18 amu.) Similarly, the **molar mass** of a molecule is the mass (in grams) of 1 mol of a substance; so the molar mass of H_2O is also roughly 18.

Now try calculating some molar masses and formula weights on your own by filling in the following chart.

Example

Substance	Molar mass	Number of moles	Mass in grams	Number of particles
Carbon dioxide, CO_2		3.0		
Oxygen, O_2			64.0	
Methane, CH_4		0.279		
Nitrogen, N_2				9.50×10^{25}

Explanation

Three significant digits were used throughout, with the exception of molar masses, where two decimal places were used. But don't stress over significant figures for this test: it's multiple choice, and the answers will never be that precise. Here's the table, filled in.

Substance	Molar mass	Number of moles	Mass in grams	Number of particles
Carbon dioxide, CO_2	44.01	3.00	132	1.81×10^{24}
Oxygen, O_2	32.00	2.00	64.0	1.20×10^{24}
Methane, CH_4	16.05	0.279	4.48	1.68×10^{23}
Nitrogen, N_2	28.02	158.00	4430	9.50×10^{25}

Now that you've had some practice figuring out molecular weights, let's talk about how you'll be expected to use them, and other stoichiometric tools, on the exam. For example, you will almost certainly be asked to find the percent composition of a compound, so let's talk about that first.

Percent Composition of Compounds

There are two different ways to describe the composition of a compound: in terms of the number of its constituent atoms (like C_2H_6) and in terms of the percentages (by mass) of its elements. When showing the constituent atoms of a molecule, you can either show the chemical formula, which shows the real number of atoms in the molecule, like C_2H_6, or show the **empirical formula**, which merely shows their relative amounts in a substance, so the above molecular formula would be expressed as CH_3.

You can describe the composition of a compound in terms of the weights of its constituent elements by determining the percent composition of particular elements in the molecule. To calculate percent compositions, you would find the weight of each constituent atom, then figure out what percent of the total molecular weight it makes up. Consider ethanol, C_2H_5OH. Taking subscripts into consideration, you have 2 mols of carbon, 6 mols of hydrogen (5 + 1), and 1 mol of O. Now convert moles into grams for each constituent element as well as for the entire molecule:

$$\text{Mass of C} = 2 \text{ mol} \times 12.01 \frac{g}{mol} = 24.02 \text{ g}$$

$$\text{Mass of H} = 6 \text{ mol} \times 1.01 \frac{g}{mol} = 6.06 \text{ g}$$

$$\text{Mass of O} = 1 \text{ mol} \times 16.00 \frac{g}{mol} = 16.00 \text{ g}$$

$$\text{Mass of 1 mol of } C_2H_5OH = 46.08 \text{ g}$$

Now use the formula you learned above to find the percent compositions of the constituent elements:

$$\text{Mass percent of C:} \frac{24.02 \text{ g}}{46.08 \text{ g}} \times 100\% = 52.14\%$$

$$\text{Mass percent of H:} \frac{6.06 \text{ g}}{46.08 \text{ g}} \times 100\% = 13.15\%$$

$$\text{Mass percent of O:} \frac{16.00 \text{ g}}{46.08 \text{ g}} \times 100\% = 34.77\%$$

Not so bad, right?

More Complex Stoichiometric Calculations

When you're asked to do stoichiometric calculations on the SAT II Chemistry exam, make sure that if you need to write out the chemical formulas, you do this correctly. No matter how good you are at math and how well you understand the stoichiometric rules that follow, you won't get the right answer if your chemical formulas are wrong! If you feel that you're weak in this area, see the review (in Appendix II) of chemical formula naming and writing.

Perhaps the easiest way to approach problems that ask you to calculate the amounts of reactants consumed or products produced during the course of a reaction is to start by creating a table or chart. Let's work through a typical example. Say the SAT II Chemistry test asks you what mass of oxygen will react completely with 96.1 grams of propane. Notice that for this question, you'll need to start by writing the chemical formulas. Now follow these steps:

1. Write the chemical equation.
2. Calculate the molar masses and put them in parentheses above the formulas; soon you'll figure out you don't have to do this for every reactant and product, just those you're specifically asked about.

3. Balance the equation.

4. Next put any amounts that you were given into the table. In this example, you were told that the reaction started with 96.1 g of propane.

5. Find the number of moles of any compounds for which you were given masses. Here you'd start with propane: you divide 96.1 grams by the molar mass of propane (44.11 g/mol) to get the number of moles of propane (2.18 mol).

6. Use the mole:mole ratio expressed in the coefficients of each of the compounds to find moles of all of the necessary compounds involved. The only one you really need to know is oxygen, but let's run through all of them for practice. If the coefficient for propane, which is 1, is equal to 2.18 moles of propane, then the number of moles of oxygen must be $5 \times 2.18 = 10.9$, the moles of CO_2 is $3 \times 2.18 = 6.54$, and the moles of $H_2O = 4 \times 2.18 = 8.72$.

Molar mass	(44.11)	(32.00)	(44.01)	(18.02)
Balanced equation	$C_3H_8 +$	$5O_2 \rightarrow$	$3CO_2 +$	$4H_2O$
No. of moles	2.18	10.9	6.54	8.72
Amount	96.1 g			

8. Reread the problem to determine which amount was asked for. The question asks for the mass of oxygen, so convert moles of oxygen to grams and you have the answer:

$$10.9 \text{ mol} \times 44.01 \text{ g/mol} = 349 \text{ g oxygen}$$

Molar mass	(44.11)	(32.00)	(44.01)	(18.02)
Balanced equation	$C_3H_8 +$	$5O_2 \rightarrow$	$3CO_2 +$	$4H_2O$
Mole:mole	1	5	3	4
No. of moles	2.18	10.9	6.54	8.72
Amount	96.1 g	349 g		

But what if this question had asked you to determine the liters of CO_2 consumed in this reaction at STP (273K, 1 atm)? You would take the number of moles of CO_2 that we calculated from the table and use the standard molar volume for a gas, or 22.4 L/mol. So, 6.54 mol $\times$ 22.4 L/mol = 146 L.

Finally, what if the question had asked how many water molecules are produced? You would take the number of moles of water and multiply it by Avogadro's number, 6.02×10^{23}, to get 5.25×10^{24} molecules of water.

Molar mass	(44.11)	(32.00)	(44.01)	(18.02)
Balanced equation	C_3H_8 +	$5O_2 \rightarrow$	$3CO_2$ +	$4H_2O$
Mole:mole	1	5	3	4
No. of moles	2.18	10.9	6.54	8.72
Amount	96.1 g	349 g	146 L	5.25×10^{24}

You certainly don't have to write out several tables; we just did that to make the method clearer to you. Once you practice, you won't need to write the categories to the left, either. They will become second nature. In essence, you can work the problems faster *and* set yourself up nicely for a clear understanding of equilibrium problems in your future.

Perhaps your teacher at school taught you to solve this type of problem using dimensional analysis. If so, and if you feel comfortable solving problems using that method, don't learn to do it our way: stick to the method with which you feel comfortable. We'll go through this problem using dimensional analysis: *What mass of oxygen will react with 96.1 grams of propane?* Again, you would first write the chemical formula and make sure your equation is correctly balanced:

$$C_3H_8 + 5O_2 \rightarrow 3CO_2 + 4H_2O$$

The amount to start with, when setting up the dimensional analysis, is 96.1 g, and your goal is to calculate the number of grams of oxygen produced:

$$96.1 \text{ g } C_3H_8 \times \frac{1 \text{ mol } C_3H_8}{44.11 \text{ g } C_3H_8} \times \frac{5 \text{ mol } O_2}{1 \text{ mol } C_3H_8} \times \frac{32.00 \text{ g } O_2}{1 \text{ mol } O_2} = 349 \text{ g } O_2$$

Not too hard, right? Now, how many liters of CO_2 would be produced at STP?

$$96.1 \text{ g } C_3H_8 \times \frac{1 \text{ mol } C_3H_8}{44.11 \text{ g } C_3H_8} \times \frac{3 \text{ mol } CO_2}{1 \text{ mol } C_3H_8} \times \frac{22.4 \text{ L } CO_2}{1 \text{ mol } CO_2} = 146 \text{ L of } CO_2 \text{ at STP}$$

And how many water molecules are produced?

$$96.1 \text{ g } C_3H_8 \times \frac{1 \text{ mol } C_3H_8}{44.11 \text{ g } C_3H_8} \times \frac{4 \text{ mol } H_2O}{1 \text{ mol } C_3H_8} \times \frac{6.02 \times 10^{23} \text{ molecules } H_2O}{1 \text{ mol } H_2O}$$
$$= 5.25 \times 10^{23} \text{ molecules of } H_2O$$

Some people prefer the table method, while others are more comfortable with dimensional analysis. Use whatever method you feel more comfortable using, but just be consistent—if you always do the same types of problems the same way, you'll feel much more confident on test day. Now try the method you prefer on some problems.

Examples

1. Solid lithium hydroxide is used in space vehicles to remove exhaled carbon dioxide from the air; it reacts with carbon dioxide to form solid lithium carbonate and liquid water. What mass of gaseous carbon dioxide will be consumed in a reaction with 1.00 kg of lithium hydroxide?

Stoichiometry

Explanation

First write the reaction, then create and fill in your chart, and when you're done filling in the necessary blocks, it should look like this:

Molar mass	(23.95)	(44.01)		
Balanced equation	2LiOH +	$CO_2 \rightarrow$	Li_2CO_3 +	H_2O
No. moles	1000 g/23.95 g/mol = 41.8 moles	20.9	20.9	20.9
Amount	1.00 kg	20.9 × 44.01 = 920 g		

2. Baking soda ($NaHCO_3$) is often used as an antacid. It neutralizes excess hydrochloric acid secreted by the stomach in the reaction below:

$$NaHCO_{3(s)} + HCl_{(aq)} \rightarrow NaCl_{(aq)} + H_2O_{(l)} + CO_{2(aq)}$$

How many grams of $NaHCO_3$ would be needed to completely react with 10.0 g of HCl?

Explanation

According to the balanced equation above, 1 mole of $NaHCO_3$ reacts with 1 mole of HCl. First you need to calculate how many moles of HCl are in 10 grams of HCl. The formula weight of HCl is about 36 g/mol, so you set up the equation:

$$\frac{10 \text{ g} \times 1 \text{ mol}}{36 \text{ g}} = 0.27 \text{ moles HCl.}$$

Now, knowing that 1 mole of baking soda reacts with 1 mole of NaCl, we next need to figure out how many grams of baking soda would react with 0.27 moles of baking soda: 0.27 moles × 134 g/mol baking soda = 37.2 grams/mole $NaHCO_3$

Molar mass	(85.32)	(36.46)			
Balanced equation	$NaHCO_3$ +	HCl →	NaCl +	H_2O +	CO_2
No. moles	0.274	10.0/36.46 = 0.274			
Amount	0.274 × 85.32 = 23.4 g	10.0 g			

Limiting Reagents

Have you ever noticed that hot dogs are sold in packages of 10, while the buns come in packages of eight? In this scenario, the buns are the limiting reactant in the sense that they limit the hot dog preparation to eight. The limiting reactant or reagent is the one that is consumed first in the chemical reaction, and its consumption halts the progress of the forward reaction.

When answering questions about limiting reagents on the exam, your first step should always be to convert all the masses you were given into moles. You should set up your table as you did before, only now you'll have *two* amounts and thus two numbers of moles to get you started.

Let's look at a specific question, involving the Haber process. Basically, this is the process of making ammonia from the reaction of nitrogen and hydrogen gases. The reaction is shown below:

Molar mass	(28.02)	(2.02)	(17.04)
Balanced equation	$N_2 +$	$3H_2 \rightarrow$	$2NH_3$
No. of moles			
Amount			

Suppose you have a total of 25.0 kg of nitrogen to react with a total of 5.00 kg of hydrogen. What mass of ammonia can be produced? Which reactant is the limiting reactant? What is the mass of the reactant that's in excess? Insert the masses in the correct rows and find the number of moles of *both*.

Molar mass	(28.02)	(2.02)	(17.04)
Balanced equation	$N_2 +$	$3H_2 \rightarrow$	$2NH_3$
No. of moles	892 mol	2475 mol	
Amount	25,000 g	5000 g	

Start with nitrogen. You have 892 moles of it available, and in order for the nitrogen to react completely with hydrogen, you'd need 3(892 mol) = 2676 moles of hydrogen, which you don't have. Therefore, hydrogen is the limiting reagent. Now let's answer the other parts of the question. The mass of ammonia that can be produced is limited by the amount of hydrogen, so do your calculations based on the number of moles of hydrogen available. Your chart should look like the one below:

Molar mass	(14.02)	(2.02)	(17.04)
Balanced equation	$N_2 +$	$3H_2 \rightarrow$	$2NH_3$
No. of moles	825 mol used	2475 mol used	therefore 1650 mol produced
Amount	892 mol 825 mol × 28.02 = 23,117 g used 25,000 g 1883 g excess	5000 g	1650 mol (17.04) = 28,116 g produced

Chemical Yields

There are three types of yields you'll need to be familiar with for the SAT II Chemistry test: theoretical yields, actual yields, and percent yields. Here's a quick review of what all of these mean to you. The theoretical yield of a reaction is the amount of product formed once the limiting reactant has been completely consumed. This assumes perfect conditions and gives a maximum amount. The actual yield is what actually occurs in the course of the reaction—how much product is actually formed. Finally, the percent yield is the ratio of the actual yield to the theoretical yield, and you can get this value using the following formula:

$$\frac{\text{actual yield}}{\text{theoretical yield}} \times 100\% = \text{percent yield}$$

Going back to our last example, the 28,116 grams you calculated would be the **theoretical yield**. But what would the percent yield be if you performed this reaction and you actually collected 26,450 grams of ammonia? You would calculate it using the above formula. Here it is with the numbers plugged in:

$$\frac{26,450}{28,116} \times 100 = 94.1\%$$

Practice Questions

1. How many moles of hydrogen sulfide are contained in a 35.0 g sample of this gas?

   (A) 1.03 mol
   (B) 2.06 mol
   (C) 6.18 mol
   (D) 9.45 mol
   (E) 11.3 mol

2. What is the molar mass of ethanol (C_2H_5OH)?

   (A) 34.2
   (B) 38.9
   (C) 46.1
   (D) 45.1
   (E) 62.1

3. Ammonia can be produced by the reaction of nitrogen and hydrogen gas. Suppose the reaction is carried out starting with 14 g of nitrogen and 15 g of hydrogen. How many grams of ammonia can be produced?

(A)   17.04 g
(B)   34.08 g
(C)   51.1 g
(D)   85.2 g
(E)   102 g

4. How many atoms of hydrogen are present in 12.0 g of water?

(A) 1.1×10^{23}
(B) 2.0×10^{23}
(C) 4.0×10^{23}
(D) 8.0×10^{23}
(E) 4.8×10^{24}

5. Which compound contains the highest percent by mass of hydrogen?

(A)   HCl
(B) H_2O
(C) H_3PO_4
(D) H_2SO_4
(E)   HF

6.	In a balanced equation, the number of moles of each substance is equal.	BECAUSE	Once the limiting reagent has been consumed, the reaction can no longer continue.

7. A hydrocarbon (a compound consisting solely of carbon and hydrogen) is found to be 96% carbon by mass. What is the empirical formula for this compound?

(A) C_2H
(B) CH_2
(C) C_3H
(D) CH_3
(E) C_4H

8. An unknown compound contains the elements C, H, and O. It is known to contain 48% C and 4.0% H by mass. The molar mass of this compound has been determined in the lab to have a value of 200. The molecular formula for this compound is

(A) $C_2H_3O_2$
(B) $C_4H_6O_4$
(C) $C_4H_4O_3$
(D) $C_8H_3O_6$
(E) $C_8H_8O_6$

9. When 7.0 g of ethene (C_2H_4) burns in oxygen to give carbon dioxide and water, how many grams of CO_2 are formed?

$$C_2H_4 + 3O_2 \rightarrow 2CO_2 + 2H_2O$$

(A) 9.0 g
(B) 22 g
(C) 44 g
(D) 82 g
(E) 180 g

10. Consider the following reaction:

$$CH_{4(g)} + 4F_{2(g)} \rightarrow CF_{4(g)} + 4HF_{(g)}$$

What mass of CF_4 is formed by the reaction of 8.00 g of methane with an excess of fluorine?

(A) 19 g
(B) 22 g
(C) 38 g
(D) 44 g
(E) 88 g

Explanations

1. **A**
The formula for hydrogen sulfide is H_2S; this means that its molar mass is equal to $2(1) + 32 = 34$ g/mol. The closest answer choice, and the correct answer, is **A**, which is thus slightly more than 1 mole. Don't try to use the standard molar volume for a gas in this problem, even though the problem asks about a gas, because the volume of the gas is not mentioned at all.

2. **C**
This is a simple question: round the atomic masses that you get from the periodic table to calculate the molar mass of C_2H_5OH. The answer is $2(12) + 6(1) + 16$, which is equal to slightly more than 46 g/mol.

3. **A**
Because there are two starting amounts, you might have guessed that one of them would act as a limiting reagent. The reaction is written below, and you'll need to start by finding all the molar masses to make your determinations. Round off the numbers. The number of moles of nitrogen is 14 g (1 mol/28 g/mol) = 0.5 mol, and hydrogen = 15 g (1 mol/2 g/mol) = 7.5 mol. Now check to see which of the reactants is the limiting reagent. If you started with 0.5 mole of N_2, in order to consume this amount of nitrogen completely, you'd need to use 3(0.5) = 1.5 moles of hydrogen. You have much more hydrogen than that (you have 7.5 moles), so nitrogen is the limiting reagent. The question asks you how much ammonia would be produced, so now you know which reactant amount to use to calculate that, and the answer is 2(0.5 mol) = 1.0 moles, which is equal to 17 g of NH_3, answer choice **A**.

Molar masses	28	2	17
Reaction	$N_2 +$	$3H_2 \rightarrow$	$2NH_3$
No. of moles	0.5 mol available limiting reactant	1.5 mol used 6.0 moles excess! 7.5 mol available	1.0 mole produced
Amounts	14 g	15 g ➔	Slightly more than 17 g

4. **D**

This question gives you the grams of water but asks for atoms of hydrogen. You'll need to find the number of water molecules and then double it since H_2O contains 2 atoms of H for every 1 molecule of water. The molar mass of water is $2(1) + 16 = 18$ g/mol. The number of moles of water, then, is 12 g H_2O (1 mol/18 g/mol) = .66 mol of 6 (as in 6.02×10^{23}) is 4×10^{23} molecules of water. Doubling that you get 8×10^{23} hydrogen atoms.

5. **B**

This question is a percent composition question, so you'll be looking for the molecule that has the largest mass of H compared to its whole molar mass. Examine the analysis below, and it's clear that water has the highest percent composition of hydrogen.

(A)   HCl
    Hydrogen's atomic weight = 1, chlorine's atomic weight = 35, so hydrogen makes up 1/36, or 2.7%, of the compound.

(B) H_2O
    Hydrogen's atomic weight = 1, oxygen's atomic weight = 16; there are two hydrogens here, so it makes up 2/18 of the total weight, or 11%.

(C) H_3PO_4
    Hydrogen's atomic weight = 1, phosphorus's weight = 31, oxygen's weight = 16, so after you add up the total weight to get $3(1) + 31 + 4(16) = 98$, hydrogen makes up 3/98 = 3%.

(D) H_2SO_4
    Hydrogen's weight = 1, sulfur's = 32, and oxygen's = 16. The total weight is equal to $2(1) + 32 + 4(16) = 98$, and hydrogen makes up 2% of this.

(E)   HF
    Hydrogen's weight = 1, fluorine's weight = 19, so hydrogen makes up 1/19, or 5.2%, of the molecule by weight.
    As you can see, choice **B**, in which hydrogen makes up 11% of the total compound, is the correct answer.

Stoichiometry

6. **F, T**

(Do not fill in **CE**.) The first statement is false—in most chemical reactions, most times the number of moles of the compounds involved is not equal. The second statement, however, is true. Once a limiting reagent has been consumed in the course of a reaction, the reaction can no longer proceed.

7. **A**

To solve this problem, first turn the percentages into grams: C becomes 96 g carbon, so the remaining 4% is hydrogen, so there are 4 g of hydrogen present. Now convert these masses into moles: the moles of C = 96 g (1 mol/12 g/mol) = 8 mol. For hydrogen, H = 4 g (1 mol/1 g/mol) = 4 mol. The C:H ratio is 8:4; remember that the empirical formula is the formula that shows the relative numbers of the kinds of atoms in a molecule, so this simplifies to 2:1, and the empirical formula is C_2H.

8. **E**

Turn the percentages into grams and find the number of moles of each element. Since the compound is 48% C and 4% H, it must also be 48% O to make the percentages total 100%. Simplify the mole:mole ratio to get the empirical formula. Calculate the empirical molar mass. The molecular mass will be some multiple of the empirical mass. Mol C = 48 g (1 mol/ 12 g/mol) = 4 mol. Mol H = 4 g (1 mol/1 g/mol) = 4 mol. Mol O = 48 g (1 mol/16 g/mol) = 3 mol. The empirical formula is then $C_4H_4O_3$. The empirical molar mass = 4(12) + 4(1) + 3(16) = 100, so the molecular formula is twice the empirical formula, or $C_8H_8O_6$.

9. **B**

This is not a limiting reactant problem since only one amount is given here, 7.0 g of ethene. First find the number of moles of the substance, in this case ethene: 7 g (1 mol/28 g/mol) = 0.25 mol, then use mole:mole to determine the moles of the rest of the compounds involved in the reaction. To find the grams of CO_2, you would do the following: 1 mol × 44 g/mol = 44 g CO_2.

Molar mass	28	32	44	18
Balanced equation	C_2H_4 +	$3O_2$ →	$2CO_2$ +	$2H_2O$
No. of moles	0.25	1.25	0.5	0.5
Amount	7 g		22 g	

10. **D**

Here, determine the moles of methane and use the mole:mole ratio to determine the number of moles, then grams of CF_4 that can be produced.

Molar mass	16	38	88	20
Balanced equation	CH_4 +	$4F_4$ →	CF_4	4HF
No. of moles	0.5	2	0.5	2
Amount	8 g		44 g	

Equilibrium and Reaction Rates

Factors That Affect Reaction Rates

For the SAT II Chemistry test, you'll have to be familiar with certain aspects of chemical reactions, such as equilibrium and reaction rate. The **reaction rate** is a measure of the change in the concentration of reactants or products over time in a chemical reaction. Four main external conditions affect reaction rate. The first is the concentration of reactants. Generally speaking, if we increase the concentration of one or more reactants, the reaction will go more quickly. This is simple because the more molecules, the more collisions between molecules, and the faster the reaction will go.

The second factor that influences reaction rate is temperature. The higher the temperature of the reaction, the more quickly it will proceed. At higher temperatures, the molecules are moving around more quickly (they have more kinetic energy); this means they will collide with each other with more energy, and it's more likely that they will overcome the activation energy needed to start the reaction. It's a general rule of thumb that a 10°C increase in temperature will double the reaction rate.

The addition of a catalyst will also speed up a chemical reaction. A **catalyst** speeds up the rate of reaction by lowering the activation energy. Biological catalysts are known as enzymes. The only other important thing you need to remember about catalysts is that they are not consumed in the course of the reaction.

The final factor that affects certain reactions is the physical state of the reactants. For example, if you mix two gases or two liquids, this represents a homogenous reaction, but if reactants are in different phases, for example, if one is a gas and one is a liquid, then the reaction area is limited to the area where they touch each other, and the larger this area, the faster the reaction will proceed. For example, consider a teaspoon of salt dissolving in water. If you were to dump the salt into the beaker of water and let it float to the bottom without stirring it, it would take much longer for it to dissolve than if you stirred the solution.

Now let's quickly go through those factors that influence reaction rate again:

1. Concentration of the reactants
2. Temperature
3. Presence of a catalyst
4. Physical state of the reactants

Energy Diagrams

We know that in order for a reaction to occur, reactant molecules must collide and that both an increase in the concentration of reactant molecules and an increase in the temperature of the system can cause an increase in reaction rate. But it takes more than just a regular collision to cause a chemical reaction to occur—in fact, only a very small fraction of collisions that occur in the solution lead to a reaction. This is true for two reasons. First of all, for a reaction to occur, the colliding molecules must be oriented in exactly the correct way: they must be oriented in suitable way for the product molecule bonds to be formed. Second, the two molecules must collide with sufficient energy to overcome the activation energy of the reaction. The **activation energy** is defined as the minimum energy needed to initiate a chemical reaction, and it is symbolized by E_a.

Now let's talk about the energy diagram below.

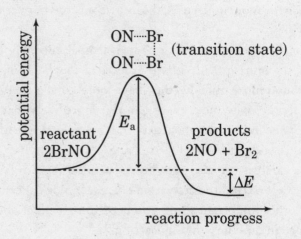

This energy diagram is a graph of the progress of a chemical reaction, versus the total energy of the system. The reactant in this case is BrNO, and the products are NO and Br_2. As you can see, after the reaction occurs, the energy of the system is lower than it was before the reaction. This energy diagram shows an exothermic reaction, one in which energy is given off. In the energy diagram for an endothermic reaction, the energy of the products would be higher than that of the reactants.

In this diagram, the activation energy is signified by the hump in the reaction pathway and is labeled. At the peak of the activation energy hump, the reactants are in the **transition state**, halfway between being reactants and forming products. This state is also known as an **activated complex**.

The figure below shows the energy diagram for a reaction in the presence of a catalyst and in the absence of a catalyst. As you can see, the catalyst has decreased the activation energy of the reaction, which means that more molecules are able to surmount it and react.

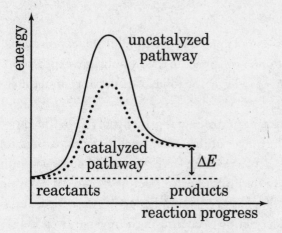

Equilibrium

Chemical equilibrium has been reached in a reaction when the rate of the forward reaction is equal to the rate of the reverse reaction. When a chemical reaction has reached equilibrium, collisions are still occurring: the reaction is now happening in each direction at the same rate. This means that reactants are being formed at the same rate as products are being formed, and this is indicated by double arrows, ⇔. At equilibrium, the reaction can lie far to the right, meaning that there are more products in existence at equilibrium, or far to the left, meaning that at equilibrium there are more reactants. The concentration of the reactants and products in a reaction at equilibrium can be expressed by an equilibrium constant, symbolized K or K_{eq}:

For the general reaction

$$aA + bB \Leftrightarrow cC + dD$$

$$\text{Equilibrium constant} = K = \frac{[C]^c[D]^d}{[A]^a[B]^b}$$

In the above expression, the brackets, as always, symbolize the concentration of the reactants and products in molarity. However, while in the above expression we used the plain symbol K to symbolize the equilibrium constant, there are several types of equilibrium constants. For example, K_c symbolizes the equilibrium constant in an aqueous solution, K_p symbolizes the partial pressures of gases in equilibrium, and K_{sp} symbolizes the solubility product of solids classified as insoluble. K values have no units, and a $K > 1$ means that the reaction favors the products at equilibrium, while a $K < 1$ means that the reaction favors the reactants at equilibrium.

Here are a couple of rules to follow when using equilibrium constant expressions on the exam:

1. Pure solids do not appear in the equilibrium expression.
2. Pure liquids do not appear in the equilibrium expression.
3. Water, either as a liquid or solid, does not appear in the equilibrium expression.
4. When a reactant or product is preceded by a coefficient, its concentration is raised to the power of that coefficient in the K_{eq} expression.
5. When the K_{eq} of a reaction has been multiplied by a number, the K is raised to the power of the multiplication factor (K^n), so if it has been multiplied by 2, K is squared, if it has been multiplied by 3, K is cubed, and so on.
6. The K_{eq} of a reaction occurring in the reverse direction is simply the inverse of the K_{eq} of the reaction occurring in the forward direction ($1/K_{eq}$).
7. The K_{eq} of a net reaction that has two or more steps is found by the product of the K_{eq}s for each of the steps: $K_s = (K_1 \times K_2 \times K_3 \ldots)$.

Let's work through an example now of an equilibrium question.

Example

Write the equilibrium expression for the following equation:

$$H_{2(g)} + I_{2(g)} \Leftrightarrow 2HI_{(g)}$$

If K is calculated to have a value of 2.5 for the reaction above, what is the value of the equilibrium constant for the following reaction?

$$4HI_{(g)} \Leftrightarrow 2H_{2(g)} + 2I_{2(g)}$$

Explanation

The equilibrium constant expression for the reaction is

$$K = \frac{[HI]^2}{[H_2][I_2]}$$

The reaction has been doubled and reversed, so the new K is the *reciprocal* of the old K *squared* (since the reaction coefficients are doubled):

$$K' = \frac{1}{2.5^2} = 0.16$$

Le Chatelier's Principle

You may see an equilibrium question that asks you to use or apply Le Chatelier's principle on the SAT II Chemistry exam. **Le Chatelier's principle** basically states that if stress is applied to a system at equilibrium, the position of the equilibrium will shift in the direction that reduces the stress to reinstate equilibrium. For example, if more reactants are added to the system, the reaction will shift in the forward direction, and if more products are added, the reaction will shift in the reverse direction. If heat is added to the system and the reaction is exothermic, heat should be thought of as a product and the reaction will shift to the left; if the reaction is endothermic and heat is added, the reaction will shift to the right. The addition of pressure will cause a shift in the direction that results in the fewer number of moles of a gas, while if pressure is relieved, the reaction will shift in the direction that produces more moles of a gas.

Practice Questions

Use the following diagram to answer questions 1–3:

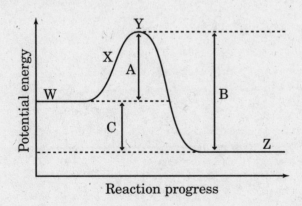

1. Which letter corresponds to the activation energy of the reaction?

(A) *A*
(B) *B*
(C) *C*
(D) *Y*
(E) *X*

2. Which letter corresponds to the change in energy for the overall reaction?

(A) *A*
(B) *B*
(C) *C*
(D) *Y*
(E) *X*

3.	The reaction shown above is exothermic.	BECAUSE	Energy difference *B* is greater than energy difference *A*.
4.	A system is at equilibrium when the rate of the forward reaction is equal to the rate of the reverse reactions.	BECAUSE	At equilibrium, the concentration of the products is equal to that of the reactants.

5. Which of the following statements best describes the condition(s) needed for a successful formation of a product in a chemical reaction?

(A) The collision must involve a sufficient amount of energy, provided from the motion of the particles, to overcome the activation energy.
(B) The relative orientation of the particles has little or no effect on the formation of the product.
(C) The relative orientation of the particles has an effect only if the kinetic energy of the particles is below some minimum value.
(D) The relative orientation of the particles must allow for formation of the new bonds in the product.
(E) The energy of the incoming particles must be above a certain minimum value and the relative orientation of the particles must allow for formation of new bonds in the product.

6. The catalyzed pathway in a reaction mechanism has a _____ activation energy and thus causes a _____ reaction rate.

(A) higher, lower
(B) higher, higher
(C) lower, higher
(D) lower, steady
(E) higher, steady

7. Write the equilibrium expression for the following reaction:

$$2A_{(g)} + B_{(g)} \Leftrightarrow 3C_{(s)} + D_{(g)}$$

(A) $[A]^2[B][D]$

(B) $\dfrac{[C]^3[D]}{[A]^2[B]}$

(C) $\dfrac{[2C][D]}{[2A][B]}$

(D) $\dfrac{[D]}{[A]^2[B]}$

(E) $\dfrac{[A]^2[B]}{[C]^3[D]}$

8. If at a given temperature the equilibrium constant for the reaction

$$H_{2(g)} + Cl_{2(g)} \Leftrightarrow 2HCl_{(g)}$$

is K_p, the equilibrium constant for the reaction

$$HCl_{(g)} \Leftrightarrow \frac{1}{2}H_{2(g)} + \frac{1}{2}Cl_{2(g)}$$

can be represented as

(A) $\dfrac{1}{K_p^2}$

(B) K_p^2

(C) $\dfrac{1}{\sqrt{K_p}}$

(D) $\sqrt{K_p}$

(E) K_p^3

9. The value of the equilibrium constant, K, is dependent on

      I.   The temperature of the system
      II.   The concentration of the reactants
      III.   The concentration of the products
      IV.   The nature of the reactants and products

(A)   I, II
(B)   II, III
(C)   III, IV
(D)   I and IV
(E)   I, II, and IV

10. Consider the following system at equilibrium:

$$N_{2(g)} + 3H_{2(g)} \Leftrightarrow 2NH_{3(g)} + 92.94 \text{ kJ}$$

Which of the following changes will shift the equilibrium to the right?

    I.   Increasing the temperature
    II.   Decreasing the temperature
    III.   Increasing the pressure on the system

(A)   I only
(B)   II only
(C)   III only
(D)   I and III
(E)   II and III

Explanations

---

1.   **A**

The activation energy is the energy that must be overcome for the reaction to proceed. Also remember that for a reaction to occur, the collisions between molecules must be sufficiently energetic and of the proper geometric orientation.

2.   **C**

The energy change for the *overall* reaction is simply the difference between the energies of the products and reactants, and this is indicated by the letter C on the diagram.

3.   **T, T**

(Fill in **CE**.) The energy change indicated by A on the diagram represents the activation energy of the reaction—the energy investment required to form the activated complex Y, also known as the energy that must be put into the system to make the reaction go. B on the diagram represents the energy released when the unstable transition state molecule Y goes to a lower energy state as the products Z. The reaction is exothermic when the energy pay-off *exceeds* the energy investment, and since the second statement is the reason for the first statement, you would fill in the **CE** oval.

4.   **T, F**

(Do not fill in **CE** oval.) The first statement is true—when a chemical reaction is at equilibrium, the rate of the forward reaction is equal to the rate of the reverse reaction, in which the reactants are formed. However, statement II is incorrect and is a common misconception. The amount of reactant and product remain constant at equilibrium but usually do not equal each other. Since the second statement is false, you would not fill in the **CE** oval.

5.   E

Two conditions must be met in order for a chemical reaction to occur. First of all, the molecules must collide with sufficient energy, and second, the molecules must collide with such an orientation that the product bonds can be formed.

6.   C

The addition of a catalyst lowers the activation energy, thus speeding up a chemical reaction.

7.   D

First, be on the lookout for pure liquids and pure solids: These *do not* appear in equilibrium constant expressions. C is a solid, so do not include it in the expression. Second, remember that the expression is written as the product of the products raised to the power of their coefficients *over* the product of the reactants raised to the power of their coefficients. Thus, the correct answer is

$$\frac{[D]}{[A]^2[B]}.$$

8.   C

The reaction is reversed, so take the reciprocal of K_p, and the coefficients in the balanced equation are halved, so you'll raise K_p to the $\frac{1}{2}$ power, which is the same as finding the square root of K_p. The correct answer is $\dfrac{1}{\sqrt{K_p}}$

9.   D

Look through the statements carefully, one by one. First, you know that the value of K depends on the temperature of the system: if you change the temperature, the value of K changes, so item I is correct. Next, K is independent of the concentrations of the reactants or products, so both items II and III are incorrect. K is dependent on the nature of the products and reactants, however, so IV is correct.

10.   E

This question combines two concepts. The reaction is exothermic, so think of heat as a product. Increasing the temperature has the same effect as increasing a product's concentration, so it causes a shift to the left, meaning statement I cannot be in the answer choice. Decreasing the temperature (removing heat) would have the same effect as removing a product (since the reaction is exothermic), so this would cause a shift to the right, and II must be in the correct answer choice. Finally, since all reactants and products are in the gas phase, and there is a total of four moles of gas on the left and a total of two moles of gas on the right, increasing the pressure will push the reaction toward the side with the fewest moles of gas. In this case, the side with the fewer moles of gas is the products side, so this also causes a shift to the right. III is also correct, and answer choice **E** is correct.

Equilibrium

Thermodynamics

Chapter Contents

The SAT II Chemistry exam will test your ability to understand the concepts of enthalpy, entropy, and free energy for various systems. All of these concepts fall under the broad category of chemical thermodynamics, and **thermodynamics** is the area of chemistry that deals with energy relationships. You will also be expected to find values for these energy relationships and use specific heat and energy changes in different systems. We will begin this chapter by introducing some terms and concepts that are probably already familiar to you.

The **law of conservation of energy** (also known as the **first law of thermodynamics**) states that in the course of a chemical reaction, energy can neither be created nor destroyed. But what exactly is energy? So far we've talked about it only tangentially, but here we can define **energy (E)** as the ability to do work or produce heat. Energy is measured in joules. **Heat (q)** refers to the transfer of energy in a physical or chemical process: heat always flows from a warmer object to a cooler one. Heat is also measured in joules. The sum of all of the potential and kinetic energy in a system is known as the internal energy of the system.

Energy comes in several different forms. Let's go through a few of them now. **Potential energy**, in chemical terms, is the energy stored in chemical bonds. Energy is needed in order to break bonds and is given off when bonds form. Another type of energy, called **kinetic energy**, exists in matter in motion. Usually the energy of particles is proportional to the temperature, in kelvins, of the system as well as the mass and the velocity of the object: $KE = \frac{1}{2}mv^2$.

Enthalpy

Often chemical changes result in either the release or the absorption of heat, and this change in heat in the system is measured in terms of the system's **enthalpy (H)**. A reaction in which there is a net absorption of heat energy is called an **endothermic reaction**, and in this type of reaction energy is a reactant, and the change in enthalpy of the system, ΔH, has a positive value. A reaction in which there is a net production of heat by the system is called an **exothermic reaction**. In this type of reaction, energy is a product, and the change in enthalpy of the system, ΔH, has a negative value. The figure below shows an exothermic reaction—you can see that the products have lower energy than the reactants and that the ΔH of the reaction has a positive value—890 kJ.

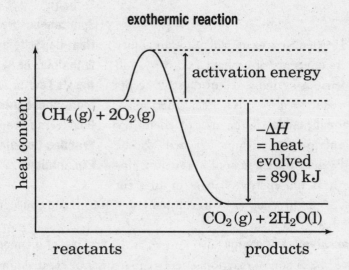

exothermic reaction

There are several different forms of enthalpy you might encounter on the SAT II Chemistry exam, so make sure to study the following list so nothing surprises you on test day.

- **Enthalpy of reaction (ΔH_{rxn})**—The amount of heat absorbed or released by the chemical reaction
- **Enthalpy of combustion (ΔH_{comb})**—The amount of heat absorbed or released by combustion (burning; usually in the presence of O_2)
- **Enthalpy of formation (ΔH_f)**—The amount of heat absorbed or released when 1 mole of a compound is formed from elements in their standard states
- **Enthalpy of fusion (ΔH_{fus})**—The amount of heat that must be absorbed to melt 1 mole of solid to liquid at the normal melting point
- **Enthalpy of vaporization (ΔH_{vap})**—The amount of heat that must be absorbed to change 1 mole of liquid to gas at the normal boiling point

Some final notes about enthalpy before we move on. First of all, enthalpy is a state function, meaning that its value is fixed when temperature, pressure, composition, and physical form are specified. Second, at a constant pressure, $\Delta H = q$, meaning that at constant pressure, the enthalpy of a system is equal to the heat, in joules, of a system. Finally, the enthalpy changes of a reaction can be calculated in several ways, including by using stoichiometry, calorimetry, tables of standard values, Hess's law, and the bond energies of the substances involved. Let's now move on to determining ΔH values of systems using the above methods.

Spontaneous Reactions

A reaction is said to be spontaneous if it occurs without being driven by some outside force. There are two driving forces for all chemical reactions. The first is enthalpy, and the second is entropy. **Entropy (ΔS)** is a measure of the disorder of a system, and systems tend to favor a more disordered system: nature tends toward chaos. Spontaneous reactions occur without outside intervention. They may occur quickly, like the combustion of hydrogen, or slowly, like when graphite turns to diamond.

Let's try a problem that might come up on the SAT II Chemistry test.

Example

The addition of 14.0 g solid potassium hydroxide pellets to water causes the following reaction to take place:

$$KOH_{(s)} \rightarrow KOH_{(aq)} + 43 \text{ kJ}$$

1. Does the beaker get warmer or colder as the reaction takes place?
2. Is the reaction endothermic or exothermic?
3. What is the enthalpy change for the dissolution of the 14.0 grams of KOH?

Explanation

1. This is an exothermic reaction (heat is a product), so heat is released to the surroundings and the beaker gets warmer.
2. As stated above, this is an exothermic reaction: Heat is a product and the ΔH is positive.
3. To solve this problem, you would first convert the grams of KOH to moles and then multiply that by the energy change seen when 1 mol of KOH is added to water, in the following proportions:

$$14.0 \text{ g KOH} \times \frac{1 \text{ mol KOH}}{56 \text{ g KOH}} = 0.25 \text{ mol KOH} \times -43 \text{ kJ} = -10.7 \text{ kJ}$$

Heat Capacity and Specific Heat

We can determine the value of ΔH for a reaction in the lab by using a calorimeter, which measures the heat flowing into and out of a system as the reaction proceeds. We'll talk more about this in chapter 11, the Laboratory chapter. The **heat capacity** of a substance is the amount of heat energy it must consume in order to raise its temperature by 1K or 1°C; it can be expressed using either the units joules or calories. A **calorie** is defined as the amount of heat needed to raise the temperature of 1.00 gram of water by 1.00°C, and joules are the SI units for energy; 1 calorie = 4.184 joules.

Every pure substance involved in a chemical reaction has a unique heat capacity, and the heat capacity of 1 mol of a pure substance is known as its molar heat capacity (J/mol-K or J/mol-°C). The heat capacity of 1 gram of a substance is known as its specific heat (J/g-K). The following equation relates the specific heat of a substance, the temperature change, the mass of the substance, and how much energy was put into the system:

$$q = mC_p\Delta T$$

where

  q = quantity of heat (joules or calories)
  m = mass in grams
  $\Delta T = T_f - T_i$ (final – initial)
  C_p = specific heat capacity (J/g °C)

One thing about specific heats that you should probably remember for the SAT II Chemistry test is that the specific heat of liquid water is 4.184 J/g °C (or 1.00 cal/g °C), which is unusually high (this is due to hydrogen bonding).

Example

How much energy would be needed to heat 450 grams of copper metal from a temperature of 25.0°C to a temperature of 75.0°C? The specific heat of copper at 25.0°C is 0.385 J/g °C.

Explanation

Given mass, two temperatures, and a specific heat, you have enough values to plug into the specific heat equation

$$q = mC_p\Delta T$$

and plugging in your values you get

$$q = (450 \text{ g}) (0.385 \text{ J/g °C}) (50.0°C)$$

$$= 8700 \text{ J}$$

Example • 151

Example

100.0 mL of 1.0 M NaOH and 100.0 mL of 1.0 M HCl are mixed in a calorimeter. Both solutions were originally at 24.6°C. After the reaction, the final temperature is 31.3°C. Assuming that the solution has a density of 1.0 g/cm³ and a specific heat capacity of 4.184 J/g °C, calculate the enthalpy change for the neutralization of HCl by NaOH. Assume that no heat is lost to the surroundings or the calorimeter.

Explanation

We are looking for energy in this problem too. Remember that the solution has a density of 1.08/cm³, and we have a total of 200 ml of solution, so the total mass to be considered is 200 g. You have all of the information you need, so again plug it into the formula $q = mC_p\Delta T$:

$$q = (200 \text{ g}) (4.184 \text{ J/g °C}) (6.7 \text{ °C})$$

The answer is –5.6 kJ/mol.

Enthalpies of Reactions

You can find the overall enthalpy of a reaction by subtracting the enthalpy at the beginning of the reaction from the enthalpy at the end of the reaction:

$$\Delta H = H_{final} - H_{initial}$$

which is virtually the same as saying

$$\Delta H = H_{products} - H_{reactants}$$

under the thermodynamic standard states 25°C (298K), 1 atm, and 1 M. Try using this equation in a problem.

Example

Calculate the ΔH for the following:

$$3Al_{(s)} + 3NH_4ClO_{4(s)} \rightarrow Al_2O_{3(s)} + AlCl_{3(s)} + 3NO_{(g)} + 6H_2O_{(g)}$$

given the following values:

Substance	H_f° (kJ/mol)
$NH_4ClO_{4(s)}$	–295
$Al_2O_{3(s)}$	–1676
$AlCl_{3(s)}$	–704
$NO_{(g)}$	90
$H_2O_{(g)}$	–242
$Al_{(x)}$	0 (since it's an element)

Explanation

$$[1(-1676) + 1(-704) + 3(90) + 6(-242)] - [3(0) + 3(-295)] = -2677 \text{ kJ}$$

This is an exothermic reaction since ΔH is negative. Don't forget to multiply values by coefficients since each coefficient represents the number of moles of each substance!

Try another one:

Example

Find the ΔH_f of $C_6H_{12}O_{6(s)}$ using the following information:

$$C_6H_{12}O_{6(s)} + 6O_{2(g)} \rightarrow 6CO_{2(g)} + 6H_2O_{(l)} + 2800 \text{ kJ}$$

Substance	H_f° (kJ/mol)
$CO_{2(g)}$	−393.5
$H_2O_{(l)}$	−285.8

Explanation

$$[6(-393.5) + 6(-285.8)] - [1(x) + 6(0)] = -2800 \text{ kJ}$$

Now solve the above for x and you have your answer! The value 2800 is negative because this reaction is exothermic. Oxygen is considered an element in its free state, so it is assigned a value of zero. (All diatomic molecules are assigned zeros for the same reason.) After solving for x, you get $H_f^\circ = -1276$ kJ/mol for glucose.

Hess's Law

The total enthalpy of a reaction is independent of the reaction pathway. This means that if a reaction is carried out in a series of steps, the enthalpy change (ΔH) for the overall reaction will be equal to the sum of the enthalpy changes for the individual steps. This idea is also known as **Hess's law**. Here are some rules for using Hess's law in solving problems:

1. Make sure to rearrange the given equations so that reactants and products are on the appropriate sides of the arrows.
2. If you reverse equations, you must also reverse the sign of ΔH.
3. If you multiply equations to obtain a correct coefficient, you must also multiply the ΔH by this coefficient.

Finally, in doing Hess's law problems, it's often helpful to begin by working backward from the answer that you want. In other words—write the final equation first. Try it out.

Example • 153

Example

Given the following equations

$$H_3BO_{3(aq)} \rightarrow HBO_{2(aq)} + H_2O_{(l)} \; \Delta H_{rxn} = -0.02 \text{ kJ}$$

$$H_2B_4O_{7(aq)} + H_2O_{(l)} \rightarrow 4HBO_{2(aq)} \; \Delta H_{rxn} = -11.3 \text{ kJ}$$

$$H_2B_4O_{7(aq)} \rightarrow 2B_2O_{3(s)} + H_2O_{(l)} \; \Delta H_{rxn} = 17.5 \text{ kJ}$$

find the ΔH for this overall reaction:

$$2H_3BO_{3(aq)} \rightarrow B_2O_{3(s)} + 3H_2O_{(l)}$$

Explanation

Multiply the first equation by 4:

$$4H_3BO_{3(aq)} \rightarrow 4HBO_{2(aq)} + 4H_2O_{(l)} \; \Delta H_{rxn} = 4(-0.02 \text{ kJ}) = -0.08$$

Reverse the second equation:

$$4HBO_{2(aq)} \rightarrow H_2B_4O_{7(aq)} + H_2O_{(l)} \; \Delta H_{rxn} = +11.3 \text{ kJ}$$

Leave the last equation as is:

$$H_2B_4O_{7(aq)} \rightarrow 2B_2O_{3(s)} + H_2O_{(l)} \; \Delta H_{rxn} = 17.5 \text{ kJ}$$

Cross out common terms and you are left with:

$$4H_3BO_{3(aq)} \rightarrow 2B_2O_{3(s)} + 6H_2O_{(l)} \; \Delta H_{rxn} = 28.8 \text{ kJ}$$

Divide the above equation and the enthalpy by 2 and you see that the answer is 14.4 kJ (the reaction is endothermic).

Bond Energies

As we mentioned earlier, another way of calculating the enthalpy change in a chemical reaction is by using bond energies. You are probably aware that energy must be added or absorbed to break bonds and that energy is released when bonds are formed. Therefore, you can calculate the total enthalpy of the reaction using the following formula:

$$\Delta H = \textbf{bonds broken} - \textbf{bonds formed}$$

Now try this on a problem.

Example

Using bond energies, calculate the change in energy that accompanies the following reaction:

$$H_{2(g)} + F_{2(g)} \rightarrow 2HF_{(g)}$$

Bond type	Bond energy
H—H	432 kJ/mol
F—F	154 kJ/mol
H—F	565 kJ/mol

Explanation

$$[1(432) + 1(154)] - [2(565)] = -544 \text{ kJ}$$

The answer is –544 kJ.

If the problem you're trying to solve involves more complex molecules, be sure to draw out their structures to determine how many bonds of each type you have.

More About Entropy

For the SAT II Chemistry exam, you'll be expected to be have an understanding of all of the laws of thermodynamics, so to refresh your memory, the first law of thermodynamics says that energy can neither be created nor destroyed. The **second law of thermodynamics** says that the disorder of the universe, meaning its entropy, or ΔS, is constantly increasing. The **third law of thermodynamics** says that the entropy of a perfect crystal at 0K is zero. What does the third law mean to you? It means that we can calculate the entropy of any substance that's at a temperature higher than 0K. Here are some rules about determining the entropy of a system:

1. The greater the disorder or randomness in a system, the larger the entropy.
2. The entropy of a substance always increases as it changes state from solid to liquid to gas.
3. When a pure solid or liquid dissolves in a solvent, the entropy of the substance increases.
4. When a gas molecule escapes from a solvent, there is an increase in entropy.
5. Entropy generally increases with increasing molecular complexity.
6. Reactions that increase the number of moles of particles often increase the entropy of the system.

Example

Which of the following reactions results in the *largest* increase in entropy?

(A) $CO_{2(s)} \rightarrow CO_{2(g)}$
(B) $H_{2(g)} + Cl_{2(g)} \rightarrow 2HCl_{(g)}$

(C) $KNO_{3(s)} \rightarrow KNO_{3(l)}$

(D) $C_{(diamond)} \rightarrow C_{(graphite)}$

Explanation

All of the reactions result in an increase in disorder, but **A**, in which CO_2 moves from a solid state to a gaseous one, represents the largest change in disorder.

You can calculate entropy using a table of standard values in much the same way that you calculated enthalpy earlier by using the equation below:

$$\Delta S^{\circ}_{rxn} = \sum \Delta S^{\circ}_{(products)} - \sum \Delta S^{\circ}_{(reactants)}$$

The units of entropy are J/K. The higher the S value, the more disordered the system, so a positive (+) S value is more disordered, and a $-S$ value is less disordered. Remember that disorder is the favored condition, according to the second law of thermodynamics. Now try a problem that involves using standard S values.

Example

Calculate the entropy change at 25°C in J/K for

$$2SO_{2(g)} + O_{2(g)} \rightarrow 2SO_{3(g)}$$

given the following data:

$SO_{2(g)}$: 248.1 J/mol-K

$O_{2(g)}$: 205.3 J/mol-K

$SO_{3(g)}$: 256.6 J/mol-K

Explanation

$$[2(256.6)] - [2(248.1) + 1(205.3)] = -188.3 \text{ J/K}$$

Don't forget to multiply by coefficients, just as you did in enthalpy, because the given data are still per 1 mole.

Gibb's Free Energy

As we said earlier, the two driving forces for chemical reactions are enthalpy and entropy. If a chemical reaction is endothermic, it must result in an increase in entropy, and if a reaction results in a decrease in entropy, it must be exothermic. For the SAT II Chemistry test, you will be expected to know how to use given entropy (S) and enthalpy (H) values to calculate if a reaction will be spontaneous or not, and you can do so by using the **Gibb's free energy (G)** equation:

$$\Delta G = \Delta H - T\Delta S$$

The Gibb's free energy equation combines all the information that we have learned thus far. But what does the Gibb's free energy value tell us about a reaction? It tells us the following:

1. If G is negative, the reaction is spontaneous in the forward direction.
2. If G is equal to zero, the reaction is at equilibrium.
3. If G is positive, then the reaction is nonspontaneous in the forward direction, but the reverse reaction will be spontaneous.
4. $G_f^\circ = 0$ for elements at standard state (pure elements at 25°C and 1 atm are assigned a value of zero).

The Gibb's free energy equation can be used to calculate the phase change temperature of a substance. During a phase change, equilibrium exists between phases, so if the G is zero, we know that the reaction is in equilibrium.

Example

Find the thermodynamic boiling point of

$$H_2O_{(l)} \rightarrow H_2O_{(g)}$$

given the following information:

$$H_{vap} = +44 \text{ kJ} \qquad S_{vap} = 118.8 \text{ J/K}$$

Explanation

You would solve this problem by setting the equation equal to zero since in equilibrium, G has a value of 0.

$$0 = (44,000 \text{ J}) - (T)(118.8 \text{ J/K})$$

Now solve for T: the answer is 370K, the boiling point of water.

Here's a handy reference table for interpreting what enthalpy and entropy values say about chemical reactions:

ΔH	ΔS	Result
Negative	Positive	Spontaneous at all temperatures
Positive	Positive	Spontaneous at high temperatures
Negative	Negative	Spontaneous at low temperatures
Positive	Positive	*Never* spontaneous

Much as is the case with both enthalpy and entropy, you can calculate ΔG using the following equation:

$$\Delta G_{rxn}^\circ = \sum \Delta G_{(products)}^\circ - \sum \Delta G_{(reactants)}^\circ$$

Example • 157

The units for ΔG are the same as the units as for enthalpy: J/K.

Now try using the above equation in a problem.

Example

Find the free energy of formation for the oxidation of water to produce hydrogen peroxide.

$$2H_2O_{(l)} + O_{2(g)} \rightarrow 2H_2O_{2(l)}$$

given the following information:

	$\underline{\Delta G_f^\circ}$
$H_2O_{(l)}$	–56.7 kcal/mol
$O_{2(g)}$	0 kcal/mol
$H_2O_{2(l)}$	–27.2 kcal/mol

Explanation

Plugging all of the values you were given into the equation (remember that elements have a ΔG_f° of 0), you get

$$[2(-27.2)] - [2(-56.7) + 1(0)] = 59.0 \text{ kcal/mol}$$

Practice Questions

$$2H_{2(g)} + O_{2(g)} \rightarrow 2H_2O_{(l)}$$

$$\Delta H_{rxn}^\circ = -572 \text{ kJ}$$

1.	The reaction shown above is exothermic.	BECAUSE	The total enthalpy of the products in this reaction is less than that of the reactants.

2. Use the bond energies given below to estimate the enthalpy, ΔH, for the following reaction:

$C_2H_4 + Cl_2 \rightarrow ClH_2C-CH_2Cl$

Bond energies:	kJ/mol
C—C	347
C=C	612
C—Cl	341
C—H	414
Cl—Cl	243

(A) $\Delta H = -800$ kJ
(B) $\Delta H = -680$ kJ
(C) $\Delta H = -150$ kJ
(D) $\Delta H = +150$ kJ
(E) $\Delta H = +200$ kJ

3. Each of two solutions are mixed separately, and both solutions are found to be the same temperature. The two solutions are mixed, and a thermometer shows that the mixture's temperature has decreased in temperature. Which of the following statements is true?

(A)   The chemical reaction is exothermic.
(B)   The chemical reaction is absorbing energy.
(C)   The chemical reaction is releasing energy.
(D)   The energy released could be found by multiplying the temperatures together.
(E)   The energy absorbed by the solution is equal to the difference in temperature of the solutions.

4. Consider the reaction

$$C_2H_5OH_{(l)} + 3O_{2(g)} \rightarrow 2CO_{2(g)} + 3H_2O_{(l)}$$
$$\Delta H = -1.40 \times 10^3 \text{ kJ}$$

When a 45.00 gram sample of ethanol is burned with excess oxygen, about how much energy is released as heat?

(A)   0.995 kJ
(B) 5.1×10^2 kJ
(C) 1.40×10^3 kJ
(D) 2.80×10^3 kJ
(E)   5000 kJ

5. In neutralizing 500 mL of 1.0 M HCl with 500 mL of 1.0 M NaOH, the temperature of the solution rises 5.0°C. Given that the density of the solution is 1.0 g/mL and the specific heat of the solution is 4.184 J/g °C, calculate the approximate energy released from this experiment.

(A)   20 J
(B)   1000 J
(C)   4200 J
(D) 2.1×10^4 J
(E) 1.0×10^4 kJ

6. Based on the relationship of entropy to the degree of disorder of a system, which response includes all the occurrences listed that represent a decrease in entropy?

    I.   The freezing of water
    II.   The vaporization of water
    III.   Sublimation (vaporization) of dry ice, solid CO_2
    IV.   The extraction of Mg and pure water from seawater

(A)   I and II
(B)   II and IV
(C)   I and IV
(D)   III
(E)   II and III

7. Spontaneous reactions are driven by

(A)   Low enthalpy values and high entropy values
(B)   Low enthalpy values and low entropy values
(C)   High enthalpy values and low entropy values
(D)   High enthalpy values and high entropy values
(E)   High temperatures and low pressures

8. If an exothermic process is spontaneous, which of the following statements must be true?

(A) ΔG must be positive.
(B) ΔS must be positive.
(C) ΔS must be negative.
(D) The temperature must be over 500K.
(E) ΔG must be negative.

9. Consider the following hypothetical reaction (at 375K). The standard free energies in kJ/mol are given below each substance in parentheses.

$$2A \quad \rightarrow \quad B \quad + \quad C \quad \Delta G° = ?$$
$$(-20.0) \qquad (150.0) \qquad (-350.0)$$

What is the value of the Gibb's free energy for the reaction at this temperature? Is the reaction spontaneous?

(A) -220; yes
(B) -180; no
(C) -160; yes
(D) $+180$; no
(E) -160; no

10. Which of the following events is *least* likely to occur with an increase in temperature for the reaction given?

$$N_2 + 3H_2 \Leftrightarrow 2NH_3$$
$$\Delta H = -45.9 \text{ kJ/mol}$$

(A) The gas particles will move more quickly.
(B) The reaction will produce more ammonia in a shorter time.
(C) The reaction will reverse and ammonia will decompose.
(D) The entropy of the system will increase.
(E) The equilibrium constant will become smaller.

Explanations

1. **T, T**

(Fill in **CE**.) In an exothermic reaction, the ΔH value is negative—energy is given off in the course of the reaction, and the products are at a lower energy than the reactants. The first statement is true since you see that the ΔH value is negative, and the second statement is also true: the enthalpy value of the products is less than that of the reactants in an exothermic reaction. The second statement is the reason for the first, so fill in the **CE** oval.

2. **C**

This question asks you to do a little arithmetic. The formula for finding enthalpy from bond energies is bonds broken minus bonds formed (this translates into the energy of the reactants broken minus the energy of the products formed). You need to draw the structures so that you see what is going on:

$$H-\underset{\underset{H}{|}}{\overset{\overset{H}{|}}{C}}=\underset{\underset{H}{|}}{\overset{\overset{H}{|}}{C}}-H+Cl-Cl \rightarrow Cl-\underset{\underset{H}{|}}{\overset{\overset{H}{|}}{C}}-\underset{\underset{H}{|}}{\overset{\overset{H}{|}}{C}}-Cl$$

Bonds broken: 4 C—H bonds; 1 C=C bond; 1 Cl—Cl bond

Bonds formed: 4 C—H bonds; 1 C—C bond; 2 C—Cl bonds

The C—H bonds cancel each other out, so you don't need to include them in your calculations.

So, $\Delta H = (612 + 243) - [347 + 2(341)] = -174$. Choice **C** is closer to this.

3.   B

After a quick survey of the answer choices, it is evident that choices **A, C**, and **D** are all saying essentially the same thing—the reaction is exothermic. Reread the question—the temperature is going down, so the reaction is endothermic. Choice **B** is the correct answer.

4.   C

To solve this problem, you must first convert the grams of ethanol to moles. The mass of ethanol, C_2H_5OH, is about 46 g/mol. Since the initial mass is 45.00 grams, you have about 1 mole of ethanol. Multiply 1 mole by the ΔH value given in the equation, and the answer is **C**.

5.   D

If you remembered the formula for calculating energy from specific heat, this problem isn't hard at all. If not, that formula is $q = mC_p\Delta T$. The total mass in the solution would be 500 mL + 500 mL = 1000 mL = 1000 g (since the density is 1.0 g/mL). The specific heat is 4.184 J/g °C (round to 4). The change in temperature is 5.0°C. Essentially, you have 20 × 1000 = 20,000 J. The only answer that is close to this value is **D**.

6.   C

Remember the laws of thermodynamics—a decrease in entropy means that a system becomes more organized. Before looking at the answer choices, decide whether each statement represents a system becoming more or less organized, then make your selections. Statement I gets more organized—solids represent the most organized state. II is becoming more disorganized—vapors are gases and are more disorganized than liquids. III is also more disorganized—vapors are more disorganized than solids. IV is more organized— when purifying a mixed-up solution you are organizing the solution. Therefore, I and IV represent a decrease in entropy, and the answer is **C**.

7. **A**

This question tests your knowledge of Gibb's equation, $\Delta G = \Delta H - T\Delta S$. Before approaching all of the choices and getting confused, decide what should happen if all conditions are favored. In order for the reaction to be spontaneous, its ΔG must be negative. You know that exothermic reactions, which have negative enthalpy values, are favored. You also know that entropy is favored and that the more positive the value of ΔS, the higher the entropy. You are looking for something that says little enthalpy, large entropy. Choice **A** states just this.

8. **E**

Answering this question correctly just takes some close reading. The question tells you that the reaction is exothermic and spontaneous, which means that ΔH is negative and ΔG is negative. **A** can be eliminated immediately because a positive free energy value would mean a nonspontaneous reaction. **B** and **C** could both be true—depending on temperature—but the question asks which *must* be true. Choice **D** gives a specific temperature. This fact is insignificant without any other numerical values. So **E** must be the answer—a negative ΔG value means a spontaneous reaction.

9. **C**

To solve this problem, you must remember the formula for calculating Gibb's free energy using standard values provided. The general equation is $\Delta G = \Sigma \Delta G$ products $- \Sigma \Delta G$ reactants. Making the math easy, this gives you $[150 + (-350)] - [2(-20)] = -160$. There is only one answer choice with this value—**C**: when ΔG is negative, the reaction is spontaneous.

10. **B**

This reaction is an exothermic equilibrium reaction. You are looking for the statement that represents an event that's least likely to occur. Option **A** should happen, according to kinetic molecular theory: the more energy, the faster the particles' movement. Choice **C** also seems true—when temperature is increased for an exothermic reaction, the tendency is a shift to the reactants. Statement **D** would definitely be true—the more energy, the more random the particle movement. Statement **E** basically restates choice **C**—there is a shift of equilibrium to the reactants, so K decreases. Statement **B** is the correct answer. With the reaction shifting to the reactants, less product will be produced, not more.

Descriptive Chemistry

This chapter is a collection of various physical and chemical properties of some of the more common elements and compounds encountered in chemistry. The SAT II Chemistry test devotes about 10 questions to this group of subjects, so take this chapter seriously!

Organic Chemistry

Simple Organic Compounds

Organic chemistry is the branch of chemistry that studies carbon compounds. This field is very important since carbon compounds are all around us—they make up a wide array of common substances such as plastics, oil, gasoline, and alcohols and are also a part of many of the foods we eat, such as proteins, carbohydrates, and fats.

One reason that there are so many carbon compounds is because of carbon's unique ability for bonding. Recall the electron structure of carbon:

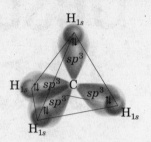

Carbon has four valence electrons, and these electrons can hybridize into sp^3, sp^2, and sp atomic orbitals. This enables carbon to join with other elements and be involved in single, double, and triple bonds. Organic compounds that contain only carbon and hydrogen are called **hydrocarbons**.

Some general properties of organic compounds are

1. They usually have low melting points.
2. They usually are nonpolar (unless they bear functional groups).
3. They are usually nonconductors of electricity.
4. They can exist in solid, liquid, and gaseous form. Compounds with:

- 1–4 carbons tend to be gases at room temperature; **butane** and **propane** are among the lightest hydrocarbons and are used for fuel
- 5–10 carbons tend to be in the liquid state at room temperature; compounds that fall in this size range are used to make gasoline and solvents
- 12–18 carbons make up jet fuels and kerosene
- More than 18 carbons tend to be solids at room temperature

Organic compounds can exist as **polymers**, in which many repeating units (called **monomers**) make up a larger molecule. **Amino acids** are monomers of **proteins** when amino acids are bonded in a chain, they make a polypeptide or protein. **Starches** are polymers of the monomer **glucose**. Plastics are polymers of organic molecules extracted from crude oil. Some common examples include

- **Polyethylene** — Many ethenes strung together with covalent bonds (ethylene is another name for ethene); shopping bags and plastic bottles are made of polyethylene.
- **Polypropylene** — Many propenes strung together; glues and carpets are made of polypropylene.
- **Polystyrene** — A clear, hard, brittle polymer used in CD cases; if you blow carbon dioxide into it during manufacture and you get the soft, opaque, foamy polymer used in a coffee cup.

Common Functional Groups

Functional groups are atoms or groups of atoms attached to an organic compound that impart characteristic shapes and chemical properties to the compound. There are a few functional groups that you should be able to recognize for the SAT II Chemistry test.

1. **Hydroxyl group, −OH**: Compounds that contain an −OH group are considered **alcohols**. An example of an alcohol, ethanol, is shown below:

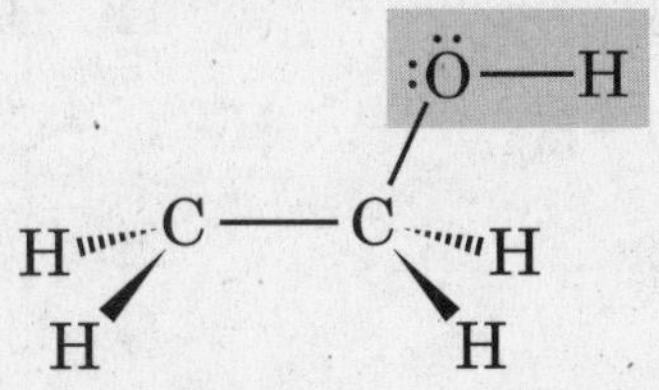

2. **Carboxylic acid group, −COOH**: In a carboxyl group, the carbon is doubly bonded to one oxygen and singly bonded to an OH group. An example of an organic compound containing a carboxyl group, trichloroethanoic acid, is shown below:

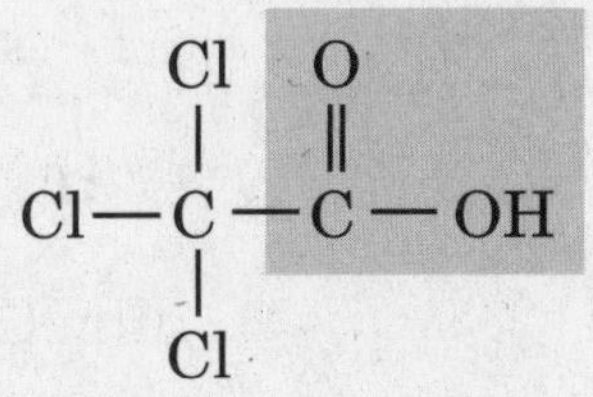

3. **Amine group, −NH₂**: An amino group contains a nitrogen and two hydrogens. In organic chemistry, an R, like the one in the diagram below, is often used as a shorthand notation to signify the rest of the molecule. This notation is generally used when only a specific part of the molecule is being discussed.

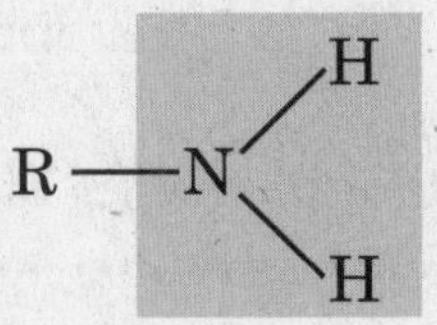

Naming Organic Compounds

Take this opportunity to look through Appendix II, Chemical Formulas Review, if you need a refresher on how to name organic compounds. It might come in handy on test day.

Isomerism

Isomers are compounds that have the same number and kinds of atoms but have different structures—meaning that the atoms are arranged differently in the molecule. Generally the number of isomers increases dramatically as the number of carbon atoms increases because there are more options for molecular structure.

1. **Different carbon skeletons (one or more bonds differ).** An example is C_4H_{10}:

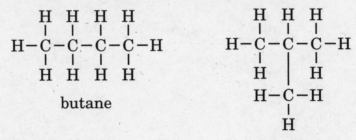

butane

2-propane

2. **Different functional groups.** An example is C_2H_6O:

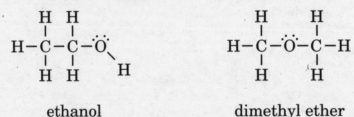

ethanol   dimethyl ether

3. Different positions of functional groups. An example is $C_3H_7NH_2$.

propylamine   isopropylamine

Don't worry about memorizing all of the names of these compounds. They are only included to show that isomers are completely different compounds, with different names.

Simple Organic Reactions

You will be expected to be familiar with a few simple, common organic reactions for the SAT II Chemistry exam, so we'll go through them briefly now. Let's start with combustion reactions. **Combustion reactions** are reactions that occur between oxygen and hydrocarbons, or $C_xH_yO_z$. There are two main types of combustion reactions—complete and incomplete.

Complete combustion occurs when excess oxygen is present; this type of reaction produces carbon dioxide and water.

$$CH_4 + 2O_2 \rightarrow CO_2 + 2H_2O$$

Incomplete combustion occurs when a limited amount of oxygen is present, and the products of incomplete combustion are often difficult to determine. There may be carbon monoxide, carbon, and water or some mixture of all of these. When cooking outdoors on a grill, you often are left with pure carbon (soot) on utensils. Space heaters and automobiles often undergo incomplete combustion and produce deadly carbon monoxide (CO) gas. Here's the reaction for an incomplete combustion:

$$2CH_4 + 3O_2 \rightarrow 2CO + 4H_2O$$

Another common organic reaction is called an addition reaction. In an **addition reaction**, two reactants join to form a single product:

$$H_2C = CH_2 + H_2 \rightarrow H_3C - CH_3$$

Finally, we have the substitution reactions. In a **substitution reaction**, one group replaces another group on the main carbon chain. The atom that's most commonly replaced in a substitution reaction is hydrogen. One common example of this is halogenation, which is the addition of a halide—remember, group 7A on the periodic table.

$$CH_4 + Cl_2 \rightarrow CH_3Cl + HCl$$

Chemistry of Some Common Substances

There will probably be several questions on the SAT II exam that will ask about some common properties of chemicals. The list below constitutes some of the things that everyone should know about chemistry.

Group 1A (Alkali Metals)

This group consists of the most active metals on the periodic table; these metals react with water at room temperature to form bases. They react readily with acids to produce hydrogen gas and get even more reactive as you move down the family. This makes sense because as you move down the family, there are more energy levels, more shielding, so it's harder for the nucleus to hold on to the lonely valence electron, and so on. Many drain cleaners contain sodium hydroxide.

Group 7A (Halogens)

This group contains the most reactive nonmetals on the periodic table, and all of these elements are diatomic. Fluorine is a gas, bromine is a liquid, and iodine is a solid, which makes sense because as the molecules get larger, there are more intermolecular forces to hold them together. Fluorine is the most reactive of the halogens. Chlorine is a very common antibacterial agent, found in bleach and muriatic acid (HCl), and is added to every city's water supply. Fluorine is the anti-tooth-decay element. Most cities also add fluoride ion to the water supply.

Group 8A (Noble Gases)

The noble gases are considered the most stable family on the periodic table. Many of these gases appear in signs (such as neon signs). Helium is used to fill balloons because it is much less dense than air. Argon is fairly abundant in our atmosphere.

Metals

You might recall from our earlier discussions (see "The Structure of Matter") that metals have a positive center surrounded by a sea of electrons. This sea of electrons makes metallic substances very good conductors of electricity. *Alloys* are substances that contain a mixture of elements that have metallic properties. An alloy is often much stronger than the individual metal itself. Some of the more common alloys include

Brass: mixture of copper and zinc

Sterling silver: mixture of silver and copper

Steel: mixture of iron and carbon

Bronze: mixture of copper, zinc, and other metals

Pewter: mixture of tin, copper, bismuth, and antimony

Properties of Some Common Gases

Hydrogen: H_2 is a colorless, odorless gas. It was once used to fill blimps because of its low density, but now helium is used since hydrogen is very flammable. When hydrogen gas is collected in a test tube in the lab, a burning splint inserted into the test tube filled with hydrogen will "bark" as the hydrogen ignites.

Oxygen: O_2 makes up about 21% of our atmosphere (the other major gases that make up the atmosphere are nitrogen and argon). It is a colorless, odorless gas that is necessary for life and supports combustion reactions. When oxygen is collected in a test tube in the laboratory, a glowing wooden splint will reignite.

Carbon dioxide: CO_2 is also a colorless, odorless gas that does not support combustion; many fire extinguishers use carbon dioxide to extinguish flames. When carbon dioxide gas is collected in a test tube in the laboratory, a burning wooden splint will go out when placed into the gas. Another common lab test for CO_2 is to bubble it into limewater, $Ca(OH)_2$. The clear solution will turn cloudy as calcium carbonate, $CaCO_3$, begins to precipitate.

Chlorine: Cl_2 is a deadly yellow-green gas. It has often been used as a weapon in warfare.

Environmental Chemistry

Fuels

The major sources of energy in the United States are coal, petroleum, and natural gas, all of which are known as fossil fuels. Fossil fuels were formed millions of years ago by the decomposition of animals and plants and thus are in limited supply. We are quickly depleting the available fossil fuels.

Coal is solid and is composed of large hydrocarbons and other compounds that contain sulfur, oxygen, and nitrogen. When it's combusted, the sulfur it contains is converted to SO_2, which is an air pollutant. **Petroleum** is a liquid made up of hundreds of different components, but mostly hydrocarbons. It also contains some compounds that have functional groups containing sulfur, nitrogen, or oxygen. The first step in refining (processing) petroleum is to separate it into fractions based on the different boiling points of its components. **Natural gas** consists of hydrocarbons in the gas phase, primarily methane (CH_4).

Air Pollution

Air pollution is the contamination of air by a variety of substances, causing health problems and damaging our environment. It has thinned the ozone layer above the earth, exposing us to harmful UV radiation from the sun. Some of the major pollutant gases are listed below.

Carbon monoxide: CO is produced from incomplete combustion of all types of natural and synthetic products, including cigarette smoke. When it builds up in high concentrations, it can be very toxic. Cities with heavy traffic problems are known for dangerous CO levels.

Carbon dioxide: CO_2 is the principal greenhouse gas and is primarily responsible for the greenhouse effect. It can be formed from all types of common human activity, such as burning fuels and even breathing.

Chlorofluorocarbons: Chlorofluorocarbons, or CFCs, are used in great quantities in industry, for refrigeration and air-conditioning, and in consumer products. When released into the air, they rise into the stratosphere, where they readily react with the ozone that constitutes the ozone layer, effectively degrading it.

Ozone: O_3 gas occurs naturally in the upper atmosphere, where it shields the earth from the sun's dangerous ultraviolet rays. When found at ground level, however, it's a pollutant. It can cause damage to humans (especially our respiratory system), the environment, and a wide range of natural and artificial materials. Vehicle exhaust and industry waste are major sources of ground-level ozone.

Nitrogen oxide and sulfur dioxide: NO_x and SO_x are major contributors to smog and acid rain. These gases both react with volatile organic compounds to form smog, which can cause respiratory problems in humans. Acid rain can harm vegetation, change the chemistry of river and lake water by lowering the pH so that it's harmful to animal life, and react with the marble of statues and buildings and decompose them.

Practice Questions

1. Which statement is INCORRECT?

(A) All of the gases in the atmosphere mix completely unless they react with each other.
(B) The atmosphere of our planet consists of a mixture of gases and various particles in the liquid and solid state.
(C) The major gaseous components of our atmosphere are nitrogen, oxygen, and argon.
(D) Carbon dioxide, another major component of our atmosphere, has concentrations that are relatively the same everywhere within our atmosphere.
(E) The amount of moisture in our atmosphere varies with location.

2.	Refining of petroleum requires the separation of its components into different fractions.	BECAUSE	The hydrocarbon chains that make up petroleum have the same basic carbon chain (same number of C's in the parent).

3. Alloys are mixtures of metallic substances. Which of the following pairs are matched INCORRECTLY?

(A) Brass—copper and zinc
(B) Steel—iron and copper
(C) Bronze—copper, zinc, and others
(D) Pewter—tin, copper, bismuth, and antimony
(E) Sterling silver—silver and copper

4. Which of the following hydrocarbons would be expected to have the highest boiling point?

(A) CH_4
(B) C_3H_8
(C) C_4H_{10}
(D) C_5H_{12}
(E) C_6H_{14}

5. When methane, CH_4, burns in excess oxygen, the products would be

(A) CH_4O_2
(B) $CO + H_2O$
(C) $CO + CH_2OH$
(D) $CO_2 + H_2O$
(E) $CO_2 + 2H_2$

6. A student performed an experiment and a gas was produced. After the gas was collected and tested with a burning splint, a loud popping noise was heard. Which of the following gases was produced?

(A)   Hydrogen
(B)   Oxygen
(C)   Carbon dioxide
(D)   Chlorine
(E)   Methane

7. Which of the following gases is known to shield the earth from harmful ultraviolet radiation?

(A)   CO
(B) CO_2
(C)   CFCs
(D) SO_2
(E) O_3

8. Which compound is INCORRECTLY matched to the functional group that it contains?

(A) CH_3COOH hydroxyl
(B) CH_3OH hydroxyl
(C) $CH_3CH_2NH_2$ amine
(D) CCl_3COOH carboxylic acid
(E) C_6H_5COOH carboxylic acid

Explanations

1.   **D**

If you don't know which is the incorrect answer here, at least try to eliminate choices that you know are true. Choice **A** is true. Chemical reactions are taking place in the atmosphere. For example, water freezes to form snow. Choice **B** is also a true statement. Clouds form when water vapor collects on a dust particle. Choice **C**: you know that oxygen and nitrogen are major components of the atmosphere, and argon is the next most abundant. Choice **D** must be false because it states that the concentration of carbon dioxide is basically the same everywhere on the planet! If you live in New York City, the concentration of CO_2 in your neighborhood is definitely higher than in the neighborhood of someone who lives in rural Kansas. Choice **E** is true. The United States and many other countries have desert climates as well as rainy ones.

2.   **T, F**

(Do not fill in **CE**.) First look at statement I—the first step in processing petroleum is to separate its components based on their different boiling points. For instance, gasoline is one of the components and can be separated out in this way. This statement is true. Now look at the second statement. If petroleum were made up of hydrocarbon chains that had the same number of carbons in them, we would not be able to separate out the components

Descriptive Chemistry

based on their boiling points since they would all have the same boiling point. So this second statement is false, and you would not fill in the **CE** oval.

3.   B

Choice B, steel, is actually composed of iron and varying combinations of carbon. All of the rest of the alloys are listed next to the correct components.

4.   E

You should always think about intermolecular forces in your head when you see the term *boiling point*. In order to boil, molecules must separate from each other, and this takes energy. The molecules that are held most tightly to each other would require the most energy. Since all the molecules listed are nonpolar, the determining factor is polarizability—the more electrons available to have London dispersion forces of attraction. The largest molecule, hexane, choice **E**, will have the greatest attractive forces.

5.   D

When excess oxygen is present, combustion will occur. Hydrocarbon combustion produces carbon dioxide and water. Choice **B** shows possible products for an incomplete combustion.

6.   A

This question requires you to know the properties of the various gases listed. Hydrogen, choice **A**, is odorless, is colorless, and readily ignites with a popping noise. This is the answer. Oxygen, choice **B**, is also odorless, colorless, and flammable but does not produce any sound when ignited. Carbon dioxide, choice **C**, would not ignite. It would put out a flame. Chlorine, choice **D**, is a yellow-green gas that has a pungent odor. It does not readily ignite with a noise. Choice **E** might be familiar to you as a gas that you use in the laboratory. Though methane is flammable, it does not make a particular sound when ignited.

7.   E

This is simply a recall question. The ozone layer in the atmosphere protects us from UV rays. The other four gases listed in this question do cause air pollution. CFCs, choice **C**, are thought to contribute to the depletion of the ozone layer. Choices **A** and **B** are some of the "greenhouse" gases, especially **B**, carbon dioxide. Carbon dioxide is thought to be the reason for global warming. Choice **D** is one of the gases that contributes to the acid rain problem when the gas is released into the atmosphere.

8.   A

A hydroxyl group is OH, an amine is the NH_2 group attached to a carbon chain, and carboxylic acids contain the COOH group. Choice **B** is methanol, wood alcohol, and does have the hydroxyl group. Choice **C** is clearly an amine. Choice **D** and **E** are both carboxylic acids since they contain –COOH. Choice **A** is acetic acid, vinegar, and should be placed with the carboxylic acid group.

Laboratory

T hough the SAT II Chemistry exam cannot test extensively on the laboratory experience, there will be questions that attempt to accomplish this task. A good chemistry course does include some basic laboratory skills, and we will review those skills in this chapter.

Rules for Basic Laboratory Safety

1. Safety goggles must be worn at all times in the laboratory.
2. No eating or drinking in the laboratory.
3. Never taste or touch the laboratory chemicals.
4. Always wash your hands before leaving the laboratory.
5. Wear proper clothing—safety glasses, closed-toed shoes, and an apron; tie long hair back and remove all jewelry.
6. Always follow the written directions, and never perform an unauthorized experiment.
7. Always add acid to water. This prevents the acid from spattering.
8. Point heating test tubes away from others and yourself, and heat them slowly.
9. Never return unused chemicals to their original containers. This prevents contamination.
10. Always use a pipette bulb or a pipetter to transfer when using a pipette. Never use your mouth.
11. Always use a fume hood when working with toxic substances. Never inhale fumes directly.
12. Never use an open flame near flammable liquids.
13. Dispose of chemicals in the designated disposal site—not in the sink or trash can.

Common Laboratory Equipment

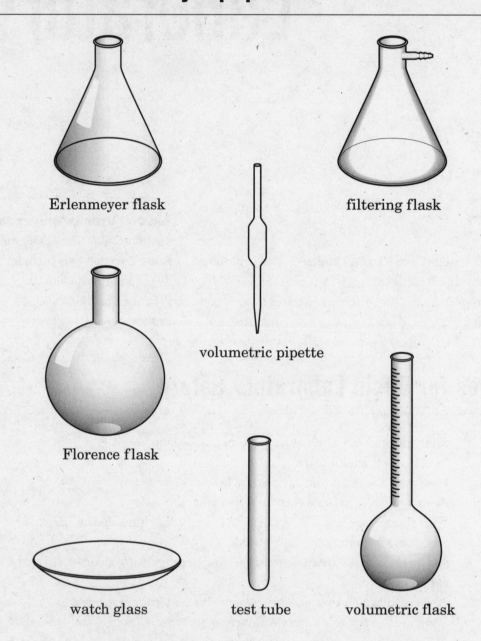

Erlenmeyer flask

filtering flask

volumetric pipette

Florence flask

watch glass

test tube

volumetric flask

Laboratory

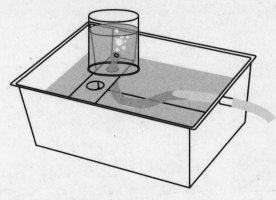

pneumatic trough

crucible tongs

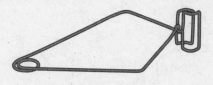

test tube holder

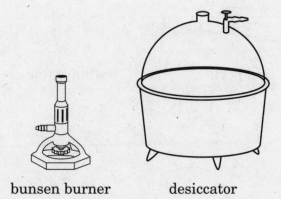

bunsen burner   desiccator

Laboratory

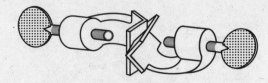

clamp holder

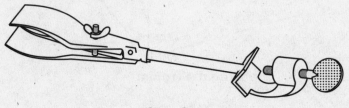

utility clamp

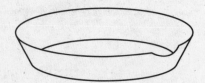

evaporating dish

mortar and pestle

buchner funnel

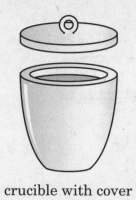

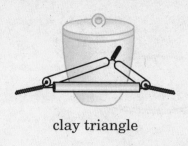

clay triangle

crucible with cover

beaker

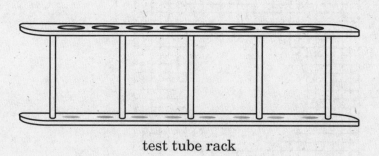

test tube rack

Laboratory

funnel

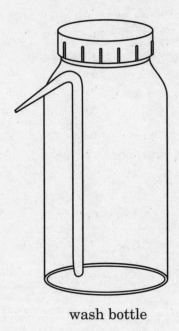

wash bottle

wire mesh

Some Common Lab Techniques

Massing solids: When obtaining the mass of solid chemicals, always use some type of weighing paper to protect the pan of the balance. Remember that the mass of the weighing paper must be written down and subtracted from the total weight when you are determining the amount of solid obtained.

Measuring liquids: When measuring out a particular volume of a liquid, you must choose an instrument that will measure as accurately as possible. For small quantities it would be appropriate to use a pipette or burette. For larger quantities a graduated cylinder might be appropriate. Remember that beakers are not accurate measuring instruments! Remember always to take measurements of liquids from the *bottom* of the meniscus.

Filtering: When filtering a solid from a mixture by gravity filtration, always weigh the filter paper, fold it, place it in the funnel, and wet it down to hold it in place before beginning the filtering process. After filtering, the solid on the filter paper must be dried and weighed. The initial weight of the filter paper is subtracted to find the mass of the solid obtained. The liquid that comes through the filter paper is known as the *filtrate*.

Color Review

One way to identify elements is by performing a simple flame test in the laboratory. When the electrons are heated, they get excited and jump away from the nucleus. As they fall back down, they release energy, often in the form of visible light. Some of the most common colors of flames are listed. You may recognize many of these from fireworks displays!

Ion	Flame color
Li^+, Sr^{2+}, Ca^{2+}	Red
Na^+	Yellow
K^+	Purple (pink)
Ba^{2+}	Light green
Cu^{2+}	Blue-green
Fe^{3+}	Gold

Many solutions in chemistry also have color, which is often the result of unpaired electrons. Metal ions often are colored.

Ion	Solution color
Cu^{2+}	Blue
Fe^{3+}	Yellow to orange (rusty)

Laboratory

Ni^{2+}	Green
MnO$_4^-$	Purple
CrO$_4^{2-}$	Yellow
Cr$_2$O$_7^{2-}$	Orange

Common Experiments

Chromatography

The purpose of chromatography is to separate out parts of a solution—to isolate substances. You might have used paper chromatography in your chemistry lab. In paper chromatography, a small drop of the substance to be separated is placed on one end of the chromatography paper. A pencil is used to mark the spot where the substance was placed, and then the tip of the paper is placed into a container with solvent. As the solvent travels up the paper, the substance separates into its various components. Whatever component is most like the solvent travels the greatest distance. At the end of the experiment, measurements are taken of how far each component traveled. The distance that the solvent traveled and the distance that the solutes (the components) traveled are usually measured in centimeters. A ratio, called the R_f value, is then calculated for each component. This information can be used to identify various parts of the mixture.

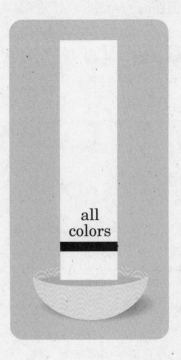
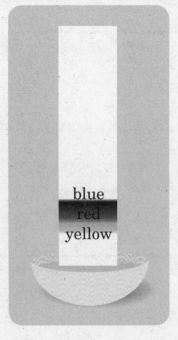
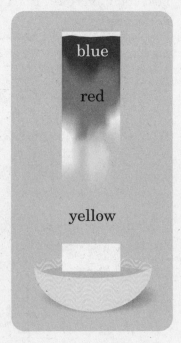

Example • 181

The formula for the calculation is

$$R_f = \frac{\text{distance traveled by solute}}{\text{distance traveled by solvent}}$$

Example

Data:

Distance solvent traveled: 10.0 cm

Distance red dye traveled: 7.0 cm

Distance blue dye traveled: 4.0 cm

Calculate the R_f for the red dye and the blue dye.

Explanation

Just plug your numbers into the equation:

$$R_f \text{ for red dye: } \frac{7.0 \text{ cm}}{10.0 \text{ cm}} = 0.7$$

$$R_f \text{ for blue dye: } \frac{4.0 \text{ cm}}{10.0 \text{ cm}} = 0.4$$

Density of Liquids and Solids

Density is defined as a pure substance's mass over its volume. Density is a property of matter that is often used to identify an unknown substance since pure substances have known densities. The units of density are usually grams divided by milliliters or cubic centimeters:

$$D = \frac{\text{mass (g)}}{\text{volume (cm}^3)}$$

Density of a solid: Typically the solid sample is massed on the balance first. The mass is recorded in grams. If the solid is a regularly shaped object, the length, width, and height may be measured with a metric ruler. These three measurements are then multiplied together to obtain the volume in cubic centimeters (cm³) or some similar unit. If the solid is irregular, the volume can be obtained by water displacement. A known amount of water is recorded, the object is immersed, and the final volume of water is recorded. The difference in volumes will give the volume of the object. Density can then be calculated by dividing the mass by the volume.

    Density of a liquid: The density of a liquid is obtained in much the same way as above. To obtain the mass of the liquid, the mass of a container must first be measured, the liquid poured in, and the total mass recorded. The difference in mass is the mass of the liquid. It is often convenient to measure the liquid in a graduated cylinder. Now try a density problem.

Example

Data (for an irregular solid):

Mass of the solid:	5.00 g
Initial volume of water:	30.0 mL
Final volume of water:	32.5 mL

Find the density of the unknown solid.

Explanation

Volume of solid: (final − initial volumes) = 32.5 − 30.0 = 2.5 mL

Density of solid: $\dfrac{5.00 \text{ g}}{2.5 \text{ mL}} = 2.0$ g/mL

Titration

A **titration** (also called volumetric analysis) is a laboratory procedure that usually involves either an acid and base neutralization reaction or a redox reaction. In a titration, two reagents are mixed, one with a known concentration and known volume (or a solid with a known mass) and one with an unknown concentration. The purpose of a titration is to find the concentration of the unknown solution. There must be some way to indicate when the two reagents have reacted essentially completely, and at the end of the titration the unknown solution's concentration can be calculated since the volume of the solution required to complete the reaction has been accurately measured.

The **titrant** is the solution of known concentration and is usually placed in the burette. The burette must be rinsed with the solution to be placed in it *before* filling.

Example • 183

The solution from the burette is added to a flask that contains either a measured volume of a solution or a weighed quantity of solid that has been dissolved. An indicator that changes color at or near the equivalence point is usually added to the solution to be analyzed before titration. The solution of known concentration is then added to the flask from the burette until the color changes. The **equivalence point** is the point in the reaction where enough titrant has been added to completely neutralize the solution being analyzed. The **end point** is the point during the titration where the indicator changes color. It is important to choose an indicator that has an end point that is at the same pH as your expected equivalence point. The burette has graduations that are used to read the volume of titrant that's added to the flask.

The data required for titrations include the mass of the dry substance to be analyzed *or* an accurately measured volume of the substance to be analyzed, the *initial* volume and *final* volume of titrant required to reach the end point, and the molarity of the titrant. At the equivalence point, the moles of the titrant will be equal to the moles of the substance analyzed. To obtain the moles of the unknown substance, multiply the molarity of the titrant by the volume (in liters) of the titrant. Once moles are known, just divide moles by volume and you have the molarity of the unknown substance

$$M = \frac{\text{moles of solute}}{\text{liter solution}}$$

If the substance to be analyzed is a solid, you will be trying to calculate the molecular weight of the unknown solid. Remember that molecular weight is grams per mole. The mass in grams will be known from the beginning of the experiment, when the solid sample was massed. You can find the moles of the unknown substance by multiplying the molarity of the titrant by the volume (in liters) of the titrant. Divide grams by moles to get molecular weight.

If you are doing a titration of a strong base with a strong acid, the equivalence point occurs at a pH of 7.00. The dilution formula can be used to calculate the moles of acid, which will equal the moles of base at the equivalence point:

$$M_1 V_1 = M_2 V_2$$

or moles of acid = moles of base. Don't try to use this formula if either the acid or base is weak!

Example

Data:

Volume of unknown acid sample: 10.0 mL

Initial volume of titrant (base): 0.0 mL

Final volume of titrant (base): 20.0 mL

Molarity of titrant (base) (must be given): 1.0 M

Find the molarity of the unknown acid solution.

Explanation

Don't forget to change mL to L.

0.020 L (titrant) × 1.0 mole/liter (titrant molarity) = 0.020 mole of base titrant

At the equivalence point: moles acid = moles base = 0.020 mole of acid

$$M = \frac{\text{moles of solute}}{\text{liter solution}} \text{ so } \frac{.020 \text{ moles}}{.010 \text{ L}} = 2.0 \ M \text{ acid}$$

Calorimetry

Calorimetry is used to determine the amount of heat released or absorbed during a chemical reaction. In the lab we can experiment with finding the energy of a particular system by using a **coffee-cup calorimeter**. The coffee-cup calorimeter (shown below) can be used to determine the heat of a reaction at constant (atmospheric) pressure or to calculate the specific heat of a metal. The coffee-cup calorimeter is a double plastic foam cup with a lid; the lid has a hole in it where the thermometer pokes through.

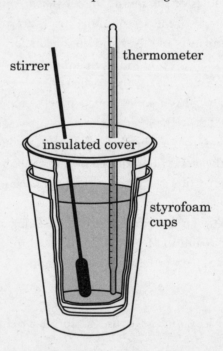

The data to be collected include the volumes of the solutions to be mixed, the initial temperatures of each solution, and the highest temperature obtained after mixing. Accurate results depend on measuring precisely and starting with a dry calorimeter. The total volume recorded must be changed into grams (use the density and multiply density × volume = grams). The change in temperature must be calculated by subtracting the final and initial temperatures. To find the heat of reaction, multiply the specific heat capacity, the mass, and the change in temperature: $q = mC_p\Delta T$.

Example • 185

Example

Data (for a specific heat of a metal):

Mass of the solid metal:	24.00 g
Initial temperature of the metal:	100.0°C
Mass of water in plastic foam cup:	100.00 g
Initial temperature of the water:	25.0°C
Highest temperature of the water:	30.0°C

Find the specific heat of the metal.

$$q = mC_p\Delta T \ (C_p = 4.18 \text{ J/g °C})$$

Explanation

Temperature change for the metal = 100.0 – 30.0 = 70.0°C
Temperature change for the water = 30.0 – 25.0 = 5.0°C
We can assume that the heat lost by the metal should equal the heat gained by the water.
Calculate the heat gained by the water:

Heat gained by water = (sp. heat water)(mass of water)(ΔT water)
= (4.18 J/g °C)(100.0 g)(5.0°C)
= 2090 joules gained

Then find the specific heat of metal:

$$\text{Sp. heat} = \frac{\text{energy (Joules)}}{\text{(mass)(change in temp.)}} = \frac{2090 \text{ J}}{(24.00 \text{ g})(70.0°\text{C})} = 1.24 \text{ J/g} \cdot °\text{C}$$

(Small values for metals are very typical!)

Stoichiometry

Many experiments require the use of **stoichiometry** to find an unknown. One typical experiment is the neutralization of an acid with a base to produce a salt and water. If a known volume and concentration of an acid and a base are reacted, the amount of salt produced can be predicted. Typical data would require the accurate recording of molarities and volumes of the acid and the base. The mass of the reacting vessel must be recorded, and then the two solutions are mixed. The mixed solution is then evaporated over a low flame (to avoid spattering and loss of mass) to dryness. The vessel is allowed to cool, and the final weight is then recorded. The vessel should be heated to a constant mass in this type of experiment. This requires heating, cooling, and weighing until two consecutive measurements are within an acceptable range of each other. The mass of the solid salt obtained is calculated by subtracting the mass of the vessel from the total mass of the vessel with the salt. This mass is known as the actual (or experimental) yield. To find the theoretical yield (what should have been produced), a balanced chemical equation must be written. The moles of each substance reacted must be determined (multiply molarity by volume) and also the moles of the limiting reagent (using coefficients). From the moles of limiting reagent, multiply by the mole ratio and then convert to grams using the formula weight of the salt from the periodic table. This gives the theoretical yield of salt. It is typical to calculate the percent yield. The closer to 100%, the better your results were!

$$\% \text{ yield} = \frac{\text{actual yield}}{\text{theoretical yield}} \times 100$$

Practice Questions

1. Which instrument would be best suited for use in a volumetric analysis to find the unknown molarity of base when titrated with a known acid?

(A) Graduated cylinder
(B) Pipette
(C) 250 mL beaker
(D) Burette
(E) Triple beam balance

2. In a neutralization reaction performed in lab, a student mixed 0.20 M NaOH with 0.10 M HCl until the reaction was complete. After the liquid left in the container was dried, which of the following statements must be true?

  I. The student produced a salt and water. All that was left in the container was the salt.
  II. The total mass of the products in the evaporating dish at the end of the experiment had a lower mass than before heating.
  III. The student was left with an ionically bonded, white, crystalline solid.

(A) I only
(B) II only
(C) I and II only
(D) I and III only
(E) I, II, and III all are true

3. Which of the following laboratory techniques would not be a physical change in components of a mixture?

(A) Chromatography
(B) Precipitation
(C) Filtering
(D) Distillation
(E) Evaporation

4. A student mixes 10.0 mL of 0.10 M $AgNO_3$ with excess copper metal. The reaction should produce 0.107 gram of silver; however, the student obtains a mass of 150 grams of silver. Plausible explanations for this yield >100% might include

    I.   The student did not subtract the mass of the filter paper before recording results.

    II.   The student did not thoroughly dry the sample before massing.

    III.   The copper metal did not react completely.

(A)   I only

(B)   II only

(C)   I and II only

(D)   I and III only

(E)   I, II, and III

5. Which of the following mixtures would best be separated by gravity filtration?

(A)   A solid precipitate in a liquid solution

(B)   A mixture of oil and water

(C)   A mixture of solid iron with solid sulfur

(D)   Carbon dioxide gas bubbles in a soft drink

(E)   A mixture of dyes in a felt-tip pen

6. Which of the following statements is the most probable explanation for color in solutions?

(A)   Solutions with color contain oxygen.

(B)   Solutions with color contain metals.

(C)   Solutions with color are ionically bonded with water.

(D)   Solutions with color usually contain transition metals with unshared electron pairs.

(E)   Solutions with color have electron configurations that are isoelectronic with the noble gases.

Explanations

1.   **D**

Choosing the appropriate instrument is a typical laboratory question on the test. When the question states *volumetric analysis* and then the word *titrated* in the same sentence, a burette, choice **D**, should be your first thought. Choice **E** is an easy elimination: a balance measures mass in grams and would be used in gravimetric analysis. Choice **C** is the next elimination: Beakers are not accurate measuring instruments. The markings on a beaker may only be accurate to within a 5–10% range! A pipette, choice **B**, and a graduated cylinder, choice **A**, are both very accurate measuring instruments. However, this question discussed a titration, so the best answer is the burette.

2.   **E**

This question requires that you understand the reaction that will occur. In this question, NaOH will react with HCl in a double replacement (neutralization) reaction and produce a salt, NaCl, and water. The concentration of each solution is irrelevant information and is thus ignored. Focus on what the question asks—after drying, what will remain? Statement I is a true statement. If you evaporate all of the water away, NaCl will be the only remaining product. Statement II is a bit tricky. If you read quickly and are thinking law of conservation of matter, you'll think that this must be false. However, the question states that after drying has occurred, water will evaporate and the mass will be less since some is given off as water vapor. You know then, that the answer contains I and II. Just for confirmation, you could check statement III. This answer is also correct. A metal and a nonmetal bond ionically and salt crystals will be white in color so, **E** is the answer.

3.   **B**

Answering this question makes you think about physical and chemical changes. You are looking for the one process that is chemical; changing substances, not physical. Chromatography, choice **A**, is a physical separation of a substance by polarities (as in paper). Filtering, choice **C**, is also a physical separation of a solid from a liquid. Distillation, choice **D**, and evaporation, choice **E**, both involve changes of state, which are also physical changes. Choice **B** is the only chemical change listed. Precipitation is the formation of a solid when two or more liquids are combined. The formation of a precipitate is one indicator that a chemical change may have taken place.

4.   **C**

Once again, you are in search of the true statements. Statement I is true. If the student forgot to subtract out the mass of the filter paper, the mass obtained would appear larger. Statement II is also correct. If the substance was not completely dry, the moisture would cause the mass to be greater. Statement III is a true statement, but it should not increase the mass of silver unless the student failed to separate all of the silver from the copper before massing. The question states that copper is in excess, meaning that it would not all react. Statement IV, the concentration of the silver nitrate needed to be stronger, does not match the problem—we had too much silver! So the answer is **C**.

5.   **A**

Choice **A** is the correct answer. Using a filter paper and funnel, you can easily separate a solid from a liquid. The solid stays in the paper, and the liquid runs through the paper. Choice **B** would not separate easily using a filter paper. Oil and water would layer and could easily be separated using a pipette. Choice **C**, two solids, would not separate with filter paper. The easiest separation technique for these two solids would be to use a magnet to gather all of the iron particles. Choice **D**, gas bubbles, would not be trapped in piece of solid filter paper. To remove the gas, a hose could be attached to the soda, and the soda could be heated or shaken to remove the carbon dioxide gas. Choice **E**, a mixture of dyes, could be separated with filter paper but not with filtration. The technique to separate the dyes is known as chromatography.

6.   **D**

Color is a result of the way light is reflected. When unshared electrons are present, especially in different energy levels, as is possible with the transition elements and their *d* orbitals, color is often a result. Most of the color comes in solutions of transition metals. Thus, choice **D** gives the correct answer. Choices **A** and **B** are partial statements of fact but are neither reasons nor explanations. Many solutions of transition elements do contain oxygen in the polyatomic ion, such as nickel (II) nitrate—nitrate contains oxygen, but this has nothing to do with the color. The term *metals* in statement **B** is too broad. Over three-quarters of the periodic table is composed of metals, and there are not that many colored solutions! Statement **C** is also a partially true statement. Most transition metals will be ionically bonded when in salt form, but bond type does not give rise to color. Statement **E** makes the incorrect assumption that noble gases are all colored. This may have tricked you since you know that neon lights have color. However, the color of the neon light is the direct result of electrons getting excited and falling back to a lower energy level.

Laboratory

Basic Measurement and Calculation Review

T he SAT II Chemistry test will not directly test you on any of the skills that this appendix discusses. However, a good working knowledge of the information in this chapter will still prove very helpful during the exam. Remember, you can't use a calculator during the test!

The SI System

The Système Internationale (International System), SI, more commonly known as the metric system, is the only system of measurement that you'll see on the SAT II Chemistry test. Here's a quick refresher course on how to use this system.

Standard Prefixes

The metric system is fairly straightforward. The table of prefixes below is only partial, but it includes the ones that you need to be familiar with for the test.

Prefix	Power	Meaning	Examples of measurements
nano (n)	10^{-9}	one-billionth	nanometer (nm): wavelength of light
micro (μ)	10^{-6}	one-millionth	micrometer (μm): width of a hair
milli (m)	10^{-3}	one-thousandth	milliliter (mL): volume of acid in burette
centi (c)	10^{-2}	one-hundredth	centimeter (cm): length of paper
deci (d)	10^{-1}	one-tenth	deciliter (dL): amount of liquid
kilo (k)	10^{3}	one thousand times	kilogram (kg): your weight

Also useful to know are the units in the table below. Most of them will probably be familiar to you.

What is being measured	Common units
length	meter (m)
mass	gram (g)
volume	liter (L) or cm^3
temperature	degree Celsius (°C) and kelvin (K)
time	second (s)
pressure	kilopascal (kPa); atmosphere (atm); mmHg
energy	joules (J); calorie (cal)
amount of substance	mole (mol)

Scientific Notation

This is an easy way to express really large or really small numbers conveniently. The general format for numbers expressed this way is

$$\text{some number} \times 10^{\text{some power}}$$

For instance, 6.022×10^{23} is really big, and 3.00×10^{-6} is really small. Notice that the proper position for the decimal is to the right of the first nonzero digit. If you must move the decimal to get it into this position, moving the decimal to the left makes the exponent appear larger, while moving decimal to the right makes the exponent appear smaller. For example, 0.000567 in scientific notation would be 5.67×10^{-4}.

You need to be able to handle numbers of this sort without a calculator. Basically, you need to remember the following. For *multiplication, add* exponents, and for *division, subtract* exponents. To get the *log* of a value, raise it to the *power of ten*. This is mostly useful for pH calculations. Now try some problems.

Basic Measurement

Example • 193

Example

$(4.5 \times 10^5)(3.0 \times 10^8)$.

Explanation

The answer is 1.35×10^{14} (or rounded, 1.4×10^{14}). In solving this, think: $3 \times 5 = 15$, and then add the exponents: $5 + 8 = 13$. Move the decimal to the right of the first nonzero digit, or one place to the left.

Example

Try another one: $\dfrac{6.8 \times 10^{-2}}{2.0 \times 10^{10}}$.

Explanation

The answer is 3.4×10^{-12}. In solving this, think: $6.8/2 = 3.4$, and then subtract the exponents: $(-2) - (10) = -12$.

Example

Let's try another: Find the log of 1.0×10^{-7}.

Explanation

The answer is -7. The thought process is as follows. The log of 1.00 is 0. The log of 10^{-7} is just the power of 10.

Temperature Conversions

The only two temperature scales that are needed for the SAT II Chemistry test are the **Celsius** scale and the **Kelvin** scale. One degree on the Celsius scale is the same increment as 1 kelvin on the Kelvin scale.

Celsius scale: This is the scale used in the chemistry laboratory for most experiments. The freezing point of water is 0°C, and the boiling point of water is 100°C. This was the original metric standard for temperature.

Kelvin scale: This is the scale used for working through gas law problems. There are no negative numbers on this scale. At 0K, all motion theoretically ceases.

Calculations Involving Metric Measurements (Dimensional Analysis)

Dimensional analysis offers an easy way to solve problems using conversion factors and unit cancellations. *Conversion factors* are ratios that equal 1. You know many of these ratios of equivalencies from everyday living. For example, 1 gallon equals 4 quarts, 12 inches equals 1 foot, etc. This is a useful technique for calculations that might come up on the test, so work through the following problems to practice it.

Example

How many inches tall is a person who is 5 feet, 4 inches tall?

Explanation

$$5 \text{ ft } \times \frac{12 \text{ in.}}{1 \text{ ft.}} = 60 \text{ in.} + 4 \text{ in.} = 64 \text{ in.}$$

Example

How many milliliters would there be in 3.5 liters of soda?

Explanation

$$3.5 \text{ L} \times \frac{1000 \text{ mL}}{1 \text{ L}} = 3500 \text{ mL.}$$

You'll have to do plenty of conversions like the one above to solve problems on the exam. Be sure that you are familiar with all the metric prefixes listed earlier so that you can be successful when you need to convert numbers.

Density

Density is a complex unit. It is defined as mass per unit of volume:

$$\text{Density} = \frac{\text{mass (g)}}{\text{volume (mL)}}$$

All pure substances have a unique density at a given temperature. Density is an intensive physical property, meaning that it does not change with sample size. Usually the solid form of a pure substance is denser than the liquid form of the same substance. This makes sense because in most solids, the particles are much closer together than in their liquid counterparts.

Typical units for density of solids and liquids are grams per milliliter or grams per cubic centimeter. (Remember: $1 \text{ cm}^3 = 1 \text{ mL}$.) Typical units for density of gases are grams per liter.

Example

Find the density of a substance that has a mass of 45.0 g and a volume of 3.0 mL.

Basic Measurement

Explanation

$$D = \frac{45.0 \text{ g}}{3.0 \text{ mL}} = 15 \text{ g/mL}$$

Example

What would be the mass of a substance that occupies a space of 2.0 cm³ and has a density of 7.5 g/cm³?

Explanation

$D = \dfrac{M}{V}$. Rearrange the equation to solve for mass: $M = D \times V$.

Then

$$M = (7.5 \text{ g/cm}^3)(2.0 \text{ cm}^3) = 15 \text{ g}$$

Basic Measurement

Chemical Formulas Review: Nomenclature and Formula Writing

Chapter Contents

Naming Simple Compounds

There are four naming systems you should familiarize yourself with to succeed on the SAT II Chemistry exam. The trick is recognizing *which* naming system to use. Here are the guidelines:

- If the compound **starts with H**, it is an acid. Use the **naming acids** rules.
- If the compound **starts with C** and contains quite a few H's and perhaps some O's, it is organic. Use the **naming organic compounds** rules.
- If the compound **starts with a metal**, it is most likely ionic. Use the **naming binary ionic compounds** rules.
- If the compound **starts with a nonmetal other than H or C**, use the **naming binary molecular compounds** rules.

It is also *essential* that you memorize some common polyatomic ions. Polyatomic ions behave as a unit. If you need more than one of them, enclose them in parentheses when you write formulas. You need to know their names, formulas, and charges. If you learn the nine that follow, you can get many others from applying two simple patterns.

Name of polyatomic ion	Formula and charge
Ammonium ion	NH_4^+
Acetate ion	$C_2H_3O_2^-$
Cyanide ion	CN^-
Hydroxide ion	OH^-
Nitrate ion	NO_3^-
Chlorate ion	ClO_3^-
Sulfate ion	SO_4^{2-}
Carbonate ion	CO_3^{2-}
Phosphate ion	PO_4^{3-}

- **Pattern 1**: The *-ates* "ate" one more oxygen than the *-ites* and their charge doesn't change as a result! For instance, if you know nitrate is NO_3^-, then nitrite is NO_2^-. If you know phosphate is PO_4^{3-}, then you know phosphite is PO_3^{3-}. You can also use the prefixes *hypo-* and *per-* with the chlorate series. Perchlorate, ClO_4^-, was really "hyper and ate yet another oxygen" when compared to chlorate, ClO_3^-. Hypochlorite is a double whammy: it is *-ite* and therefore "ate" one less oxygen than chlorate *and* it is *hypo-*, which means "below," so it "ate" even one less oxygen than plain chlorite, so its formula is ClO^-. You can also substitute the other halogens for Cl and make additional sets of the series.

- **Pattern 2**: The *-ates* with charges less than negative 1 (that is, ions with charges of −2, −3, etc.) can have an H added to them to form new polyatomic ions. For each H added, the charge is increased by a +1. For instance, CO_3^{2-} can have an H added and become HCO_3^-. HCO_3^- is called either the bicarbonate ion *or* the hydrogen carbonate ion. Since phosphate is −3, it can add one or two hydrogens to make two new polyatomic ions, HPO_4^{2-} and $H_2PO_4^-$. These are named hydrogen phosphate and dihydrogen phosphate, respectively. If you keep adding hydrogen ions until you reach neutral, you've made an acid! That means you need to see the naming acids rules.

- **Pattern 3**: The following periodic table will also come in handy. Notice there are simple patterns for determining the most common oxidation states of the elements based on their family's position in the periodic table. Notice the 1A family is +1, while the 2A family is +2; then skip across to the 3A family and see that aluminum is +3. Working backward from the halogens, or 7A family, the oxidation states are most commonly –1, while the 6A family is –2, and the 5A family is –3. The 4A family is "wishy-washy": they can be several oxidation states, with the most common being +4.

1A												3A	4A	5A	6A	7A	8A
	2A													N^{3-}	O^{2-}	F^-	
Li^+																	
Na^+	Mg^{2+}											Al^{3+}			S^{2-}	Cl^-	
K^+	Ca^{2+}			Cr^{2+} Cr^{3+}	Mn^{2+} Mn^{3+}	Fe^{2+} Fe^{3+}	Co^{2+} Co^{3+}		Cu^+ Cu^{2+}	Zn^{2+}						Br^-	
Rb^+	Sr^{2+}								Ag^+	Cd^{2+}			Sn^{2+} Sn^{4+}			I^-	
Cs^+	Ba^{2+}								Hg_2^{2+} Hg^{2+}				Pb^{2+} Pb^{4+}				

■ Common type I cations   □ Common type II cations   ▨ Common monatomic anions

Naming Acids

How do you know it's an acid? The compound's formula begins with an H, and water doesn't count! Naming acids is extremely easy if you know your polyatomic ions. There are three rules to follow:

- **H + element**: When the acid has *only* an element following the H, use the prefix *hydro-*, followed by the element's root name and an *-ic* ending. HCl is hydrochloric acid; H_2S is hydrosulfuric acid. When you see an acid name beginning with *hydro-*, think: Caution, element approaching! HCN is an exception since it is a polyatomic ion without oxygen, so it is named hydrocyanic acid.
- **H + -ate polyatomic ion**: If the acid has an *-ate* polyatomic ion after the H, that makes it an *-ic* acid. H_2SO_4 is sulfuric acid.
- **H + -ite polyatomic ion**: When the acid has an *-ite* polyatomic ion after the H, that makes it an *-ous* acid. H_2SO_3 is sulfurous acid.

Chemical Formulas Review

Acids have enough H^+ added to the anion to make the compound neutral. Supply either the acid's name or its formula to complete the table below:

Acid formula	Acid name
HCl	
	Hypochlorous acid
	Chlorous acid
	Chloric acid
	Hyperchloric acid (or perchloric acid)
HNO_3	
	Hydrobromic acid
H_3PO_4	
H_3PO_3	
	Hydrocyanic acid
$HC_2H_3O_2$	
	Carbonic acid
	Hydroiodic acid
HF	

Naming Organic Compounds

How do you know it's organic? The formula will start with a C followed by H's. Most of the organic carbons you will encounter will be either hydrocarbons or alcohols, and luckily for you, these are the simplest of all to name. Learn the list of prefixes in the table following this section: they correspond to the number of carbons present in the compound. The following silly statement will help you remember the order of the first four prefixes since they are not ones you are familiar with: "Me eat peanut butter." This corresponds to *meth-*, *eth-*, *prop-*, and *but-*, which correspond to one, two, three, and four carbons, respectively.

Now that we have a stem, we need an ending. There are three common hydrocarbon endings; the ending changes depending on the structure of the molecule:

- *-ane* = alkane (all single bonds and saturated); C_nH_{2n+2}; *saturated*: it contains the maximum number of H's
- *-ene* = alkene (contains double bond, unsaturated); C_nH_{2n}
- *-yne* = alkyne (contains triple bond, unsaturated); C_nH_{2n-2}; *polyunsaturated*: it contains more than one double or triple bond

For any hydrocarbon, you can remove one H and replace it with a hydroxyl group, or —OH group, to form an alcohol. Do *not* be fooled—this looks like a hydroxide group but isn't! The OH does *not* make this hydrocarbon an alkaline or basic compound, *nor* do you name it as a hydroxide! C_2H_6 is ethane, while C_2H_5OH is ethanol. Fill in the missing formulas and names for each compound in the table:

No. of carbon atoms = n	Prefix or stem	-ane C_nH_{2n+2}	-ene C_nH_{2n}	-yne C_nH_{2n-2}	-anol C_nH_{2n+1} + OH
1	meth-		Must have 2 carbons		CH_3OH
2	eth-				
3	prop-		C_3H_6		
4	but-				
5	pent-	C_5H_{12}			
6	hex-				
7	hept-				$C_7H_{15}OH$
8	oct-			C_8H_{14}	
9	non-				
10	dec-				

Naming Binary Ionic Compounds

How will you know a compound is ionic? You'll know because the formula will begin with a metal cation or the ammonium cation. Formulas often end with a polyatomic anion. If only two elements are present, they are usually from opposite sides of the periodic table, like in KCl. If the metal is one of the transition metals, be prepared to use a Roman numeral to indicate which oxidation state the metal is exhibiting. Silver, cadmium, and zinc are exceptions to the Roman numeral rule! First, let's name the ions.

Naming positive ions (usually metals)

- Monatomic, metal, cation: simply the name of the metal from which it is derived. Al^{3+} is the aluminum ion (these are often referred to as group A metals).
- Transition metals form *more than one ion*; Roman numerals (in parentheses) follow the ion's name. Cu^{2+} is copper (II) ion. *Exception*: mercury (I) is Hg_2^{2+}, that is, two Hg^+ bonded together covalently.
- NH_4^+ is ammonium.

Chemical Formulas Review

- Roman numerals are not usually written with silver, cadmium, and zinc. Arrange their symbols in alphabetical order—the first one is 1+ and the other two are 2+.

Naming negative ions (usually nonmetals or polyatomic ions)

- Monatomic, nonmetal, anion: add the suffix *-ide* to the stem of the nonmetal's name. Halogens are called the *halides*. Cl^- is the chloride ion.
- Polyatomic anion: you must memorize the polyatomic ion's name. NO_2^- is the nitrite ion.

Naming ionic compounds: The positive ion name is given *first* (remember, if it's a transition metal, the Roman numeral indicating its charge is part of its name), followed by the name of the negative ion. *No* prefixes are used.

Naming Binary Molecular Compounds

How will you know if it's a molecular compound? Well, it will be a combination of nonmetals, both of which lie near each other on the periodic table. Use the following set of prefixes, and don't forget the *-ide* ending to the name.

Subscript	Prefix
1	*mono-*
	(usually used only on the second element, such as carbon monoxide or nitrogen monoxide)
2	*di-*
3	*tri-*
4	*tetra-*
5	*penta-*
6	*hexa-*
7	*hepta-*
8	*octa-*
9	*nona-*
10	*deca-*

If the second element's name begins with a vowel, the *a* at the end of the prefix is usually dropped. N_2O_5 is dinitrogen pentoxide, *not* dinitrogen pentaoxide. PCl_5 is phosphorous pentachloride, not phosphorous pentchloride.

Formula Writing

The naming is the tricky bit! Once you've been given the name, the formula writing is easy *as long as you know the formula and charges of the polyatomic ions*. The prefixes of a molecular compound make it really easy since the prefix tells you how many atoms are present! Roman numerals are your friend: they tell you the charge on the transition metal. *Remember*, Ag, Cd, and Zn are usually not written with a Roman numeral—arrange the symbols in alphabetical order, and the first listed is +1, while the other two are +2. **Most important, the sum of the charges must add up to** *zero* **in order to form a neutral compound**. The "crisscross method" is very useful—the charge on one ion becomes the subscript on the other. Always double-check to see that the subscripts are in their lowest terms! Here are some examples:

potassium oxide → $K^{1+}\ O^{2-}$ → K_2O_2 → K_2O

iron (III) chlorate → $Fe^{3+}\ ClO_3^{1-}$ → $Fe_3(ClO_3)_3$ → $Fe(ClO_3)_3$

tin (IV) sulfite → $Sn^{4+}\ SO_3^{2-}$ → $Sn_2^4(SO_3)_2$ → $Sn_2(SO_3)_4$ → $Sn(SO_3)_2$

zinc acetate → $Zn^{2+}C_2H_3O_2^{1-}$ → $Zn_2(C_2H_3O_2)_1$ → $Zn(C_2H_3O_2)_2$

Fill in the following chart with the proper chemical formulas. If the charges are missing, it's because you should already know them or be able to determine them from their position in the periodic table.

	Ag	Si^{2+}	Cu^+	Ba	NH_4	P^{5+}	Mn^{7+}
N							
O							
Br							
S							
SO₄							
ClO₂							
PO₃							

Chemical Formulas Review

Fill in the following chart with the proper chemical names. If the charges are missing, again, it is because you should already know them or be able to determine them from their position in the periodic table.

	Ag	Si^{2+}	Cu^+	Ba	NH_4	P^{5+}	Mn^{7+}
N							
O							
Br							
S							
SO_4							
ClO_2							
PO_3							

Answers to the Table Exercises

Naming Acids Exercise

Acid formula	Acid name
HCl	Hydrochloric acid
HClO	Hypochlorous acid
$HClO_2$	Chlorous acid
$HClO_3$	Chloric acid
$HClO_4$	Perchloric acid (or hyperchloric acid)
HNO_3	Nitric acid
HBr	Hydrobromic acid
H_3PO_4	Phosphoric acid
H_3PO_3	Phosphorous acid
HCN	Hydrocyanic acid
$HC_2H_3O_2$	Acetic acid
H_2CO_3	Carbonic acid
HI	Hydroiodic acid
HF	Hydrofluoric acid

Naming Organic Compounds Exercise

No. of carbon atoms = n	Prefix or stem	*-ane* C_nH_{2n+2}	*-ene* C_nH_{2n}	*-yne* C_nH_{2n-2}	*-anol* $C_nH_{2n+1}+OH$
1	*meth-*	CH_4 methane	Cannot form*		CH_3OH methanol
2	*eth-*	C_2H_6 ethane	C_2H_4 ethene	C_2H_2 ethyne	C_2H_5OH ethanol
3	*prop-*	C_3H_8 propane	C_3H_6 propene	C_3H_4 propyne	C_3H_7OH propanol
4	*but-*	C_4H_{10} butane	C_4H_8 butene	C_4H_6 butyne	C_4H_9OH butanol
5	*pent-*	C_5H_{12} pentane	C_5H_{10} pentene	C_5H_8 pentyne	$C_5H_{11}OH$ pentanol
6	*hex-*	C_6H_{14} hexane	C_6H_{12} hexene	C_6H_{10} hexyne	$C_6H_{13}OH$ hexanol
7	*hept-*	C_7H_{16} heptane	C_7H_{14} heptene	C_7H_{12} heptyne	$C_7H_{15}OH$ heptanol
8	*oct-*	C_8H_{18} octane	C_8H_{16} octene	C_8H_{14} octyne	$C_8H_{17}OH$ octanol
9	*non-*	C_9H_{20} nonane	C_9H_{18} nonene	C_9H_{16} nonyne	$C_9H_{19}OH$ nonanol
10	*dec-*	$C_{10}H_{22}$ decane	$C_{10}H_{20}$ decene	$C_{10}H_{18}$ decyne	$C_{10}H_{21}OH$ decanol

*Must have two carbons for a double or triple bond!

Chemical Formulas Review

Formula Writing and Naming Exercise

	Ag^+	Si^{2+}	Cu^+	Ba^{2+}	NH^{4+}	P^{5+}	Mn^{7+}
N^{3-}	Ag_3N silver nitride	Si_3N_2 trisilicon dinitride	Cu_3N copper (I) nitride	Ba_3N_2 barium nitride	$(NH_4)_3N$ ammonium nitride	P_3N_5 triphosphorus pentanitride	Mn_3N_7 manganese (VII) nitride
O^{2-}	Ag_2O silver oxide	SiO silicon monoxide	Cu_2O copper (I) oxide	BaO barium oxide	$(NH_4)_2O$ ammonium oxide	P_2O_5 diphosphorus pentoxide	Mn_2O_7 manganese (VII) oxide
Br^-	$AgBr$ silver bromide	$SiBr_2$ silicon dibromide	$CuBr$ copper (I) bromide	$BaBr_2$ barium bromide	NH_4Br ammonium bromide	PBr_5 phosphorus pentabromide	$MnBr_7$ manganese (VII) bromide
S^{2-}	Ag_2S silver sulfide	SiS silicon sulfide	Cu_2S copper (I) sulfide	BaS barium sulfide	$(NH_4)_2S$ ammonium sulfide	P_2S_5 diphosphorus pentasulfide	Mn_2S_7 manganese (VII) sulfide
SO_4^{2-}	Ag_2SO_4 silver sulfate	$SiSO_4$ silicon sulfate	Cu_2SO_4 copper (I) sulfate	$BaSO_4$ barium sulfate	$(NH_4)_2SO_4$ ammonium sulfate	$P_2(SO_4)_5$ diphosphorus pentasulfate	$Mn_2(SO_4)_7$ manganese (VII) sulfate
ClO_2^-	$AgClO_2$ silver chlorite	$Si(ClO_2)_2$ silicon chlorite	$CuClO_2$ copper (I) chlorite	$Ba(ClO_2)_2$ barium chlorite	NH_4ClO_2 ammonium chlorite	$P(ClO_2)_5$ phosphorus pentachlorite	$Mn(ClO_2)_7$ manganese chlorite
PO_3^{3-}	$Ag(PO_3)_3$ silver phosphite	$Si_3(PO_3)_2$ silicon phosphite	Cu_3PO_3 copper (I) phosphite	$Ba_3(PO_3)_2$ barium phosphite	$(NH_4)_3PO_3$ ammonium phosphite	$P_3(PO_3)_5$ triphosphorus pentaphosphite	$Mn_3(PO_3)_7$ manganese (VII) phosphite

Chemical Formulas Review

Practice Tests

Practice Tests Are Your Best Friends

Believe it or not, the SAT II Chemistry test has some redeeming qualities. One of them is reliability. The test doesn't change much from year to year. While individual questions will never repeat from test to test, the topics that are covered and the way in which they're covered *will* remain constant.

This constancy can be of great benefit to you as you study for the test. To show how you can use the similarity between different versions of the SAT II Chemistry to your advantage, we provide a case study.

Taking Advantage of the Test's Regularity

One day an eleventh grader named Marie Pasteur sits down at her desk and takes an SAT II Chemistry practice test. Because it makes this example much simpler, imagine she takes the entire test and gets only one question wrong.

The question Marie missed dealt with mitosis. Because she doesn't have the best grasp on mitosis, she mistakenly thought that anaphase preceded metaphase, when it's the other way around. So she takes a few minutes to study up on cell reproduction and sorts out when the different phases take place and what happens in each. All this takes about ten minutes, after which Marie vows never again to miss a question involving mitosis.

Analyzing Marie Pasteur

Marie wasn't content simply to see what the correct answer was and get on with her day; she wanted to see *how* and *why* she got the question wrong and what she should have done, or needed to know, in order to get it right. She spent a little time studying the question, discovered her mistaken understanding of mitosis, and learned the subject thoroughly. If Marie were to take that same test again, she definitely wouldn't get that question wrong.

Skeptical readers might say, "But she'll never take that test again, and she'll never see that particular question again, so wasn't figuring out her mistake a waste of time?"

No! It's definitely *not* a waste of time. If you take the time to learn why you got a question wrong and to learn what you need to know to get it right, you'll probably remember what you learned the next time you're faced with a similar question. And chances are excellent that you will be faced with a similar question.

Marie and You

So what if you take a practice test and get 15 questions wrong, and your errors span many of the major topics in biology? Do exactly what Marie did. Take your test and *study it*. Identify every question you got wrong, figure out why you got it wrong, and then teach yourself what you should have done to get the question right. If you can't figure out your error, find someone who can.

A wrong answer on the SAT II Chemistry identifies a weakness in your test taking, whether that weakness is an unfamiliarity with a particular topic or a tendency to be careless. As you study each wrong answer, you are actually learning how to answer questions that will appear in similar form on the real SAT II Chemistry. You are discovering your exact weaknesses and addressing them, and you are learning to understand not just the knowledge behind the question, but also the *way* that ETS asks questions.

True, if you got 15 questions wrong, studying your first practice test will take some time. But if you invest that time and study your practice test properly, you will be eliminating future mistakes. Each successive practice test you take should have fewer errors, meaning you'll spend less time studying those errors. More importantly, you'll be pinpointing what you need to study for the real SAT II Chemistry, identifying and overcoming your weaknesses, and learning to answer an increasing variety of questions on the specific topics covered by the test. Taking practice tests and studying them will allow you to teach yourself how to recognize and handle whatever the SAT II Chemistry throws at you.

Taking a Practice Test

Through the example of Marie Pasteur, we've shown you why studying practice tests is an extremely powerful stratgey. Now we're going to backtrack and explain what you should do while you're actually taking a practice test.

Controlling Your Environment

Do everything in your power to make the practice test feel like the real SAT II Chemistry. The closer your practice resembles the real thing, the more helpful it will be. When taking a practice test, follow these rules:

Time the test

Don't give yourself any extra time. Be stricter with yourself than the meanest proctor you can think of. Also, don't give yourself time off for bathroom breaks. If you have to go to the bathroom, let the clock keep running; that's what will happen on the real SAT II.

Take the test in a single sitting

Training yourself to endure an hour of test taking is part of your preparation.

Find a place to take the test that offers no distractions

Don't take the practice test in a room with lots of people walking through it. Go to a library, your bedroom, a well-lit closet, anywhere quiet.

Now, having stated the rules of practice test taking, we can relax a little bit: don't be so strict with yourself that studying and taking practice tests becomes unbearable. The most important thing is that you actually study. Do whatever you have to do in order to make your studying interesting and painless enough for you to actually do it.

Practice Test Strategy

You should take each practice test as if it were the real SAT II Chemistry. Don't be more daring than you would be on the actual test, guessing blindly even when you can't eliminate an answer. Don't carelessly speed through the test. Don't flip through this book while taking the practice exam just to sneak a peek. Follow the rules for guessing and for skipping questions that we outlined in the chapter on strategy. The more closely your attitude and strategies during the practice test reflect those you'll employ during the actual test, the more predictive the practice test will be of your strengths and weaknesses and the more fruitful your studying of the test will be.

Scoring Your Practice Test

After you take your practice test, you'll want to score it and see how you did. When you score your test, don't just write down how many questions you answered correctly and tally your score. Instead, keep a list of every question you got wrong and every question you skipped. This list will be your guide when you study your test.

Studying Your . . . No, Wait, Go Take a Break

Go relax for a while. You know how to do that.

Studying Your Practice Test

After grading your test, you should have a list of the questions you answered incorrectly or skipped. Studying your test involves going through this list and examining each question you answered incorrectly. When you look at each question, you shouldn't just look to see what the correct answer is, but rather why you got the question wrong and how you could have gotten the question right. Train yourself in the process of getting the question right.

Why Did You Get the Question Wrong?

There are three reasons why you might have gotten an individual question wrong:

- **Reason 1:** You thought you knew the answer, but actually you didn't.
- **Reason 2:** You managed to eliminate some answer choices and then guessed among the remaining answers. Sadly, you guessed wrong.
- **Reason 3:** You knew the answer but made a careless mistake.

You should know which of these reasons applies to every question you got wrong.

What Could You Have Done to Get the Question Right?

The reasons you got a question wrong affect how you should think about it while studying your test.

If You Got a Question Wrong for Reason 1, Lack of Knowledge

A question answered incorrectly for reason 1 identifies a weakness in your knowledge of the material tested on the SAT II Chemistry. Discovering this wrong answer gives you an opportunity to target your weakness. When addressing that weakness, make sure that you don't just look at the facts.

For example, if you missed a question about the properties of solutions, first figure out why you were confused (maybe you mixed it up with the properties of gasses?) and then study up on the correct structure. But don't stop there. If you had some trouble, you're probably not so hot on the properties of solutions. Remember, you won't see a question exactly like the one you got wrong. But you probably *will* see a question that covers the same topic. Learn the broader topic of which the question tests only a piece.

If You Got a Question Wrong for Reason 2, Guessing Wrong

If you guessed wrong, review your guessing strategy. Did you guess intelligently? Could you have eliminated more answers? If yes, why didn't you? By thinking in this critical way about the decisions you made while taking the practice test, you can train yourself to make quicker, more decisive, and better decisions.

If you took a guess and chose the incorrect answer, don't let that sour you on guessing. Even as you go over the question and figure out if there was any way for you to have answered the question without having to guess, remind yourself that if you eliminated at least one answer and guessed, even if you got the question wrong, you followed the right strategy.

If You Got a Question Wrong for Reason 3, Carelessness

If you discover you got a question wrong because you were careless, it might be tempting to say to yourself, "Oh, I made a careless error," and assure yourself you won't do that again. That is not enough. You made that careless mistake for a reason, and you should try to figure out why. Whereas getting a question wrong because you didn't know the answer constitutes a weakness in your knowledge of the test subject, making a careless mistake represents a weakness in your *method of taking the test.*

To overcome this weakness, you need to approach it in the same critical way you would approach a lack of knowledge. Study your mistake. Reenact your thought process on the problem and see where and how your carelessness came about: were you rushing? Did you jump at the first answer that seemed right instead of reading all the answers? Know your error and look it in the eye. If you learn precisely what your mistake was, you are much less likely to make that mistake again.

If You Left the Question Blank

It is also a good idea to study the questions you left blank on the test, since those questions constitute a reservoir of lost points. A blank answer is a result either of:

1. Total inability to answer a question
2. Lack of time

In the case of the first possibility, you should see if there was some way you might have been able to eliminate an answer choice or two and put yourself in a better position to guess. In the second case, look over the question and see whether you think you could have answered it. If you could have, then you know that you are throwing away points by working too slowly. If you couldn't, study the relevant material and review your guessing strategy.

The Secret Weapon: Talking to Yourself

Yeah, it's embarrassing. Yeah, you may look silly. But talking to yourself is perhaps the best way to pound something into your brain. As you go through the steps of studying a question, talk it out. When you verbalize something to yourself, it makes it much harder to delude yourself into thinking that you're working if you're really not.

SAT II Chemistry
Practice Test I

SAT II CHEMISTRY TEST

Note: For all questions involving solutions and/or chemical equations, assume that the system is in pure water unless otherwise stated.

Time: 1 hour

Part A

Directions: Each set of lettered choices below refers to the numbered questions or statements immediately following it. Select the one lettered choice that best answers each question or best fits each statement, and then fill in the corresponding oval on the answer sheet. A choice may be used once, more than once, or not at all in each set.

Questions 1–4

(A) AB
(B) AB_2
(C) A_2B
(D) AB_3
(E) A_2B_3

Which of the above represents the formula for the most common compound of A and B, where A and B represent given pairs of elements or polyatomic ions as indicated below?

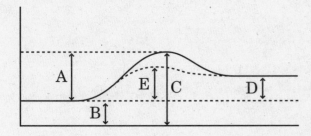

	$\underline{A}$	$\underline{B}$	
1.	Be	F	B
2.	NH_4^+	Cl	A
3.	H	S	H_2 C
4.	Al	O	E

Questions 5–7

5. Which letter corresponds to the activation energy in this reaction without the addition of a catalyst? *E*

6. Which letter corresponds to the total change in energy for the overall reaction? *D*

7. Which letter corresponds to the activation energy of the reaction after the addition of a catalyst? *E*

Questions 8–11

(A) H_2
(B) O_2
(C) N_2
(D) CO_2
(E) NH_3

8. Which molecule is polar? *D*

9. Which molecule contains a triple bond? *B*

10. Which molecule has no unshared electron pairs? *A*

11. Which molecule has trigonal pyramidal molecular geometry? *E*

(A) A
(B) B
(C) C
(D) D
(E) E

Questions 12–15 refer to the following compounds:

(A) C_2H_6
(B) C_2H_4
(C) C_2H_2
(D) C_2H_5OH
(E) C_3H_8

12. Exists as a liquid at room temperature.

13. Contains carbons that are sp^2 hybridized.

14. Is a linear molecule.

15. Dissolves in water.

GO ON TO THE NEXT PAGE

Questions 16–20

(A) $1s^2 2s^2 2p^6 3s^2 3p^2$ Si

(B) $1s^2 2s^2 2p^6 3s^2 3p^4$ S

(C) $1s^2 2s^2 2p^6 3s^2 3p^5$ Cl

(D) $1s^2 2s^2 2p^6 3s^2 3p^6$ Ar

(E) $1s^2 2s^2 2p^6 3s^2 3p^6 4s^1$ K

16. Is the electron configuration for an element that reacts exothermically with water to produce an alkaline solution and hydrogen gas.   A

17. Is isoelectronic with Ca^{2+}.   B

18. Forms diatomic molecules.   C

19. Has the largest atomic radius.   E

20. Has the greatest first ionization energy.   D

Questions 21–25

(A) SO_2

(B) $Ba(OH)_2$

(C) KCl

(D) $Fe(NO_3)_3$

(E) $LiC_2H_3O_2$

21. Is known to produce acid rain.   A

22. Is a salt that forms acidic aqueous solutions.   E

23. Is a salt that forms basic aqueous solutions.   D

24. Is a salt that forms neutral aqueous solutions.   B

25. Is a strong base.   B

GO ON TO THE NEXT PAGE

SAT II CHEMISTRY TEST

PLEASE GO TO THE SPECIAL SECTION OF YOUR ANSWER SHEET LABELED CHEMISTRY AND ANSWER QUESTIONS 101–115 ACCORDING TO THE FOLLOWING DIRECTIONS:

Part B

Directions: Each question below consists of two statements, statement I in the left-hand column and statement II in the right-hand column. For each question, determine whether statement I is true or false <u>and</u> whether statement II is true or false and fill in the corresponding T or F ovals on your answer sheet. <u>Fill in oval **CE** only if statement II is a correct explanation of statement I.</u>

	Statement I	BECAUSE	Statement II
101.	Increasing the pressure on a confined sample of a gas will decrease its volume.	BECAUSE	Gas molecules move more slowly as their kinetic energy decreases.
102.	Water droplets form on the outside of a beaker containing an ice bath.	BECAUSE	Water vapor molecules in the air lose energy when they collide with the cold glass surface and condense.
103.	Alpha particles are the most penetrating radioactive particle.	BECAUSE	Alpha particles are the smallest of the radioactive particles.
104.	Atomic radius generally increases as you move across the periodic table from left to right.	BECAUSE	The atomic number is increasing from left to right as you move across the periodic table.
105.	The ionization energy generally increases as you move from left to right across the periodic table.	BECAUSE	Shielding increases as you move from left to right across the periodic table.
106.	Water has a higher boiling point than expected.	BECAUSE	Each molecule forms a hydrogen bond with an adjacent molecule.
107.	Evaporation is an endothermic process.	BECAUSE	Heat is absorbed as a substance cools.
108.	Nonmetallic oxides are usually basic anhydrides.	BECAUSE	Nonmetal oxides form acids when placed in water.
109.	Nitrogen gas effuses faster than oxygen gas.	BECAUSE	Nitrogen gas has a molecular mass of 14 g/mol while oxygen gas has a molecular mass of 16 g/mol.
110.	The fluoride ion has a larger radius than the fluorine atom.	BECAUSE	The fluoride ion has 8 electrons and 9 protons.
111.	The Al^{3+} ion needs to be reduced to form aluminum metal.	BECAUSE	Reduction is a gain of electrons.
112.	Metals are great conductors of electricity.	BECAUSE	Metals exist as positive ions with delocalized electrons.
113.	The transmutation decay of carbon-14 can be shown as $^{14}_{6}C \rightarrow ^{0}_{7}\beta + ^{14}_{7}N$.	BECAUSE	The decay of carbon-14 is accompanied by the release of a beta particle.
114.	$^{14}_{6}C$ and $^{12}_{6}C$ isomers of the element carbon.	BECAUSE	Isomers contain the same number of protons but a different number of neutrons.
115.	A sample of gas is heated at constant pressure from 200K to 400K and volume doubles.	BECAUSE	Each molecule expands to twice its original volume.

RETURN TO THE MAIN SECTION OF YOUR ANSWER SHEET AND ANSWER
QUESTIONS 26–70.

GO ON TO THE NEXT PAGE

SAT II CHEMISTRY TEST

Part C

26. A certain mass of sulfur required 16 grams of oxygen to be converted into sulfur dioxide, SO_2. If this same mass of sulfur were to be converted into sulfur trioxide, SO_3, the mass of oxygen required would be

    (A) 4.0 g
    (B) 8.0 g
    (C) 12 g
    (D) 24 g
    (E) 32 g

Questions 27–28

Consider the following equilibrium:

$$X_{2(g)} + 2H_{2(g)} \Leftrightarrow 2H_2X_{(g)} + energy$$

27. Addition of X_2 to a system described by the above equilibrium will

    (A) Increase the equilibrium concentration of $[H_2]$
    (B) Increase the equilibrium concentration of $[H_2X]$
    (C) Decrease the equilibrium concentration of $[H_2X]$
    (D) Have no effect on the equilibrium concentrations
    (E) Decrease the amount of heat energy given off by the system

28. Addition of argon to the above equilibrium will

    (A) Increase the equilibrium concentration of $[H_2]$
    (B) Increase the equilibrium concentration of $[H_2X]$
    (C) Decrease the equilibrium concentration of $[H_2X]$
    (D) Have no effect on the equilibrium concentrations
    (E) Decrease the amount of heat energy given off by the system

29. Which compound contains the highest percent by mass of hydrogen?

    (A) HCl   1 : 12
    (B) H_2O 2 : 16 →1.8
    (C) H_2SO_4 2 : ✓
    (D) H_2S
    (E) HF

Questions 30–31:

Consider the following equilibrium system:

$$3H_{2(g)} + N_{2(g)} \rightleftharpoons 2NH_{3(g)}$$

30. What is the mass action expression (equilibrium constant expression) for the equilibrium mixture above?

    (A) $K = \dfrac{1}{[H_2]}$
    (B) $K = \dfrac{1}{[H_2][N_2]}$
    (C) $K = [H_2][N_2][NH_3]$
    (D) $K = \dfrac{[NH_3]^2}{[H_2]^3[N_2]}$
    (E) $K = \dfrac{[H_2]^3[N_2]}{[NH_3]^2}$

31. If the total pressure of the system is increased when the reaction represented above is at equilibrium, which of the following occurs?

    (A) The concentration of H_2 increases.
    (B) The concentration of N_2 increases.
    (C) The reaction will shift to the right.
    (D) The reaction will shift to the left.
    (E) The H_2 gas condenses.

32. $\underset{4}{...}Al_{(s)} + \overset{3}{...}O_{2(g)} \rightarrow \overset{2}{...}Al_2O_{3(s)}$

    When the equation for the reaction represented above is balanced and all coefficients are reduced to lowest whole-number terms, the coefficient for $Al_{(s)}$ is

    (A) 1 $4 + 2 \rightarrow 2$
    (B) 2
    (C) 3
    (D) 4
    (E) 6

GO ON TO THE NEXT PAGE

33. Nitric acid contains approximately what percent hydrogen by mass?

    (A) 2%
    (B) 5%
    (C) 7%
    (D) 10%
    (E) 20%

34. I. $X + Y \Leftrightarrow 2Z$

    II. $4Z \Leftrightarrow 2X + 2Y$

    If the equilibrium constant for the reaction represented by equation I above is 5.0, what is the value of the equilibrium constant for the reaction represented by equation II?

    (A) 1/25.00
    (B) 1/5.00
    (C) 5.00
    (D) 10.0
    (E) 25.0

35. The mass of 3.01×10^{23} molecules of a gas is 32.0 grams. What volume does 8.00 grams of the gas occupy at STP?

    (A) 2.80 L
    (B) 8.00 L
    (C) 11.2 L
    (D) 22.4 L
    (E) 64.0 L

36. $\ldots$ KOH$_{(aq)}$ + $\ldots$ H$_3$PO$_{4(aq)}$ → $\ldots$ K$_3$PO$_{4(aq)}$ + $\ldots$ H$_2$O

    When the equation for the reaction represented above is balanced and the coefficients are reduced to the lowest whole-number terms, the coefficient for H$_2$O is

    (A) 1
    (B) 2
    (C) 3
    (D) 4
    (E) 5

37. Which of the following statements about catalysts is INCORRECT?

    (A) They have no effect on the value of the equilibrium constant.
    (B) They increase the amount of product present at equilibrium.
    (C) They provide an alternate pathway for effective collisions.
    (D) They lower the activation energy.
    (E) They are reusable since they are regenerated at the end of the reaction.

38. What is the empirical formula of a compound that contains 0.05 mole of magnesium, 0.05 mole of sulfur, and 0.20 mole of oxygen?

    (A) MgSO
    (B) MgSO$_2$
    (C) MgSO$_3$
    (D) MgSO$_4$
    (E) MgS$_2$O$_2$

39. The rate at which a solid dissolves in water is increased by which of the following?

    I.   Crushing the solid into smaller pieces
    II. Agitating the mixture
    III. Placing the mixture in an ice bath

    (A) I only
    (B) II only
    (C) I and II only
    (D) I and III only
    (E) I, II, and III

40. $\ldots$ C$_6$H$_{14(l)}$ + $\ldots$ O$_{2(g)}$ → $\ldots$ CO$_{2(g)}$ + $\ldots$ H$_2$O$_{(l)}$

    When the equation for the reaction represented above is balanced and the coefficients are reduced to the lowest whole-number terms, the coefficient for H$_2$O is

    (A) 1
    (B) 2
    (C) 6
    (D) 13
    (E) 14

41. How many milliliters of 0.400 M potassium hydroxide must be added to a 200 mL solution of 0.100 M hydrochloric acid to obtain a solution with a pH of 7.00?

    (A) 10.0 mL
    (B) 25.0 mL
    (C) 50.0 mL
    (D) 100.0 mL
    (E) 200.0 mL

GO ON TO THE NEXT PAGE

Questions 42–43

$$C_{(s)} + O_{2(g)} \rightarrow CO_{2(g)} + 394 \text{ kJ}$$

42. Carbon dioxide is produced from carbon and oxygen by the exothermic reaction represented above. When 2 moles of carbon dioxide are produced by the reaction, which of the following occurs?

    (A) 197 kilojoules are absorbed.
    (B) 394 kilojoules are absorbed.
    (C) 788 kilojoules are absorbed.
    (D) 197 kilojoules are released.
    (E) 788 kilojoules are released.

43. According to the reaction above, what mass of oxygen gas is required to produce 88 g of carbon dioxide?

    (A) 12 g
    (B) 16 g
    (C) 24 g
    (D) 32 g
    (E) 64 g

CO_2
$12 + 32 . 44$

44. A 1.0 L sample of 0.05 M $Al_3(PO_4)_2$ contains a total of

    (A) 0.05 M Al^{3+}
    (B) 0.10 M Al^{3+}
    (C) 0.25 M Al^{3+}
    (D) 0.05 M PO_4^{3+}
    (E) 0.10 M PO_4^{3+}

Use the following to answer questions 45–46:

Consider three 1-L flasks at STP. Flask A contains CH_4 gas, flask B contains NO_2 gas, and flask C contains O_2 gas.

45. Which flask contains the largest number of molecules?

    (A) Flask A
    (B) Flask B
    (C) Flask C
    (D) All flasks contain the same number of molecules since they are at the same temperature.
    (E) All flasks contain the same number of molecules since they are at the same temperature and pressure.

46. In which flask do the molecules have the highest average velocity?

    (A) Flask A
    (B) Flask B
    (C) Flask C
    (D) The molecules in all of the flasks have the same velocity since they are at the same temperature
    (E) The molecules in all of the flasks have the same velocity since they are at the same temperature and pressure

47. Which of the following is the best qualitative graph of T versus V for a sample of gas at constant pressure and number of molecules?

    (A)
    (B)
    (C)
    (D)
    (E)

48. Which of the following conditions are most closely associated with the behavior of ideal gases?

    I.   High pressure
    II. High temperature
    III. High numbers of moles of gas in the sample

    (A) I only
    (B) II only
    (C) I and II
    (D) II and III
    (E) I and III

GO ON TO THE NEXT PAGE

49. A student adds $AgNO_{3(aq)}$ to $HCl_{(aq)}$. Which of the following should the student easily observe?

    I.   A precipitate is formed.
    II. The solution turns yellow.
    III. Bubbles are produced as a gas is evolved.

(A) I only
(B) II only
(C) III only
(D) I and II only
(E) I, II, and III

50. What volume of $H_2O_{(g)}$ measured at STP is produced by the combustion of 8.00 g of methane gas, CH_4, according to the following equation?

$$\tfrac{1}{?}CH_{4(g)} + 2O_{2(g)} \rightarrow CO_{2(g)} + 2H_2O_{(g)}$$

(A) 5.60 L
(B) 11.2 L
(C) 22.4 L
(D) 33.6 L
(E) 44.8 L

51. Which of the following electron configurations corresponds to a transition element?

(A) $1s^22s^22p^63s^23p^6$
(B) $1s^22s^22p^63s^23p^64s^2$
(C) $1s^22s^22p^63s^23p^63d^24s^2$
(D) $1s^22s^22p^63s^23p^63d^{10}4s^24p^1$
(E) $1s^22s^22p^63s^23p^63d^24s^24p^64f^1$

52. $.1.\,ZnS_{(s)} + ...O_{2(g)} \rightarrow .1.\,ZnO_{(s)} + .1.\,SO_{2(g)}$

When the equation for the reaction represented above is balanced and the coefficients are reduced to the lowest whole-number terms, the coefficient for SO_2 is

(A) 1
(B) 2
(C) 3
(D) 4
(E) 5

$$2\,ZnS + 3O_2$$
$$2\,ZnO + 2SO_2$$

53. Which of the following will result when the temperature is increased as the chemical reaction proceeds?

    I.   Increased molecular collision frequency
    II. Increased numbers of molecules possess energy greater than the activation energy
    III. Decreased randomness of the system

(A) I only
(B) II only
(C) I and II only
(D) I and III only
(E) I, II, and III

54. Which of the following has the highest second ionization energy?

(A) Cl
(B) S
(C) Na
(D) Mg
(E) Al

55. Which forms the largest of the –1 ions?

(A) F
(B) Cl
(C) Br
(D) I
(E) H

56. The electron dot structure for BF_3 is

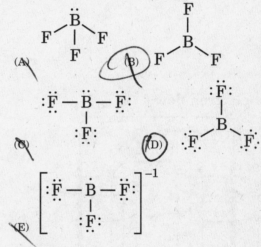

57. The hybridization on the central carbon in methane, CH_4, is

(A) sp
(B) sp^2
(C) sp^3
(D) sp^3d
(E) sp^3d^2

GO ON TO THE NEXT PAGE

Questions 58–60

The following elements are listed in order of decreasing reactivity as they appear in the electrochemical series:

Ca, Na, Mg, Zn, Fe, H, Cu, Hg, Ag, Au

58. The element that is the best oxidizing agent is

(A) Ca
(B) Au
(C) H
(D) Fe
(E) Cu

59. Of the following, the element that reacts most readily with hydrochloric acid to produce hydrogen gas is

(A) Cu
(B) Hg
(C) Ag
(D) Zn
(E) Au

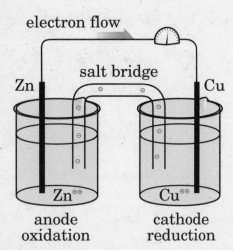

electron flow

salt bridge

Zn   Cu

Zn⊕⊕   Cu⊕⊕

anode   cathode
oxidation   reduction

60. In the electrochemical cell shown above, which of the following half-reactions occurs at the cathode?

(A) $Cu^{2+} + e^- \rightarrow Cu^+$
(B) $Zn_{(s)} \rightarrow Zn^{2+} + 2e^-$
(C) $Zn^{2+} + 2e^- \rightarrow Zn_{(s)}$
(D) $Cu_{(s)} \rightarrow Cu^{2+} + 2e^-$
(E) $Cu^{2+} + 2e^- \rightarrow Cu_{(s)}$

61. When HCO_3^- acts as a Brønsted base, which of the following is formed?

(A) CO_2
(B) CO_3
(C) CO_3^{2-}
(D) H_2CO_3
(E) $H_3CO_3^+$

62. $\ldots MgCl_{2(aq)} + \ldots NH_{3(aq)} + \ldots H_2O \rightarrow ?$
Which of the following is one of the products obtained from the reaction above?

(A) Mg_3N_2
(B) MgH_2
(C) Mg
(D) $Mg(NO_3)_2$
(E) $Mg(OH)_2$

63. Petroleum is an important source for all of the following EXCEPT

(A) Plastics
(B) Rubber
(C) Kerosene
(D) Gasoline
(E) Propane

64. The method by which we separate a mixture of pure liquids based on the differences in their boiling points is known as

(A) Condensation
(B) Distillation
(C) Fractional crystallization
(D) Hydration
(E) Chromatography

65. Which pair of ions listed below will form a precipitate when mixed together in aqueous solution?

(A) Na^+ and $C_2O_4^{2-}$
(B) Ag^+ and NO_3^-
(C) Pb^{2+} and Cl^-
(D) Mg^+ and $C_2H_3O_2^-$
(E) NH_4^+ and CO_3^{2-}

GO ON TO THE NEXT PAGE

66. A measured mass of an unreactive metal was dropped into a small graduated cylinder half filled with water. The following measurements were made:

    Mass of metal = 25.200 g
    Volume of water before addition of metal = 12.5 mL
    Volume of water after addition of metal = 15.0 mL

    The density of the metal should be reported as

    (A) 10.0800 g/mL
    (B) 10.080 g/mL
    (C) 10.08 g/mL
    (D) 10.1 g/mL
    (E) 10.0 g/mL

Questions 67–69 refer to the experiment shown below in which a sample of solid potassium chlorate ($KClO_3$) was heated in a test tube and decomposed by the following reaction:

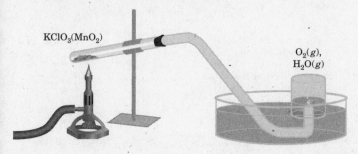

$KClO_3(MnO_2)$

$O_2(g),$
$H_2O(g)$

$$2KClO_{3(s)} \rightarrow 2KCl_{(s)} + 3O_{2(g)}$$

The oxygen produced was collected by displacement of water at 22°C and a pressure of 750 mmHg. The volume of the gas collected was 2.24 L. (The vapor pressure of water at 22°C is 20.0 mmHg.)

67. The partial pressure of O_2 in the gas collected is

    (A) 790 mmHg
    (B) 770 mmHg
    (C) 750 mmHg
    (D) 730 mmHg
    (E) 710 mmHg

68. If 61.0 g of solid $KClO_3$ (molar mass = 122 g/mol) were to be completely decomposed by this method, what mass of $KCl_{(s)}$ would you expect to remain in the test tube?

    (A) 111 g
    (B) 74 g
    (C) 56 g
    (D) 37 g
    (E) 19 g

69. Which of the following is NOT a possible source of error in this experiment?

    (A) Inaccurate weighing of the KCl
    (B) Leakage around the rubber stopper
    (C) Failure to correct for the water vapor present
    (D) Insufficient amount of the catalyst added
    (E) Misreading of the thermometer

70. Which of the following gases is LEAST dense when all are measured under the same conditions?

    (A) N_2
    (B) Cl_2
    (C) CH_4
    (D) NO_2
    (E) CO_2

S T O P

IF YOU FINISH BEFORE TIME IS CALLED, YOU MAY CHECK YOUR WORK ON THIS TEST ONLY.
DO NOT TURN TO ANY OTHER TEST IN THIS BOOK.

SAT II Chemistry Practice Test I Explanations

Answers to SAT II Chemistry Practice Test I

Question Number	Answer	Right	Wrong	Question Number	Answer	Right	Wrong
Part A				**Part C**			
1.	B	✓		26.	D	✓	
2.	A	✓		27.	B		✓
3.	C	✓		28.	D		✓
4.	E	✓		29.	B	✓	
5.	A		✓	30.	D		✓
6.	E		✓	31.	C		✓
7.	E		✓	32.	D	✓	✓
8.	E		✓	33.	A		✓
9.	C		✓	34.	A		✓
10.	A	✓		35.	A	✓	
11.	E	✓		36.	C	✓	
12.	D		✓	37.	B	✓	
13.	B		✓	38.	D		
14.	C		✓	39.	C	✓	
15.	D		✓	40.	E	✓	
16.	E		✓	41.	C	✓	
17.	D		✓	42.	E	✓	
18.	C	✓		43.	E		
19.	E		✓	44.	E		✓
20.	D		✓	45.	E	✓	
21.	A	✓		46.	A	✓	✓
22.	D		✓	47.	B	✓	
23.	E		✓	48.	B		✓
24.	C		✓	49.	A		✓
25.	B	✓		50.	C		✓
Part B				51.	C		✓
101.	T T		✓	52.	B	✓	
102.	T T CE	✓		53.	C		
103.	F F	✓		54.	C		
104.	F T	✓		55.	D	✓	
105.	T F		✓	56.	D		
106.	T T CE	✓		57.	C		✓
107.	T F	✓		58.	B		✓
108.	F T		✓	59.	D		✓
109.	T F	✓		60.	E		✓
110.	T F			61.	D		
111.	T T			62.	E		
112.	T T CE	✓		63.	B		
113.	T T	✓		64.	B		
114.	F F	✓		65.	C		
115.	T F	✓		66.	E		
				67.	D		
				68.	D		
				69.	D		
				70.	C		

Calculating Your Score

Your raw score for SAT II Chemistry test is based on the number of questions you answer correctly and incorrectly. Once you have determined your raw score, use the conversion table on page 14 of this book to calculate your scaled score.

To Calculate Your Raw Score

1. Count the number of questions you answered correctly: __34__ (A)
2. Count the number of questions you answered incorrectly, and multiply that number by ¼: __31 37__ (B) × ¼ = ~~9.25~~ (C) 9.25
3. Subtract the value in (C) from value in (A): ~~25 24~~ (D)
4. Round the number in (D) to the nearest whole number. This is your raw score: ~~25~~ (E) 25

Part A

The first 25 questions on this exam are classification set questions. These should be some of the easier points to obtain on the exam. You need to read only one set of answer choices to complete several questions. Approach these questions by reading all of the choices, read each statement that follows, answer, and then match your answer with the best answer choice.

1. B Formula writing
The correct formula is BeF_2 since Be is in group 2A and has a charge of +2, while F is in group 7A and has a charge of –1. This means that the compound has the formula AB_2.

2. A Formula writing
The correct formula is NH_4Cl. Ammonium has a charge of +1—this is a polyatomic ion and its charge was included, luckily for you. Cl is in group 7A and has a charge of –1. This means that the compound has the formula AB.

3. C Formula writing
The correct formula is H_2S. Hydrogen is considered to be in group 1A and has a +1 charge in its cationic form. Sulfur is in group 6A and most commonly has a –2 charge. This means that the compound has the formula A_2B.

4. E Formula writing
The correct formula is Al_2O_3. Al is in group 3A and has a charge of +3 while O is in group 6A with a charge of –2. The lowest common denominator between 2 and 3 is 6. Each element must then have a subscript to achieve a total of 6. This means that the compound has the formula A_2B_3.

5.   A   Energy diagram
To be successful on this series of questions, you could label the diagram with the reactants, products, activation energy, and ΔH before beginning. Remember that the activation energy is the energy required to get the reaction going: it's the distance from the reactants' energy level to the peak of the activated complex. Letter A represents this distance.

6.   D   Enthalpy
The overall energy change in the reaction would be represented by the energy difference between the products and the reactants. If you labeled the diagram, as we suggested, this problem isn't difficult. This diagram represents an endothermic process—the products have more energy than the reactants, so energy was absorbed during the reaction.

7.   E   Catalysis
A catalyst lowers the energy of activation of a reaction. The dashed line represents a lower activation energy barrier, and **E** shows the new, lowered activation energy.

8.   E   Atomic/molecular
You should approach this block of questions by taking the time to draw the structures of these molecules. To answer this particular question, you must recall that a polar molecule has a dipole moment, and the atoms in the molecule must have fairly different electronegativity values. You can quickly eliminate choices **A, B,** and **C** since they contain only one type of atom. Ammonia has one unshared electron on nitrogen and is the only nonlinear molecule listed—this unshared pair cause polarity of the molecule.

(A)   H—H

(B)   :O≡O:

(C)   :N≡N:

(D)   :O≡C≡O:

(E)   H—N—H with H below (ammonia structure)

9.   C   Bonding
The nitrogen molecule is the only one of the above drawings that contains a triple bond. Nitrogen forms this triple bond in order for each nitrogen atom to complete its octet. Each N has five valence electrons, which means it has a total of 10 electrons that need to be distributed.

10.   A   Bonding
Each of the two hydrogens has only one electron to contribute to the bond. Therefore, these two electrons are situated between the hydrogen nuclei, and this molecule has no unshared electron pairs.

11. **E** Bonding and molecular shape

A trigonal pyramidal structure has three bonded pairs of electrons and one unshared electron pair. In ammonia, nitrogen forms three single bonds with the three hydrogens and is left with one unshared pair of electrons. It is the only molecule listed that has this shape.

12. **D** Organic chemistry

Again, the best way to begin this question would be to draw the structures for each of the choices. An OH group is the functional group of an alcohol; this hydroxyl group gives a compound the ability to hydrogen bond and thus be in the liquid state. Each of the other answer choices is nonpolar and these molecules are held by weak London forces. Remember that a general rule of thumb is that only hydrocarbon chains that contain five to 10 carbons will be present in the liquid state.

(A)
$$H-\overset{\overset{\displaystyle H}{|}}{\underset{\underset{\displaystyle H}{|}}{C}}-\overset{\overset{\displaystyle H}{|}}{\underset{\underset{\displaystyle H}{|}}{C}}-H$$

(B)
$$\overset{\displaystyle H}{}\diagdown\overset{\displaystyle H}{}\diagup C=C\diagup\overset{\displaystyle H}{}\diagdown\overset{\displaystyle H}{}$$

(C)
$$H-C\equiv C-H$$

(D)
$$H-\overset{\overset{\displaystyle H}{|}}{\underset{\underset{\displaystyle H}{|}}{C}}-\overset{\overset{\displaystyle H}{|}}{\underset{\underset{\displaystyle H}{|}}{C}}-\ddot{O}:$$

(E)
$$H-\overset{\overset{\displaystyle H}{|}}{\underset{\underset{\displaystyle H}{|}}{C}}-\overset{\overset{\displaystyle H}{|}}{\underset{\underset{\displaystyle H}{|}}{C}}-\overset{\overset{\displaystyle H}{|}}{\underset{\underset{\displaystyle H}{|}}{C}}-H$$

13. **B** Hybridization of carbon

Once you've drawn each molecule, this question should be fairly easy. sp^2 hybridization occurs when there are three areas of electrons around the carbon center. Since ethene, C_2H_4, contains one double bond between its carbons, it has a trigonal planar arrangement and thus sp^2 hybridization.

14. **C** Bonding

Acetylene, C_2H_2, which is also known as ethyne, contains a triple bond. The two hydrogen atoms will orient themselves for maximum repulsion; therefore the molecule is linear.

15. **D** Intermolecular forces

The phrase "like dissolves like" is the key to answering this question. Water is a polar molecule, and ethanol, C_2H_5OH, is also a polar molecule. Polar molecules have a dipole moment. The other four choices list molecules that are nonpolar and would not be expected to mix well with water.

16. **E** Electron configuration

In a set such as this, first check and make sure that all of the electron configurations are plausible ones. All of these choices represent elements. Add the total number of electrons and write the symbol of the element next to each one—this will save time when answering the next questions in this series. The ending configuration of $4s^1$ represents an alkali metal—in particular potassium. Alkali metals are known to react violently with water. Metals also produce basic solutions in water as well as hydrogen gas. See the equation below:

$$2K_{(s)} + 2H_2O_{(l)} \rightarrow 2KOH_{(aq)} + H_{2(g)}$$

17. **D** Electron configuration

Two elements that have the same electron configuration are said to be isoelectronic. The calcium ion must have lost two electrons to have a +2 charge since calcium metal has 20 electrons – 2 electrons = the calcium ion (Ca^{2+} ion), which has 18 electrons. Choice **D** represents argon, which also has 18 electrons, so this answer choice is isoelectronic.

18. **C** Diatomic molecules

Once the elements are identified, this is just a matter of choosing chlorine; you should have memorized the diatomic molecules, and none of the other elements exist as diatomic molecules. The seven diatomic molecules are N, O, F, Cl, Br, I, H.

19. **E** Periodic trends

The more principal energy levels in an atom, the larger the atom. Choice **E** is the only one that has electrons in the fourth principal energy level.

20. **D** Periodic trends

The ionization energy of an atom is the energy that must be expended to remove an electron. Which elements in the periodic table do not want to lose their electrons? Right—the noble gases—group 8A. Argon, with 18 electrons, has a filled energy level and so is in a very stable energy state and will require much more energy to remove an electron than any of the others; thus it has the highest first ionization energy.

21. **A** Environmental chemistry

An acid is produced from a nonmetal oxide dissolved in water. Remember that some of the gases in the air that act as pollutants are the SO_x and NO_x gases. SO_2 is the only choice listed that fits this category.

22. **D** Salt hydrolysis

$Fe(NO_3)_3$ is an acidic salt. In order to be *neutral*, the salt must have been formed from a strong acid and a strong base (or from a weak acid/base that have the same K_a/K_b values). Since you know that nitric acid is a strong acid and $Fe(OH)_3$ is not a very soluble hydroxide (it is a weak base), the resulting salt must be acidic.

23. **E**   Salt hydrolysis

$LiC_2H_3O_2$ is a salt that forms basic solutions. Using the same reasoning as in the problem above, you will know that acetic acid is a weak acid and LiOH must be a strong base since it is in group 1A.

24. **C**   Salt hydrolysis

KCl is a neutral salt. KOH is a strong base, and HCl is a strong acid. Therefore, the salt that they form, KCl, will be neutral.

25. **B**   Solubility rules

Many strong bases have a hydroxide group with a metal cation, as choice **B** does. The strong bases are those in group 1A and the larger atoms in group 2A with hydroxide. Barium hydroxide is the only strong base in this list.

Part B

By now you are well versed in how these questions work. Remember that to be successful on this type of question, you should read each statement individually and decide whether it is true or false. Then if both statements are true, read the second statement again and see if it is the *reason* the first statement is true.

101. **T T**   Gas laws

Statement I is true. Boyle's law states that increasing the pressure on a fixed amount of gas will decrease the volume when the number of particles and temperature remain constant. Statement II is also true. When kinetic energy is decreased, particles will slow down. However, slowing down gas particles is not the reason for the pressure-volume relationship in statement I. Therefore you should not have filled in the **CE** oval.

102. **T T CE**   States of matter

Statement I is true. You have probably noticed that water droplets form on the outside of a glass of ice water. Statement II is also true. When particles of water vapor in the air hit the cold glass, they will slow down. If they slow enough, intermolecular forces of attraction will take over. As a substance moves from a less-ordered state (gas) to a more-ordered state (liquid), energy will be released. Statement II explains why water droplets form on the outside of the glass beaker, so the **CE** oval should also be filled in for this question.

103. **F F**   Nuclear chemistry

Statement I is false. Alpha particles are the least penetrating form of radiation: these particles can be stopped by paper, skin, and clothing. Statement II is also false. Alpha particles are the largest of the main types of radiation. An alpha particle is a helium nucleus—^4_2He. Since both statements are false, the **CE** oval should not be bubbled in.

104. F T Periodic trends

Statement I is false. As you move across the periodic table within a period, the atoms become smaller. The effective nuclear charge increases, the shielding stays constant, and with the same number of energy levels, the nucleus pulls more tightly and thus the atoms become smaller. Statement II is a true statement. Atomic number does increase as you move across a period on the periodic table. Since statement I was false, however, this second true statement cannot be a correct explanation for it. **CE** should not be filled in.

105. T F Periodic trends

Statement I is true. Ionization energy is the energy needed to remove an electron from an atom. Group 8A, and specifically He, would be the most unwilling to give up an electron; therefore it has the greatest ionization energy. Statement II is a false statement. As you move across a period on the periodic table, the atoms do not have an increased number of principal energy levels; therefore shielding stays constant. Since statement II is false, the **CE** oval should not be filled in.

106. T T CE Hydrogen bonding

Statement I is true. Other molecules that have a mass near the mass of water are all gases at room temperature. Statement II is also true. Since water is a polar molecule and contains the highly electronegative oxygen atom, hydrogen bonding (a strong intermolecular force) will attract water molecules to each other. Since both statements are true, check to see if statement II is the reason for statement I. In this case, fill in the **CE** oval because hydrogen bonding is the reason for water's high boiling point.

107. T F Thermochemistry

Statement I is true. When a substance evaporates, it must change from a relatively condensed state (liquid) to a very random state (gas), and this change requires the input of energy. Since energy must be put into the system to make this change happen—the reaction is endothermic. Statement II is false. This statement is in direct disagreement with statement I. When a substance cools, molecules slow down and must release energy. Do not fill in the **CE** oval.

108. F T Acid-base reactions

Statement I is false. An example of a nonmetallic oxide would be CO_2. When carbon dioxide dissolves in water, it forms carbonic acid. Therefore, it is known as an acidic anhydride. This explanation shows that statement II is true.

109. T F Gas laws

Statement I is true. Graham's law states that the rate of effusion is inversely proportional to the square root of the masses of the two gases. Statement II is false, but this is hard to catch. The masses given are for single elements—both of these gases are diatomic, so the masses should be doubled.

110. **T F**   Atomic size

Statement I is true. As an atom gains one electron, its size will increase. Statement II is false. Fluoride ion has 10 electrons and nine protons. The fluoride ion tends to gain one electron to form an ion; it bears a negative charge.

111. **T T**   Oxidation-reduction

Statement I is a true statement. In order for Al^{3+} to form Al^0, three electrons must be gained; it must be reduced. Statement II is also true, but it does not constitute an explanation for how an aluminum ion forms aluminum metal.

112. **T T CE**   Bonding—metals

Statement I is true: metals are good conductors of electricity. Statement II is also true: it gives a description of metallic bonding. Statement II gives the reason that metals are such good conductors—because of their sea of electrons—so fill in the **CE** oval.

113. **T T**   Nuclear chemistry

Statement I is true. The nuclear reaction shown is properly balanced and does represent the decay of carbon-14. Statement II is also true. A beta particle is shown as a product with nitrogen-14. However, the reason that carbon-14 releases a beta particle has to do with the stability (or lack thereof) of the nucleus. You should not fill in the **CE** oval.

114. **F F**   Nuclear chemistry

Statement I and statement II are both false. By changing the word *isomer* to *isotope* each of the statements would be true. Isomers are compounds that have the same molecular formula but different structures. These are encountered frequently in organic chemistry.

115. **T F**   Gas laws

Statement I is true. Charles's law states that as temperature increases, the volume increases when pressure and number of particles are held constant. Gas laws are worked using the Kelvin scale; if the temperature in Kelvin doubles, the volume should also double. Statement II is false. This statement implies that the gas molecule itself changes size—gases are mostly empty space. The space that they must occupy to keep the same pressure must double at the given temperature, but the molecules themselves do not change in size.

Part C

The remaining questions on the test are the traditional multiple choice that you know and love. Eliminate any choices that you can initially, then see which answer choice is most similar to your answer.

26. D   Stoichiometry

This problem requires that you write two balanced equations. The first equation is the formation of SO_2:

$$S + O_2 \rightarrow SO_2$$
$$?\qquad\quad 16\ g$$

Since sulfur and oxygen, O_2, have the same molecular masses, this reaction should require 16 grams of sulfur. This same amount of sulfur was used in the following reaction:

$$2S + 3O_2 \rightarrow 2SO_3$$
$$16\ g$$

The question here is the amount of oxygen needed. The ratio is not 1:1, so try to simplify.

Molar mass	32	32	80
Balanced equation	2S +	$3O_2 \rightarrow$	$2SO_3$
Number of moles	0.5 moles	1.5	0.5
Amount	16 g	24 g	

27. B   Le Chatelier's principle

Since X_2 is a reactant, adding more of it will cause a shift in equilibrium toward the products. The only product listed in the answer choices is H_2X, so this is the correct answer.

28. D   Le Chatelier's principle

Adding an inert gas will not effect equilibrium concentrations since it is not involved in the reaction.

29. B   Percent composition

You can solve this problem by putting the total mass of hydrogen in each compound over the total mass of the compound. There is no need to calculate—it should be obvious which fraction is closest to 1/1.

$HCl = 1/36$ $H_2O = 2/18$ $H_2SO_4 = 2/98$ $H_2S = 2/32$ $HF = 1/20$

The answer is water, with 2/18

30. D   Equilibrium expression

The equilibrium expression is the ratio of products to the reactants, each raised to the power of their coefficients. All substances are in the gaseous state, so all should appear in this expression; knowing this means that you can eliminate choices **A** and **B**. Only choice **D** places shows NH_3 in the numerator of the expression.

31. C   Equilibrium

When the pressure of a gaseous system is increased, the volume is decreased. The increase in pressure places a stress on the side of the reaction that has the most moles of gas and will shift to the side with the lesser number of moles in order to decrease the stress in the system. The reactant side contains 4 moles of gas and the product side contains 2 moles of gas. Therefore, the shift will be to the products—NH_3.

32. **D**   Balancing equations
The balanced equation should be as follows:

$$4Al_{(s)} + 3O_{2\,(g)} \rightarrow 2Al_2O_{3(s)}$$

Since oxygen had 2 on the reactant side and 3 on the product side, the common denominator of 6 had to be obtained by multiplying by 3 and 2 respectively. This made 4 aluminums on the product side, so place a coefficient of 4 on the reactant side, and you've got it.

33. **A**   Percent composition
The formula for nitric acid is HNO_3. The relative amount of hydrogen in this molecule is about 1/63. Make the math easy since you will not have a calculator—1/60th. 10% would mean 6/60; 5% would be 3/60—by process of elimination it must be the smallest choice given, **A**.

34. **A**   Equilibrium constants
Compare equation I and equation II to each other. Equation II is the reverse of equation I and has been doubled. Reversing the equation will give you the value of $1/K$. Doubling the equation raises the expression to 2 exponentially, so the expression should be squared. Since the value of K is 5.0 for equation I, the reverse reaction would give a K of 1/5; this should then be squared: $(1/5) \times (1/5)$; 1/25.00 is the answer.

35. **A**   Gas laws
At STP, 1 mole of any gas occupies 22.4 L of gas. 1 mole of gas = 6.02×10^{23}. The problem states that 3.01×10^{23} molecules of this gas has a mass of 32.00 g, so 0.50 mole of the gas has a mass of 32.00 g. Therefore, we would expect this gas to occupy a volume of 11.2 L at STP. 8.00 g is ¼ of this mass, so we would expect that it should occupy ¼ of 11.2 L. ¼ of 10 would be 2.5—you are looking for an answer that's in this range. Choice **A** is the closest answer, so it is correct.

36. **C**   Balancing equations
The balanced equation should be as follows:

$$3KOH_{(aq)} + H_3PO_{4(aq)} \rightarrow K_3PO_{4(aq)} + 3H_2O$$

Counting the hydrogens here is a bit tricky. By placing a 3 in front of KOH, you are left with 6 total H's on the reactant side (3 from KOH and 3 from H_3PO_4). Since H's are found only in water on the product side, you need to give water a coefficient of 3, resulting in 6 hydrogens.

37. **B** Catalysis

You are in search of the one false statement. Choice **A** is a true statement. A catalyst speeds up the rate of the forward reaction and the reverse reaction, and the equilibrium constant of the reaction is unaffected. Choice **B** must then be a false statement since equilibrium concentrations are not affected. Choices **C** and **D** are both true statements. A catalyst gives a reaction an alternate pathway by decreasing the energy of activation. Choice **E** is a true statement. A catalyst is not consumed during the reaction.

38. **D** Empirical formula

To find the empirical formula for a compound, you must set up the mole ratio for each element. Divide each of the moles given by the smallest number of moles and this should give the subscripts.

$$\frac{0.05 \text{ mole Mg}}{0.05} = 1 \qquad \frac{0.05 \text{ mole S}}{0.05} = 1 \qquad \frac{0.20 \text{ mole O}}{0.05} = 4$$

These are your subscripts: $MgSO_4$.

39. **C** Solution formation

First determine whether the statements given are true or false. Statement I is true. By crushing the solid into smaller pieces, you increase the surface area, and the solvent is able to come in contact with solute at a faster rate; thus it dissolves more quickly. Statement II is a true statement. By stirring the mixture, you bring solute and solvent in contact with each other more often, and the solid will dissolve more quickly. Statement III is false. When the temperature of the system is lowered, the molecules move more slowly, which prevents the solute and solvent from making contact as often. Look for the choice that includes only I and II; it's **C**.

40. **E** Balancing equations

The balanced equation should be as follows:

$$2C_6H_{14} + 19O_2 \rightarrow 12CO_2 + 14H_2O$$

In this equation, begin by balancing the carbons so you have six on each side, but then you'll end up with an odd number of oxygens. When this happens, the trick is to double the hydrocarbon number and start over. When you're done, make sure you can't reduce them all by a common number.

41. **C** Reactions, acid-base

First write the reaction and determine what you're starting with:

KOH	+	HCl	→	KCl	+	H_2O
0.400 M		0.100 M				
?		200 mL				

This represents a reaction between a strong acid and a strong base. When the moles of acid equal the moles of base, the reaction will have a pH of 7.00. In this case, the KOH is 4 times more concentrated than the HCl, so it should take only ¼ the volume to obtain an equal number of moles: 200/4 = 50 mL.

42. **E** Thermochemistry

The reaction is written with energy as a product: 394 kJ of energy are produced along with every 1 mole of CO_2. You would expect two moles of CO_2 to be double this number—788 kJ. Be careful: there are two answer choices with this number, so read closely. Since energy is a product, energy is released, and the correct answer is choice **E**.

43. **E** Stoichiometry

Here setting up a table really helps:

Molar mass	12	32	44
Balanced equation	C +	$O_2 \rightarrow$	CO_2
Number of moles	2	2	2
Amount		64 g	88

44. **E** Stoichiometry

The easiest way to solve this problem is to figure out concentrations and then match them to the answer.

$$Al_3(PO_4)_2 \rightarrow \quad 3Al^{3+} \quad + \quad 2PO_4^{3-}$$
$$0.05\ M \qquad 3(0.05) = 0.15 \qquad 2(0.05) = 0.10$$

The only answer that agrees is choice **E**—0.10 M phosphate ions.

45. **E** Gas laws

All flasks contain gases that have the same volume, the same temperature, and the same pressure; therefore Avogadro's law indicates that the number of molecules should be equal. Choices **D** and **E** give almost the same answer, but choice **E** is the best answer.

46. **A** Gas laws

Since all of the molecules are at the same temperature and pressure, their average kinetic energy should be the same. Graham's law states that smaller molecules should move faster because they will have fewer collisions. CH_4 is by far the smaller of the molecules, so you would expect that the methane molecules would have the higher average velocity.

47. **B** Gas laws

For gases, temperature in kelvins and volume are directly proportional. The only graph that shows this direct relationship is choice **B**. Choice **A** would be a good Boyle's law graph (inverse relationship). Choice **E** is a good graph of kinetics data.

48. B Gas laws

An ideal gas has no intermolecular attractive or repulsive forces and occupies little or no volume. Statement I is false. The higher the pressure, the more molecules are colliding with each other. Statement II is true. The higher the temperature, the faster the particles are moving. This means that intermolecular forces will have a harder time keeping the particles together. Statement III is false. The more molecules that are in a given area, the more collisions there will be, and the greater the chance for intermolecular forces to take effect. This would not lead to ideal conditions.

49. A Laboratory

Write a reaction to see what's produced:

$$AgNO_3 + HCl \rightarrow AgCl + HNO_3$$

$$\text{Net ionic: } Ag^+ + Cl^- \rightarrow AgCl$$

Silver chloride is not soluble. It is a white precipitate. Statement I is true, but statement II is false. (Silver iodide, AgI, is a yellow precipitate.) Statement III is false. No gas is produced in this reaction.

50. C Gas stoichiometry

Molar mass	16	32	44	18
Balanced equation	$CH_4 +$	$2O_2 \rightarrow$	$CO_2 +$	$2H_2O$
Number of moles	0.50 mole	1	0.5	1
Amount	8 g			22.4 L

51. C Electron configuration

The electron configurations are not written in filling order. Transition elements fill in the *d* orbital. Choices **A** and **B** are easy to eliminate since they have no *d* levels in their configuration. Choice **C** is the correct answer. The last level to be filled here would actually be the 3*d*. Choice **D** has the 3*d* level completely filled. Choice **E** is just wrong.

52. B Balancing equations

The balanced equation should be as follows:

$$2ZnS_{(s)} + 3O_{2(g)} \rightarrow 2ZnO_{(s)} + 2SO_{2(g)}$$

Begin by placing a coefficient of 2 in front of ZnO to give you an even number of oxygens on the product side. From here, 2 in front of ZnS, then 2 in front of SO_2, and finally balance the oxygens.

53. C Thermochemistry

Statement I is true. When temperature is increased, molecules will collide more often. Statement II is true. The faster the molecules are traveling, the greater the force of their collisions and the greater the number of them that can overcome the activation energy barrier needed to become products. Statement III is false. An increase in temperature will make particles become more chaotic, which represents an increase in entropy. Choice **C** contains the true statements.

54. C Periodic trends

The second ionization energy is the energy needed to remove the second-most loosely held electron. Use the periodic table to write a simplified electron configuration for each element:

Cl [Ne] $3s^2 3p^5$
S [Ne] $3s^2 3p^4$
Na [Ne] $3s^1$
Mg [Ne] $3s^2$
Al [Ne] $3s^2 3p^1$

After writing the configurations, it should be easy to tell that the second electron removed from sodium would come from an inner energy level. The closer the electrons are to the nucleus, the harder they are to remove.

55. D Ionic size

All of the elements listed are in the same family with the exception of hydrogen. Moving down a family in the table, the number of energy levels increases and so does atomic size. Ions follow the same periodic trends. The largest would be I, which has five principal energy levels.

56. D Bonding—Lewis structure

BF_3 would have B (3 valence e$^-$) + F (3(7) valence e$^-$) = 24 electrons. By placing boron in the middle and the three F's around it, six electrons are used for bonding. This leaves 18 electrons. Place 6 on each F to complete their octet. Boron is an exception to the octet rule and ends up with only 6 electrons. This structure will be trigonal planar in shape.

57. C Bonding—hybridization

Methane has four shared pairs of electrons, a tetrahedral arrangement. The hybridization will be sp^3. Choice **A**, sp, reflects a linear arrangement. Choice **B**, sp^2, is characteristic of a trigonal planar arrangement. Choice **D**, $sp^3 d$, is characteristic of trigonal bipyramid. Choice **E**, $sp^3 d^2$, is the hybridization for an octahedral arrangement.

58. B Oxidation-reduction
The best oxidizing agent will be the element that is most easily reduced. Since the elements are listed in decreasing order, Au will be the least reactive, so it should be the most easily reduced. Choice **A**, Ca, is the most active and will be the most easily oxidized. Choices **C–E** are all scattered in the activity series and can therefore be easily eliminated.

59. D Oxidation-reduction
The most reactive metal is Ca. Zn is the closest element to Ca in the choices that are given, so it will react most readily.

60. E Electrochemistry
The cathode half-cell is clearly labeled in the diagram given. Choices **B** and **C** can be eliminated immediately since Zn is the anode half-cell. Reduction, the gain of electrons, takes place at the cathode. This allows the elimination of choice **C** since this reaction is written as an oxidation. Of the two choices left, the best choice will be **E**. Copper (II) ions will be fully reduced to copper metal if this reaction takes place at standard conditions.

61. D Acid-base
A Brønsted base is a proton acceptor. Write the equation to see what would be produced with this definition. There's only one choice after seeing it!

$$HCO_3^- \quad + \quad H_2O \quad \rightarrow \quad H_2CO_3 \quad + \quad OH^-$$

base   acid   conj. acid   conj. base

62. E Reaction prediction
You're given the reaction $MgCl_{2(aq)} + \ldots NH_{3(aq)} + \ldots H_2O \rightarrow$? Treat ammonia and water like NH_4OH and perform a double replacement reaction. One of your products will be $Mg(OH)_2$ when the formula is balanced.

63. B Organic
Choices **A, C, D**, and **E** are all known products of petroleum, but rubber has traditionally been produced from the rubber plant.

64. B Classifying matter
Choice **A**, condensation, is the change from gas to liquid. Choice **B**, distillation, is the process of vaporizing a substance and recondensing it to produce pure fractions. This process does separate substances according to their differing boiling points. Choice **C**, fractional crystallization, involves the change of liquid to solid. Choice **D**, hydration, is the dissolving of a substance into water. Choice **E**, chromatography, is the separation of substances based on their polarities to a solvent.

65. C   Solubility and precipitation

Group 1A and NH_4^+ compounds are all soluble. Choices **A** and **E** can be eliminated if you know this rule. Choice **B**, silver nitrate, would be soluble because all nitrates are soluble. Choice **C**, $PbCl_2$, would form a precipitate. Pb, Hg, and Ag are the heavy metals that will precipitate the halogens. Choice **D**, magnesium acetate, will be soluble because acetates are very soluble.

66. E   Laboratory

Density is mass per unit of volume. The mass given is 25.200 g. The volume must be calculated. 15.0 mL – 12.5 mL = 2.5 mL. Find the density using the equation 25.200 g/2.5 mL is equal to about 10 g/mL. It's tricky because all of the answers are very close. Significant figures are the key! When dividing, take the least number of significant figures; the answer should be reported to only two significant digits.

67. D   Laboratory

Dalton's law of partial pressure states $P_{total} = P_{H_2O} + P_{O_2}$. The pressure of oxygen will be the total pressure, 750 mmHg – 20 mmHg, the vapor pressure of water at this temperature; 730 mmHg is the pressure due to oxygen.

68. D   Laboratory/Stoichiometry

Molar mass	122	74	32
Balanced equation	$KClO_3 \rightarrow$	KCl +	O_2
Number of moles	0.50	0.50	1.5
Amount	61 g	37 g	

69. D   Laboratory

Choice **A** is a true statement though vague—inaccurate measurements would cause error. Choice **B** is a true statement. This is probably the largest contributor to experimental error in this experiment. Choice **C** would cause an error in the final mathematical answer. Choice **D** would not affect the answer in any way. The reaction would still proceed with or without a catalyst—just at a different rate. Choice **E** would ultimately effect the water vapor that gets subtracted, if it is misread.

70. C   Gas laws

Density is a measure of mass per unit volume. When you are dealing with gases, the units of density are usually grams per liter. Since all gases are measured under the same conditions, the only difference would be the mass. The masses are 28, 71, 16, 46, and 44, respectively. Therefore, methane, CH_4, would be the least dense of the choices since it has the least mass.

Test I Explanations

SAT II Chemistry
Practice Test II

SAT II CHEMISTRY PRACTICE TEST II ANSWER SHEET

1 Ⓐ Ⓑ Ⓒ Ⓓ Ⓔ	15 Ⓐ Ⓑ Ⓒ Ⓓ Ⓔ	29 Ⓐ Ⓑ Ⓒ Ⓓ Ⓔ	43 Ⓐ Ⓑ Ⓒ Ⓓ Ⓔ	57 Ⓐ Ⓑ Ⓒ Ⓓ Ⓔ
2 Ⓐ Ⓑ Ⓒ Ⓓ Ⓔ	16 Ⓐ Ⓑ Ⓒ Ⓓ Ⓔ	30 Ⓐ Ⓑ Ⓒ Ⓓ Ⓔ	44 Ⓐ Ⓑ Ⓒ Ⓓ Ⓔ	58 Ⓐ Ⓑ Ⓒ Ⓓ Ⓔ
3 Ⓐ Ⓑ Ⓒ Ⓓ Ⓔ	17 Ⓐ Ⓑ Ⓒ Ⓓ Ⓔ	31 Ⓐ Ⓑ Ⓒ Ⓓ Ⓔ	45 Ⓐ Ⓑ Ⓒ Ⓓ Ⓔ	59 Ⓐ Ⓑ Ⓒ Ⓓ Ⓔ
4 Ⓐ Ⓑ Ⓒ Ⓓ Ⓔ	18 Ⓐ Ⓑ Ⓒ Ⓓ Ⓔ	32 Ⓐ Ⓑ Ⓒ Ⓓ Ⓔ	46 Ⓐ Ⓑ Ⓒ Ⓓ Ⓔ	60 Ⓐ Ⓑ Ⓒ Ⓓ Ⓔ
5 Ⓐ Ⓑ Ⓒ Ⓓ Ⓔ	19 Ⓐ Ⓑ Ⓒ Ⓓ Ⓔ	33 Ⓐ Ⓑ Ⓒ Ⓓ Ⓔ	47 Ⓐ Ⓑ Ⓒ Ⓓ Ⓔ	61 Ⓐ Ⓑ Ⓒ Ⓓ Ⓔ
6 Ⓐ Ⓑ Ⓒ Ⓓ Ⓔ	20 Ⓐ Ⓑ Ⓒ Ⓓ Ⓔ	34 Ⓐ Ⓑ Ⓒ Ⓓ Ⓔ	48 Ⓐ Ⓑ Ⓒ Ⓓ Ⓔ	62 Ⓐ Ⓑ Ⓒ Ⓓ Ⓔ
7 Ⓐ Ⓑ Ⓒ Ⓓ Ⓔ	21 Ⓐ Ⓑ Ⓒ Ⓓ Ⓔ	35 Ⓐ Ⓑ Ⓒ Ⓓ Ⓔ	49 Ⓐ Ⓑ Ⓒ Ⓓ Ⓔ	63 Ⓐ Ⓑ Ⓒ Ⓓ Ⓔ
8 Ⓐ Ⓑ Ⓒ Ⓓ Ⓔ	22 Ⓐ Ⓑ Ⓒ Ⓓ Ⓔ	36 Ⓐ Ⓑ Ⓒ Ⓓ Ⓔ	50 Ⓐ Ⓑ Ⓒ Ⓓ Ⓔ	64 Ⓐ Ⓑ Ⓒ Ⓓ Ⓔ
9 Ⓐ Ⓑ Ⓒ Ⓓ Ⓔ	23 Ⓐ Ⓑ Ⓒ Ⓓ Ⓔ	37 Ⓐ Ⓑ Ⓒ Ⓓ Ⓔ	51 Ⓐ Ⓑ Ⓒ Ⓓ Ⓔ	65 Ⓐ Ⓑ Ⓒ Ⓓ Ⓔ
10 Ⓐ Ⓑ Ⓒ Ⓓ Ⓔ	24 Ⓐ Ⓑ Ⓒ Ⓓ Ⓔ	38 Ⓐ Ⓑ Ⓒ Ⓓ Ⓔ	52 Ⓐ Ⓑ Ⓒ Ⓓ Ⓔ	66 Ⓐ Ⓑ Ⓒ Ⓓ Ⓔ
11 Ⓐ Ⓑ Ⓒ Ⓓ Ⓔ	25 Ⓐ Ⓑ Ⓒ Ⓓ Ⓔ	39 Ⓐ Ⓑ Ⓒ Ⓓ Ⓔ	53 Ⓐ Ⓑ Ⓒ Ⓓ Ⓔ	67 Ⓐ Ⓑ Ⓒ Ⓓ Ⓔ
12 Ⓐ Ⓑ Ⓒ Ⓓ Ⓔ	26 Ⓐ Ⓑ Ⓒ Ⓓ Ⓔ	40 Ⓐ Ⓑ Ⓒ Ⓓ Ⓔ	54 Ⓐ Ⓑ Ⓒ Ⓓ Ⓔ	68 Ⓐ Ⓑ Ⓒ Ⓓ Ⓔ
13 Ⓐ Ⓑ Ⓒ Ⓓ Ⓔ	27 Ⓐ Ⓑ Ⓒ Ⓓ Ⓔ	41 Ⓐ Ⓑ Ⓒ Ⓓ Ⓔ	55 Ⓐ Ⓑ Ⓒ Ⓓ Ⓔ	69 Ⓐ Ⓑ Ⓒ Ⓓ Ⓔ
14 Ⓐ Ⓑ Ⓒ Ⓓ Ⓔ	28 Ⓐ Ⓑ Ⓒ Ⓓ Ⓔ	42 Ⓐ Ⓑ Ⓒ Ⓓ Ⓔ	56 Ⓐ Ⓑ Ⓒ Ⓓ Ⓔ	70 Ⓐ Ⓑ Ⓒ Ⓓ Ⓔ

CHEMISTRY

	I	II	CE
101	Ⓣ Ⓕ	Ⓣ Ⓕ	Ⓒᴇ
102	Ⓣ Ⓕ	Ⓣ Ⓕ	Ⓒᴇ
103	Ⓣ Ⓕ	Ⓣ Ⓕ	Ⓒᴇ
104	Ⓣ Ⓕ	Ⓣ Ⓕ	Ⓒᴇ
105	Ⓣ Ⓕ	Ⓣ Ⓕ	Ⓒᴇ
106	Ⓣ Ⓕ	Ⓣ Ⓕ	Ⓒᴇ
107	Ⓣ Ⓕ	Ⓣ Ⓕ	Ⓒᴇ
108	Ⓣ Ⓕ	Ⓣ Ⓕ	Ⓒᴇ
109	Ⓣ Ⓕ	Ⓣ Ⓕ	Ⓒᴇ
110	Ⓣ Ⓕ	Ⓣ Ⓕ	Ⓒᴇ
111	Ⓣ Ⓕ	Ⓣ Ⓕ	Ⓒᴇ
112	Ⓣ Ⓕ	Ⓣ Ⓕ	Ⓒᴇ
113	Ⓣ Ⓕ	Ⓣ Ⓕ	Ⓒᴇ
114	Ⓣ Ⓕ	Ⓣ Ⓕ	Ⓒᴇ
115	Ⓣ Ⓕ	Ⓣ Ⓕ	Ⓒᴇ

THE PERIODIC TABLE OF ELEMENTS

Legend / Key:

OXIDATION STATES (MOST STABLE STATE IN BOLD)
EN — ELECTRONEGATIVITY
EA — ELECTRON AFFINITY (kJ/mol)
FIP — FIRST IONIZATION POTENTIAL (eV)
AR — ATOMIC RADIUS (Å)

1, 3	79 ATOMIC NUMBER
EN 2.54	**Au** ATOMIC SYMBOL
EA 222.737	196.96654 ATOMIC MASS
FIP 9.23	Gold NAME
AR 1.44	[Xe] 4f¹⁴5d¹⁰6s¹ ELECTRON SHELL CONFIGURATION

Legend: METALS · METALLOIDS · NONMETALS

LANTHANIDE SERIES
ACTINIDE SERIES

Group headings

- 1 IA — HYDROGEN & ALKALI METALS
- 2 IIA — ALKALINE-EARTH METALS
- 3 IIIB
- 4 IVB
- 5 VB
- 6 VIB
- 7 VIIB
- 8 VIII
- 9 VIII
- 10 VIII
- 11 IB
- 12 IIB
- 13 IIIB / IIIA
- 14 IVB / IVA
- 15 VB / VA
- 16 VIB / VIA — CHALCOGENS
- 17 VIIB / VIIA — HALOGENS
- 18 0 / VIII — NOBLE GASES

Selected elements

1 Hydrogen H, EN 2.20, EA 72.770, FIP 13.598, AR 0.37, 1s¹, 1.00794

2 Helium He, EN —, EA <0, FIP 24.59, AR —, 1s², 4.002602

3 Lithium Li, EN 0.98, EA 59.63, FIP 5.392, AR 1.52, [He] 2s¹, 6.941

4 Beryllium Be, EN 1.57, EA ≤0, FIP 9.322, AR 1.13, [He] 2s², 9.01218

5 Boron B, EN 2.04, EA 26.7, FIP 8.30, AR 0.88, [He] 2s²2p¹, 10.81

6 Carbon C, EN 2.55, EA 121.85, FIP 11.26, AR 0.77, [He] 2s²2p², 12.011

7 Nitrogen N, EN 3.04, EA -7, FIP 14.53, AR 0.70, [He] 2s²2p³, 14.00674

8 Oxygen O, EN 3.44, EA 140.9760, FIP 13.62, AR 0.66, [He] 2s²2p⁴, 15.9994

9 Fluorine F, EN 3.98, EA 328.0, FIP 17.42, AR 0.64, [He] 2s²2p⁵, 18.998403

10 Neon Ne, EN —, EA <0, FIP 21.57, AR 0.51, [He] 2s²2p⁶, 20.1797

11 Sodium Na, EN 0.93, EA 52.867, FIP 5.139, AR 1.86, [Ne] 3s¹, 22.98977

12 Magnesium Mg, EN 1.31, EA ≤0, FIP 7.646, AR 1.60, [Ne] 3s², 24.3050

13 Aluminum Al, EN 1.61, EA 42.6, FIP 5.99, AR 1.43, [Ne] 3s²3p¹, 26.98154

14 Silicon Si, EN 1.90, EA 133.6, FIP 8.15, AR 1.17, [Ne] 3s²3p², 28.0855

15 Phosphorus P, EN 2.19, EA 72.03, FIP 10.49, AR 1.10, [Ne] 3s²3p³, 30.97376

16 Sulfur S, EN 2.58, EA 200.4116, FIP 10.36, AR 1.04, [Ne] 3s²3p⁴, 32.066

17 Chlorine Cl, EN 3.16, EA 349.0, FIP 12.97, AR 0.99, [Ne] 3s²3p⁵, 35.4527

18 Argon Ar, EN —, EA <0, FIP 15.76, AR 0.88, [Ne] 3s²3p⁶, 39.948

19 Potassium K, EN 0.82, EA 48.384, FIP 4.341, AR 2.27, [Ar] 4s¹, 39.0983

20 Calcium Ca, EN 1.00, EA 2.369, FIP 6.113, AR 1.97, [Ar] 4s², 40.078

21 Scandium Sc, EN 1.36, EA 18.1, FIP 6.56, AR 1.61, [Ar] 3d¹4s², 44.95591

22 Titanium Ti, EN 1.54, EA 7.6, FIP 6.83, AR 1.45, [Ar] 3d²4s², 47.88

23 Vanadium V, EN 1.63, EA 50.7, FIP 6.75, AR 1.31, [Ar] 3d³4s², 50.9415

24 Chromium Cr, EN 1.66, EA 64.3, FIP 6.77, AR 1.25, [Ar] 3d⁵4s¹, 51.9961

25 Manganese Mn, EN 1.55, EA <0, FIP 7.43, AR 1.37, [Ar] 3d⁵4s², 54.93805

26 Iron Fe, EN 1.83, EA 14.57, FIP 7.90, AR 1.24, [Ar] 3d⁶4s², 55.847

27 Cobalt Co, EN 1.88, EA 63.8, FIP 7.88, AR 1.25, [Ar] 3d⁷4s², 58.93320

28 Nickel Ni, EN 1.91, EA 111.5, FIP 7.64, AR 1.25, [Ar] 3d⁸4s², 58.69

29 Copper Cu, EN 1.90, EA 118.5, FIP 7.73, AR 1.28, [Ar] 3d¹⁰4s¹, 63.546

30 Zinc Zn, EN 1.65, EA <0, FIP 9.39, AR 1.34, [Ar] 3d¹⁰4s², 65.39

31 Gallium Ga, EN 1.81, EA 29, FIP 6.00, AR 1.53, [Ar] 3d¹⁰4s²4p¹, 69.723

32 Germanium Ge, EN 2.01, EA -120, FIP 7.90, AR 1.22, [Ar] 3d¹⁰4s²4p², 72.61

33 Arsenic As, EN 2.18, EA -80, FIP 9.81, AR 1.21, [Ar] 3d¹⁰4s²4p³, 74.92159

34 Selenium Se, EN 2.55, EA 194.967, FIP 9.75, AR 1.17, [Ar] 3d¹⁰4s²4p⁴, 78.96

35 Bromine Br, EN 2.96, EA 324.7, FIP 11.81, AR 1.14, [Ar] 3d¹⁰4s²4p⁵, 79.904

36 Krypton Kr, EN —, EA <0, FIP 14.00, AR 1.03, [Ar] 3d¹⁰4s²4p⁶, 83.8

37 Rubidium Rb, EN 0.82, EA 46.884, FIP 4.177, AR 2.47, [Kr] 5s¹, 85.4678

38 Strontium Sr, EN 0.95, EA 4.6, FIP 5.695, AR 2.15, [Kr] 5s², 87.62

39 Yttrium Y, EN 1.22, EA 29.6, FIP 6.22, AR 1.78, [Kr] 4d¹5s², 88.90585

40 Zirconium Zr, EN 1.33, EA 41.1, FIP 6.63, AR 1.60, [Kr] 4d²5s², 91.224

41 Niobium Nb, EN 1.6, EA 86.2, FIP 6.76, AR 1.49, [Kr] 4d⁴5s¹, 92.90638

42 Molybdenum Mo, EN 2.16, EA 72.0, FIP 7.09, AR 1.45, [Kr] 4d⁵5s¹, 95.94

43 Technetium Tc, EN 1.90, EA 53, FIP 7.28, AR 1.35, [Kr] 4d⁵5s², (98)

44 Ruthenium Ru, EN 2.2, EA 101.0, FIP 7.36, AR 1.32, [Kr] 4d⁷5s¹, 101.07

45 Rhodium Rh, EN 2.28, EA 110, FIP 7.46, AR 1.34, [Kr] 4d⁸5s¹, 102.90550

46 Palladium Pd, EN 2.20, EA 54.22, FIP 8.34, AR 1.38, [Kr] 4d¹⁰, 106.42

47 Silver Ag, EN 1.93, EA 125.6, FIP 7.58, AR 1.44, [Kr] 4d¹⁰5s¹, 107.8682

48 Cadmium Cd, EN 1.69, EA <0, FIP 8.99, AR 1.49, [Kr] 4d¹⁰5s², 112.411

49 Indium In, EN 1.78, EA 29, FIP 5.76, AR 1.63, [Kr] 4d¹⁰5s²5p¹, 114.82

50 Tin Sn, EN 1.96, EA 101.0, FIP 7.34, AR 1.40, [Kr] 4d¹⁰5s²5p², 118.710

51 Antimony Sb, EN 2.05, EA 103, FIP 8.64, AR 1.41, [Kr] 4d¹⁰5s²5p³, 121.760

52 Tellurium Te, EN 2.1, EA 190.15, FIP 9.01, AR 1.37, [Kr] 4d¹⁰5s²5p⁴, 127.60

53 Iodine I, EN 2.66, EA 295.2, FIP 10.45, AR 1.33, [Kr] 4d¹⁰5s²5p⁵, 126.90447

54 Xenon Xe, EN —, EA <0, FIP 12.13, AR 1.24, [Kr] 4d¹⁰5s²5p⁶, 131.29

55 Cesium Cs, EN 0.79, EA 45.505, FIP 3.894, AR 2.65, [Xe] 6s¹, 132.90543

56 Barium Ba, EN 0.89, EA 5.212, FIP 5.212, AR 2.22, [Xe] 6s², 137.327

57 Lanthanum La, EN 1.1, EA 50, FIP 5.58, AR 1.88, [Xe] 5d¹6s², 138.9055

72 Hafnium Hf, EN 1.30, EA <0, FIP 6.83, AR 1.67, [Xe] 4f¹⁴5d²6s², 178.49

73 Tantalum Ta, EN 1.5, EA 31, FIP 7.55, AR 1.49, [Xe] 4f¹⁴5d³6s², 180.9479

74 Tungsten W, EN 2.36, EA 78.6, FIP 7.86, AR 1.41, [Xe] 4f¹⁴5d⁴6s², 183.85

75 Rhenium Re, EN 1.9, EA 14.5, FIP 7.88, AR 1.37, [Xe] 4f¹⁴5d⁵6s², 186.207

76 Osmium Os, EN 2.2, EA 106, FIP 8.7, AR 1.34, [Xe] 4f¹⁴5d⁶6s², 190.2

77 Iridium Ir, EN 2.20, EA 151, FIP 8.97, AR 1.36, [Xe] 4f¹⁴5d⁷6s², 192.22

78 Platinum Pt, EN 2.28, EA 205.1, FIP 8.96, AR 1.37, [Xe] 4f¹⁴5d⁹6s¹, 195.08

79 Gold Au, EN 2.54, EA 222.737, FIP 9.23, AR 1.44, [Xe] 4f¹⁴5d¹⁰6s¹, 196.96654

80 Mercury Hg, EN 2.00, EA <0, FIP 10.44, AR 1.50, [Xe] 4f¹⁴5d¹⁰6s², 200.59

81 Thallium Tl, EN 2.04, EA 20, FIP 6.11, AR 1.47, [Xe] 4f¹⁴5d¹⁰6s²6p¹, 204.3833

82 Lead Pb, EN 2.33, EA 35.1, FIP 7.42, AR 1.75, [Xe] 4f¹⁴5d¹⁰6s²6p², 207.2

83 Bismuth Bi, EN 2.02, EA 91.3, FIP 7.29, AR 1.82, [Xe] 4f¹⁴5d¹⁰6s²6p³, 208.98804

84 Polonium Po, EN 2.00, EA 180, FIP 8.42, AR 1.67, [Xe] 4f¹⁴5d¹⁰6s²6p⁴, (209)

85 Astatine At, EN 2.20, EA 270, FIP —, AR 1.40, [Xe] 4f¹⁴5d¹⁰6s²6p⁵, (210)

86 Radon Rn, EN —, EA <0, FIP 10.75, AR 1.34, [Xe] 4f¹⁴5d¹⁰6s²6p⁶, (222)

87 Francium Fr, EN 0.7, EA <0, FIP 4.07, AR 2.7, [Rn] 7s¹, (223)

88 Radium Ra, EN 0.90, EA >0, FIP 5.279, AR 2.33, [Rn] 7s², (226)

89 Actinium Ac, EN 1.1, EA ≤0, FIP 5.17, AR 1.88, [Rn] 6d¹7s², (227.0278)

104 Rutherfordium Rf, [Rn] 5f¹⁴6d²7s², (261.1089)

105 Dubnium Db, [Rn] 5f¹⁴6d³7s², (262.1144)

106 Seaborgium Sg, [Rn] 5f¹⁴6d⁴7s², (266.1219)

107 Bohrium Bh, [Rn] 5f¹⁴6d⁵7s², (262.1229)

108 Hassium Hs, [Rn] 5f¹⁴6d⁶7s², (269.1341)

109 Meitnerium Mt, [Rn] 5f¹⁴6d⁷7s², (268.1388)

110 Ununnilium Uun, [Rn] 5f¹⁴6d⁸7s², (271.1461)

111 Unununium Uuu, [Rn] 5f¹⁴6d⁹7s², (272.1535)

112 Ununbium Uub, (277)

114 Ununquadium Uuq, (289)

116 Ununhexium Uuh, (289)

118 Ununoctium Uuo, (293)

Lanthanide Series

58 Cerium Ce, EN 1.12, EA 54, FIP 5.54, AR 1.82, [Xe] 4f¹5d¹6s², 140.115

59 Praseodymium Pr, EN 1.13, EA 54, FIP 5.46, AR 1.82, [Xe] 4f³6s², 140.90765

60 Neodymium Nd, EN 1.14, EA <0, FIP 5.53, AR 1.81, [Xe] 4f⁴6s², 144.24

61 Promethium Pm, EN 1.13, EA 50, FIP 5.55, AR 1.80, [Xe] 4f⁵6s², (145)

62 Samarium Sm, EN 1.17, EA <0, FIP 5.64, AR 1.79, [Xe] 4f⁶6s², 150.36

63 Europium Eu, EN 1.2, EA 50, FIP 5.67, AR 2.00, [Xe] 4f⁷6s², 151.965

64 Gadolinium Gd, EN 1.20, EA 50, FIP 6.15, AR 1.79, [Xe] 4f⁷5d¹6s², 157.25

65 Terbium Tb, EN 1.1, EA 50, FIP 5.86, AR 1.76, [Xe] 4f⁹6s², 158.92534

66 Dysprosium Dy, EN 1.22, EA 50, FIP 5.94, AR 1.75, [Xe] 4f¹⁰6s², 162.50

67 Holmium Ho, EN 1.23, EA 50, FIP 6.02, AR 1.74, [Xe] 4f¹¹6s², 164.93032

68 Erbium Er, EN 1.24, EA 50, FIP 6.11, AR 1.73, [Xe] 4f¹²6s², 167.26

69 Thulium Tm, EN 1.25, EA 50, FIP 6.18, AR 1.72, [Xe] 4f¹³6s², 168.93421

70 Ytterbium Yb, EN 1.1, EA 50, FIP 6.25, AR 1.94, [Xe] 4f¹⁴6s², 173.04

71 Lutetium Lu, EN 1.27, EA 50, FIP 5.43, AR 1.72, [Xe] 4f¹⁴5d¹6s², 174.967

Actinide Series

90 Thorium Th, EN 1.3, EA <0, FIP 6.08, AR 1.80, [Rn] 6d²7s², 232.0381

91 Protactinium Pa, EN 1.5, EA <0, FIP 5.89, AR 1.61, [Rn] 5f²6d¹7s², 231.03588

92 Uranium U, EN 1.38, EA <0, FIP 6.05, AR 1.54, [Rn] 5f³6d¹7s², 238.0289

93 Neptunium Np, EN 1.36, EA <0, FIP 6.19, AR 1.55, [Rn] 5f⁴6d¹7s², 237.048

94 Plutonium Pu, EN 1.28, EA <0, FIP 6.06, AR 1.53, [Rn] 5f⁶7s², (244)

95 Americium Am, EN 1.3, EA <0, FIP 5.99, AR 1.84, [Rn] 5f⁷7s², (243)

96 Curium Cm, EN 1.3, EA <0, FIP 6.02, AR —, [Rn] 5f⁷6d¹7s², (247)

97 Berkelium Bk, EN 1.3, EA <0, FIP 6.23, AR —, [Rn] 5f⁹7s², (247)

98 Californium Cf, EN 1.3, EA <0, FIP 6.30, AR —, [Rn] 5f¹⁰7s², (251)

99 Einsteinium Es, EN 1.3, EA <0, FIP 6.42, AR —, [Rn] 5f¹¹7s², (252)

100 Fermium Fm, EN 1.3, EA <0, FIP 6.50, AR —, [Rn] 5f¹²7s², (257)

101 Mendelevium Md, EN 1.3, EA <0, FIP 6.58, AR —, [Rn] 5f¹³7s², (258)

102 Nobelium No, EN 1.3, EA <0, FIP 6.65, AR —, [Rn] 5f¹⁴7s², (259)

103 Lawrencium Lr, [Rn] 5f¹⁴6d¹7s², (262)

SAT II CHEMISTRY TEST

Time: 1 hour

Part A

> Directions: Each set of lettered choices below refers to the numbered questions or statements immediately following it. Select the one lettered choice that best answers each question or best fits each statement, and then fill in the corresponding oval on the answer sheet. A choice may be used once, more than once, or not at all in each set.

Questions 1–5

    (A) K
    (B) Ca
    (C) Br
    (D) Kr
    (E) Zn

1. Which element has the smallest atomic radii?

2. Which element has the highest electronegativity?

3. Which element has the largest electron affinity?

4. Which element has the largest first ionization energy?

5. Which element reacts most explosively in water?

Questions 6–10

    (A) Nonpolar covalent substance
    (B) Polar covalent substance
    (C) Ionic substance
    (D) Metallic substance
    (E) Noble gas

6. Solid magnesium carbonate

7. Ammonia gas

8. Tungsten filament

9. Exists as cations with delocalized electrons

10. Emits energy in the form of bright red light when an electric current is passed through a confined gaseous sample

Questions 11–15 refer to the following segments on the heating curve for water:

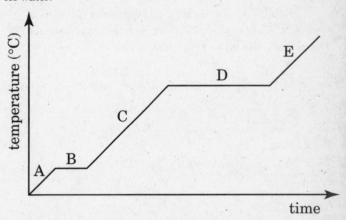

11. Corresponds to 0°C when the pressure of the system is held constant at 1.0 atm.

12. The part of the curve that represents only the vapor phase when the pressure of the system is held constant at 1.0 atm.

13. The part of the curve where the energy changes can be calculated using the formula $q = mc_{steam}T$.

14. The part of the curve that represents the following chemical equation:

$$H_2O_{(g)} \rightarrow H_2O_{(l)}$$

15. The part of the curve that corresponds to the greatest change in the average kinetic energy of the molecules.

GO ON TO THE NEXT PAGE

Questions 16–19

    (A) Miscible
    (B) Suspension
    (C) Colloid
    (D) Saturated
    (E) Supersaturated

16. Describes a solution that contains more solute than it should theoretically be able to hold at a given temperature.

17. A mixture from which some of the solute particles will settle on standing.

18. Describes a solution containing solute particles of intermediate size that do not settle but do scatter light.

19. Describes a solution that is at equilibrium and contains the maximum amount of solute for a given amount of solvent at constant temperature and pressure.

Questions 20–25 refer to the five types of chemical reactions listed below:

    (A) Decomposition
    (B) Synthesis
    (C) Combustion
    (D) Single replacement
    (E) Double replacement

20. Octane burns in air.

21. Two aqueous solutions are mixed and a precipitate is formed.

22. A solid piece of silver metal reacts with oxygen in the air and tarnishes.

23. An electric current is sent through a sample of water.

24. An iron nail, solid iron metal, rusts.

25. A solid piece of sodium reacts violently with water.

GO ON TO THE NEXT PAGE

SAT II CHEMISTRY TEST

PLEASE GO TO THE SPECIAL SECTION OF YOUR ANSWER SHEET LABELED CHEMISTRY AND ANSWER QUESTIONS 101–115 ACCORDING TO THE FOLLOWING DIRECTIONS:

Part B

> Directions: Each question below consists of two statements, statement I in the left-hand column and statement II in the right-hand column. For each question, determine whether statement I is true or false and whether statement II is true or false and fill in the corresponding T or F ovals on your answer sheet. Fill in oval **CE** only if statement II is a correct explanation of statement I.

	Statement I	BECAUSE	Statement II
101.	After a period of time in a closed container, the rate of evaporation of a liquid will equal the rate of condensation.	BECAUSE	An equilibrium will be established between a liquid and its vapor in a closed container held at constant temperature.
102.	Water boils below 100°C at high altitudes.	BECAUSE	Atmospheric pressure varies inversely with altitude.
103.	The temperature of a substance always increases as heat energy is added to the system.	BECAUSE	The average kinetic energy of the particles in the system increases with an increase in temperature.
104.	Gases are more easily compressed than liquids.	BECAUSE	Gases expand to fill their container.
105.	$MgCl_2$ is the correct formula for magnesium chloride.	BECAUSE	Chlorine is always diatomic.
106.	In general, within a family, boiling point increases with increasing molecular mass.	BECAUSE	The larger a molecule, the more likely its electron cloud is to polarize and establish dispersion intermolecular forces.
107.	A spontaneous reaction is always exothermic.	BECAUSE	Exothermic reactions release energy from the system.
108.	The rate of a chemical reaction is affected by temperature.	BECAUSE	An increase in temperature causes more effective collisions to occur between the particles reacting.
109.	The value of the equilibrium constant is affected by temperature.	BECAUSE	An increase in temperature causes more effective collisions to occur between the particles reacting.
110.	A large value for the equilibrium constant indicates that products are favored at equilibrium.	BECAUSE	The ratio of products to reactants at equilibrium is always greater than one.
111.	The freezing of water is an exothermic process.	BECAUSE	Energy is lost when covalent bonds are formed.
112.	Ionic compounds only dissolve in water.	BECAUSE	Hydration is the process of dissolving an ionic solid in water.
113.	O_2 contains a double bond.	BECAUSE	O_2 is diatomic.
114.	The electronic geometry of the ammonia molecule is tetrahedral.	BECAUSE	Ammonia obeys the octet rule.
115.	The molecular geometry of a CO_2 molecule is linear.	BECAUSE	All molecules having only three atoms form bond angles of 180°.

GO ON TO THE NEXT PAGE

RETURN TO THE MAIN SECTION OF YOUR ANSWER SHEET AND ANSWER QUESTIONS 26–70.

SAT II CHEMISTRY TEST

Part C

26. Which response includes only the true statements concerning the characteristics of covalent compounds?

    I.   These compounds can be gases, liquids, or solids with low melting points.
    II. Most are soluble in polar solvents.
    III. Liquid and molten compounds do not conduct electricity.
    IV. Aqueous solutions of these compounds are very good conductors of electricity.

    (A) I and III
    (B) II and IV
    (C) I, III, and IV
    (D) I, II, and III
    (E) IV only

27. Which of the following is the density of nitrogen at STP?

    (A) 0.33 g/L
    (B) 0.65 g/L
    (C) 0.80 g/L
    (D) 1.25 g/L
    (E) 1.60 g/L

28. The hydrogen sulfate or bisulfate ion, HSO_4^-, can act as either an acid or a base in water solution. In which of the following equations does HSO_4^- act as an acid?

    (A) $HSO_4^- + H_2O \rightarrow H_2SO_4 + OH^-$
    (B) $HSO_4^- + H_3O^+ \rightarrow SO_3 + 2H_2O$
    (C) $HSO_4^- + OH^- \rightarrow H_2SO_4 + O^{2-}$
    (D) $HSO_4^- + H_2O \rightarrow SO_4^{2-} + H_3O^+$
    (E) None of these

29. Which nuclide is formed as a result of this fission reaction?
    $$^{235}_{92}U + {}^{1}_{0}n \rightarrow 3{}^{1}_{0}n + {}^{139}_{56}Ba + \underline{\qquad}$$

    (A) $^{96}_{35}Br$

    (B) $^{96}_{36}Kr$

    (C) $^{94}_{37}Rb$

    (D) $^{94}_{36}Kr$

    (E) $^{90}_{38}Sr$

30. A substance contains 35.0 g nitrogen, 5.05 g hydrogen, and 60.0 g oxygen. How many grams of oxygen are there in a 200 g sample of the substance?

    (A) 10.1 g
    (B) 60.0 g
    (C) 70.0 g
    (D) 120 g
    (E) 140 g

31. The ground state electron configuration of the cobalt atom is characterized by which of the following?

    I.   Partially filled $3d$ orbitals
    II. The presence of unpaired electrons
    III. All electrons paired

    (A) I only
    (B) II only
    (C) I and II only
    (D) I and III only
    (E) I, II, and III

32. What would happen to the equilibrium system shown here if oxygen were added?
    $$4NH_{3(g)} + 5O_{2(g)} \Leftrightarrow 4NO_{(g)} + 6H_2O_{(g)}$$

    (A) More ammonia would be produced.
    (B) More oxygen would be produced.
    (C) The equilibrium would shift to the right.
    (D) The equilibrium would shift to the left.
    (E) Nothing would happen since the temperature is constant.

GO ON TO THE NEXT PAGE

33. You have two samples of the same gas in a 1.0 L container at 1.0 atm pressure. The temperature of the gas in the first container has a Kelvin temperature four times that of the gas in the other container. The ratio of the number of moles of gas in the first container compared to that in the second container is

    (A) 1:1
    (B) 1:2
    (C) 1:4
    (D) 2:1
    (E) 4:1

34. An atom of silicon has a mass number of 29. How many neutrons does it have?

    (A) 14
    (B) 15
    (C) 16
    (D) 28
    (E) 29

Use the following to answer questions 35–36:

Consider the chemical system $CO + Cl_2 \Leftrightarrow COCl_2$; $K = 4.6 \times 10^9$ L/mol.

35. What does the value of K indicate about the system once it has achieved equilibrium?

    (A) A great quantity of reactants remain and little product is formed.
    (B) Few reactants remain and a great deal of product is formed.
    (C) At equilibrium, the concentration of the products equals the concentration of the reactants.
    (D) The reaction is endothermic.
    (E) The reaction is exothermic.

36. If the concentration of the reactants were to double while temperature remains unchanged, how would the value of the equilibrium constant, K, be affected?

    (A) K would double.
    (B) K would become half its current value.
    (C) K would quadruple.
    (D) K would remain unchanged.
    (E) K would depend on the initial conditions of the reactants.

37. Argon has a density of 1.78 g/L at STP. Which of the following gases have a density at STP greater than that of argon?

    I. F_2
    II. H_2S
    III. NH_3
    IV. CO_2

    (A) I only
    (B) II only
    (C) IV only
    (D) I and III only
    (E) II and IV only

38. Which of the following combinations represents a 2^+ ion having a mass number of 40?

	Protons	Electrons	Neutrons
(A)	18	17	22
(B)	18	17	22
(C)	19	20	21
(D)	20	18	20
(E)	20	20	20

39. Which factor listed below is most important in determining the strength of an oxyacid?

    (A) The size of the molecule
    (B) The molecular mass of the molecule
    (C) The identity of the central atom in the molecule
    (D) The number of oxygen atoms present in the molecule
    (E) The ability of the molecule to vaporize

40. Draw the Lewis dot formula for NH_3. How many unshared pairs of electrons are in the outer shell of the central nitrogen atom?

    (A) 0
    (B) 1
    (C) 2
    (D) 4
    (E) 6

41. Which of the following would give the highest pH when dissolved in water to form a 0.10 M solution?

    (A) A strong acid
    (B) A weak acid
    (C) The sodium salt of a strong acid
    (D) The ammonium salt of a strong acid
    (E) The sodium salt of a weak acid

GO ON TO THE NEXT PAGE

42. Which of the species below, when dissolved in H_2O, will not produce a basic solution?

    (A) MgO
    (B) NH_3
    (C) K_2O
    (D) $Ba(OH)_2$
    (E) CH_3OH

43. Consider the following orderings:

    I.   Al < Si < P < Cl
    II. Be < Mg < Ca < Sr
    III. I < Br < Cl < F
    IV. $Na^+ < Mg^{2+} < Al^{3+} < Si^{4+}$

    Which of these give(s) a correct trend in ionization energy?

    (A) I only
    (B) III only
    (C) I and II only
    (D) I and IV only
    (E) I, III, and IV only

44. Of the following elements, which is most likely to form a negative ion with a charge of 1?

    (A) Ba
    (B) Ca
    (C) Si
    (D) P
    (E) Cl

45. The hybridization associated with the central atom of a molecule in which all the bond angles are 120° is _____.

    (A) sp
    (B) sp^2
    (C) sp^3
    (D) sp^3d
    (E) sp^3d^2

46. The following hydrogen halides (HF, HCl, HBr, and HI) are all polar molecules. The strength of the acid each forms in water is based on which of the following?

    I.   The polarity of the molecule
    II. The size of the molecule
    III. The strength of the bond

    (A) I only
    (B) II only
    (C) III only
    (D) I and III
    (E) II and III

47. A sample of ammonia has a mass of 51.1 g. How many molecules are in this sample?

    (A) 1.8×10^{23} molecules
    (B) 3.6×10^{23} molecules
    (C) 9.1×10^{23} molecules
    (D) 1.8×10^{24} molecules
    (E) 3.6×10^{24} molecules

48. Which of the following is true for a system whose equilibrium constant is less than 1?

    (A) It will take a short time to reach equilibrium.
    (B) It will take a long time to reach equilibrium.
    (C) The equilibrium lies to the left.
    (D) The equilibrium lies to the right.
    (E) It requires a higher concentration of reactants to reach equilibrium.

49. What is the molar mass of ammonium carbonate, $(NH_4)_2CO_3$?

    (A) 48.06 g/mol
    (B) 96.11 g/mol
    (C) 82.09 g/mol
    (D) 78.05 g/mol
    (E) 192.2 g/mol

50. If the Kelvin temperature of a gas is tripled and the volume is doubled, the new pressure will be

    (A) 1/6 of the original pressure
    (B) 1/3 of the original pressure
    (C) 2/3 of the original pressure
    (D) 3/2 of the original pressure
    (E) 3 times the original pressure

51. How many grams are in a 7.0 mol sample of sodium hydroxide?

    (A) 40.0 g
    (B) 140.0 g
    (C) 280.0 g
    (D) 340.0 g
    (E) 420.0 g

52. Hydrofluoric acid contains what percent hydrogen by mass?

    (A) 1.0%
    (B) 5.0%
    (C) 10%
    (D) 15%
    (E) 20%

GO ON TO THE NEXT PAGE

53. Determine the coefficient for O_2 when the following equation is balanced in standard form (smallest whole number integers):

$$\ldots C_4H_{10(g)} + \ldots O_{2(g)} \rightarrow \ldots CO_{2(g)} + \ldots H_2O_{(g)}$$

    (A) 4
    (B) 8
    (C) 10
    (D) 13
    (E) 26

54. An ammonium nitrate product dissolves easily in water at room temperature, and the process causes the solution to become quite cold. Which of the following are true about the dissolution of ammonium nitrate?

    I. The process is endothermic.
    II. The solubility will be greater in warmer water.
    III. S° for the reaction is negative.

    (A) I only
    (B) II only
    (C) I and II only
    (D) I and III only
    (E) I, II, and III

55. Which of the following is paired incorrectly?

    (A) HCl—strong acid
    (B) HNO_3—weak acid
    (C) $Ba(OH)_2$—strong base
    (D) HI—strong acid
    (E) NH_3—weak base

Questions 56–59 refer to the experiment shown below in which the molar volume of a gas was determined in order to calculate the ideal gas constant. Throughout the experiment, the temperature was held constant at 25°C, and the atmospheric pressure remained at 760 mmHg.

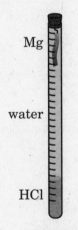

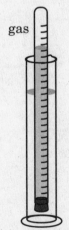

Figure 1: filled   Figure 2: reaction setup   Figure 3: measurement setup

56. Which of the following gases is produced as a result of inverting the tube in Figure 1?
    Hydrochloric acid →

    (A) H_2
    (B) O_2
    (C) N_2
    (D) CO_2
    (E) $H_2O_{(g)}$

57. What is the purpose of the procedure illustrated in Figure 3?

    (A) Raising the tube out of the water so that the numbers can be read more easily
    (B) Equalizing the pressure of the gas within the tube to atmospheric pressure
    (C) Providing more space in the graduated cylinder so that the water displaced by the gas does not cause overflow of water from the graduated cylinder
    (D) Checking to see that all of the magnesium ribbon has reacted
    (E) Raising the tube so that it is separated from any unreacted acid

58. What is the total pressure of the dry gas collected if the vapor pressure due to water at 25°C is 24 mmHg?

    (A) 24 mmHg
    (B) 240 mmHg
    (C) 736 mmHg
    (D) 760 mmHg
    (E) 784 mmHg

59. Which of the following is a possible source of error in the results of this experiment?

    I. Failure to correct for humidity
    II. The presence of unreacted magnesium
    III. Failure to convert the temperature of the gas to kelvins

    (A) I only
    (B) II only
    (C) III only
    (D) I and II only
    (E) II and III only

GO ON TO THE NEXT PAGE

60. Which of the following compounds has the same percent composition by mass as styrene, C_8H_8?

   (A) Acetylene, C_2H_2

   (B) Benzene, C_6H_6

   (C) Cyclobutadiene, C_4H_4

   (D) α-ethyl naphthalene, $C_{12}H_{12}$

   (E) All of these

61. Balanced chemical equations imply which of the following?

   I.   Numbers of molecules are conserved in chemical change.

   II. Numbers of atoms are conserved in chemical change.

   III. Mass is conserved in chemical change.

   (A) I only

   (B) II only

   (C) I and III

   (D) II and III

   (E) I, II, and III

62. The balanced net ionic equation for the reaction of calcium chloride and sodium phosphate contains which of the following terms?

   (A) $Ca^{2+}_{(aq)}$

   (B) $PO^{3-}_{4(aq)}$

   (C) $2Ca_3(PO_4)_{2(s)}$

   (D) $6NaCl_{(aq)}$

   (E) $3Ca^{2+}_{(aq)}$

63. Assume equilibrium has been reached in the following reaction:
$A(g) + B(g) \Leftrightarrow C(g) + D(g)$
On an increase in the pressure, the system will

   (A) Shift to the products

   (B) Shift to the reactants

   (C) Not change because pressure never affects equilibrium positions

   (D) Not change as long as the temperature is constant

   (E) Not change because there are equal number of moles of gas in reactant and product

Use the following to answer questions 64–66:

Aqueous solutions of magnesium chloride and silver nitrate are mixed to form solid silver chloride and aqueous magnesium nitrate.

64. The balanced molecular equation contains which one of the following terms?

   (A) $AgCl_{(s)}$

   (B) $2AgCl_{(s)}$

   (C) $2Mg(NO_3)_2$

   (D) $MgNO_3$

   (E) $3AgCl_{(s)}$

65. The balanced complete ionic equation contains which of the following terms?

   (A) $2Mg^+_{(aq)}$

   (B) $Cl^-_{(aq)}$

   (C) $2Ag^+_{(aq)}$

   (D) $NO^-_{3(aq)}$

   (E) $3NO^-_{3(aq)}$

66. The balanced net ionic equation contains which of the following terms?

   (A) $Ag^+_{(aq)}$

   (B) $Mg^{2+}_{(aq)}$

   (C) $NO^-_{3(aq)}$

   (D) $2NO^-_{3(aq)}$

   (E) $3AgCl_{(s)}$

67. Sodium forms an oxide containing one oxygen atom for every two atoms of sodium. What is the coefficient of sodium in the balanced equation for the reaction of sodium with oxygen to form this oxide?

   (A) 0

   (B) 1

   (C) 2

   (D) 3

   (E) 4

68. How many grams of H_2O will be formed when 16.0 g H_2 is mixed with 16.0 g O_2 and allowed to react to form water?

   (A) 9.0 g

   (B) 18.0 g

   (C) 32.0 g

   (D) 36.0 g

   (E) 72.0 g

GO ON TO THE NEXT PAGE

69. Consider the following reaction:
$$2X + Y \rightarrow 3Z$$
3.0 mol X and 2.0 mol Y react to form 4.0 mol Z. What is the percent yield of this reaction?

(A) 50%
(B) 67%
(C) 75%
(D) 89%
(E) 100%

70. When potassium chloride and lead (II) nitrate react in an aqueous solution, which of the following terms will be present in the balanced molecular equation?

(A) $PbCl_{(s)}$
(B) $Pb_2Cl_{(s)}$
(C) $KNO_{3(aq)}$
(D) $2KNO_{3(aq)}$
(E) $2KCl_{2(s)}$

S T O P

IF YOU FINISH BEFORE TIME IS CALLED, YOU MAY CHECK YOUR WORK ON THIS TEST ONLY.
DO NOT TURN TO ANY OTHER TEST IN THIS BOOK.

SAT II Chemistry
Practice Test II
Explanations

Answers to SAT II Chemistry Practice Test II

Question Number	Answer	Right	Wrong	Question Number	Answer	Right	Wrong
Part A				**Part C**			
1.	D			26.	A		
2.	C			27.	D		
3.	C			28.	D		
4.	D			29.	D		
5.	D			30.	C		
6.	C			31.	C		
7.	B			32.	C		
8.	D			33.	C		
9.	D			34.	B		
10.	E			35.	B		
11.	B			36.	D		
12.	E			37.	C		
13.	E			38.	D		
14.	C			39.	D		
15.	D			40.	B		
16.	C			41.	E		
17.	B			42.	E		
18.	C			43.	D		
19.	D			44.	E		
20.	C			45.	B		
21.	E			46.	E		
22.	B			47.	D		
23.	A			48.	C		
24.	B			49.	B		
25.	D			50.	D		
Part B				51.	C		
101.	T T CE			52.	B		
102.	T T CE			53.	D		
103.	F T			54.	C		
104.	T T			55.	B		
105.	T T			56.	A		
106.	T T CE			57.	B		
107.	F F			58.	C		
108.	T T CE			59.	B		
109.	T T			60.	E		
110.	T F			61.	D		
111.	T T			62.	E		
112.	F T			63.	E		
113.	T T			64.	B		
114.	T T			65.	C		
115.	T F			66.	A		
				67.	E		
				68.	B		
				69.	D		
				70.	D		

Calculating Your Score

Your raw score for SAT II Chemistry test is based on the number of questions you answer correctly and incorrectly. Once you have determined your raw score, use the conversion table on page 14 of this book to calculate your scaled score.

To Calculate Your Raw Score

1. Count the number of questions you answered correctly: _____ (A)
2. Count the number of questions you answered incorrectly, and multiply that number by $1/4$: _____ (B) × $1/4$ = _____ (C)
3. Subtract the value in (C) from value in (A): _____ (D)
4. Round the number in (D) to the nearest whole number. This is your raw score: _____ (E)

Part A

The first 25 questions on this exam are classification set questions. These should be some of the easier points to obtain on the exam. You need to read only one set of answer choices to complete several questions. Approach these questions by reading all of the choices, read each statement that follows, answer, and then match your answer with the best answer choice.

1. **D** Periodic trends—atomic size
All of the elements listed are in period 4. As you move left to right across a period, atomic size decreases as effective nuclear charge increases. Kr, choice **D**, is the element that lies farthest to the right on the table, so it is the smallest.

2. **C** Periodic trends
Electronegativity is the ability of an atom to attract a shared pair of electrons when a chemical bond is formed. Nonmetals attract electrons. Choice **C**, Br, and choice **D**, Kr, are the only nonmetals listed. Krypton is a noble gas and has a low attraction for electrons. Bromine, choice **C**, needs one more electron to minimize electron repulsion and have a filled valence shell, so it has the highest electronegativity.

3. **C** Periodic trends
Electron affinity is the attraction that an atom has for electrons, and for the same reasons listed in question 2, bromine is the answer.

4.   D   Periodic trends

The first ionization energy is the energy needed to remove the first electron from an atom. Metals tend to lose electrons readily, so traditionally they have lower first ionization energies than do nonmetals. The choice is again narrowed down to Br, choice **C**, and Kr, choice **D**. Krypton wins this time. It will take great amounts of energy to remove an electron from a completely filled energy level, and so the answer is **D**.

5.   A   Periodic trends

The most reactive metal family in the periodic table is group 1A. The most reactive nonmetal family is group 7A. Knowing these two facts, you can narrow the choice to **A** or **C**. Halogens are not known for their reactivity in water. However, choice **A**, potassium, is very reactive in water. All of group 1A metals are so reactive that they must be stored under oil.

6.   C   Bonding

Solid magnesium carbonate, $MgCO_3$, contains a polyatomic ion. This is a dead giveaway that it will bond ionically—the answer is choice **C**.

7.   B   Bonding

Ammonia gas, NH_3, is composed of two nonmetals. It contains covalent bonds. To figure out if the answer is **A** or **B**, you should draw the molecule. The one unshared pair of electrons on the nitrogen atom will make this substance polar.

8.   D   Bonding

Tungsten filament is just a fancy way of saying tungsten, which has the chemical symbol W. This metal is found in many lightbulbs and is composed of only one type of metal atom, so it is metallically bonded.

9.   D   Bonding

Metallic bonds are characterized by delocalized electrons. The delocalized electrons are what allow metals to be such good conductors.

10.   E   Atomic structure

Noble gases are often used for lighting. As the gases are heated, electrons are excited and move away from the ground state position into an excited state. As the electrons fall back into the ground state, energy is emitted, often in the form of light. Neon light has a reddish glow.

11.   B   Energy diagram

This is the energy diagram for water. Water freezes at 0°C and begins to boil at 100°C. The two plateaus represent these two phase change transitions. Line B would represent the freezing point. The line labeled A would represent ice at temperatures below 0°C.

12. E Energy diagram

The highest point of the graph would represent the vapor phase. This question is a bit tricky. Read closely: the question asks for only vapor present, so line E would be the appropriate choice.

13. E Energy diagram

The formula $q = mc_{steam} T$ is specific for steam. Water is in a vapor state (as steam) at line segment E on the graph. Along line D, both steam and liquid water are present.

14. D Energy diagram

As mentioned above, line D represents the phase change between liquid and vapor.

15. C Energy diagram

Average kinetic energy can be related to temperature change. According to this graph, the greatest temperature change occurs between ice, 0°C, and liquid water at the point of vaporization, 100°C. This segment of the curve has the greatest slope. No temperature change takes place at line segments B or D. Line A and E are not as long as line C.

16. E Solutions

A supersaturated solution is defined as one that is holding more solute than is theoretically possible. This type of solution is created by heating the solution and adding solute at a high temperature. Supersaturated solutions are usually unstable and often crystallize when disturbed.

17. B Solutions

A solution in which particles will settle on standing is known as a suspension. In a suspension, the particles may stay suspended for a period of time but will eventually settle to the bottom of the container.

18. C Solutions

Solutions that contain particles that stay suspended and have the ability to scatter light are known as colloids. The scattering of light is known as the Tyndall effect. Particles in a colloid usually range from 100 to 1000 nm in size.

19. D Solutions

A solution that holds the maximum amount of solvent that it can theoretically hold at a given temperature and pressure is called a saturated solution. In a solution, solute and solvent particles are in a state of dynamic equilibrium.

20. **C**   Chemical reactions

Write at least a sketch of the equation described to determine the type of reaction. There's no need to waste time balancing equations in this group of questions since you are just placing the reactions into categories.

$$C_8H_{18} + O_2 \rightarrow CO_2 + H_2O$$

This is a hydrocarbon combustion reaction. Octane is a hydrocarbon—it contains hydrogen and carbon only, and it combusts in the presence of enough oxygen, producing carbon dioxide and water.

21. **E**   Chemical reactions

Since a precipitate is formed when two aqueous solutions are mixed, this must be a double replacement reaction. This type of reaction might look something like the following:

$$AgNO_3 + NaCl \rightarrow NaNO_3 + AgCl_{(s)}$$

22. **B**   Chemical reactions

Write the sketch of the reaction:

$$Ag + O_2 \rightarrow Ag_2O$$

Tarnishing is the reaction of a substance with the oxygen in the air. Since silver is reacting with oxygen here, this must be a synthesis reaction.

23. **A**   Chemical reactions

Write the sketch of the reaction:

$$H_2O \rightarrow H_2 + O_2$$

The electric current passing through water serves to break water apart into its two diatomic elements, hydrogen and oxygen. A reaction in which one reactant produces two or more products is a decomposition reaction.

24. **B**   Chemical reactions

Write the sketch of a possible reaction:

$$Fe + O_2 \rightarrow Fe_2O_3$$

In rusting, iron would react with oxygen in the air to produce, among other compounds, Fe_2O_3. When two elements combine, a synthesis reaction has taken place.

25. **D**   Chemical reactions
Write the sketch of the reaction:

$$Na + H_2O \rightarrow NaOH + H_2$$

When one element reacts with one compound to produce a different element and a different compound, this is known as a single replacement reaction.

Part B

By now you are well versed in how these questions work. Remember that to be successful on this type of question, you should read each statement individually and decide whether it is true or false. Then if both statements are true, read the second statement again and see if it is the *reason* the first statement is true.

101. **T T CE**   Equilibrium
The first statement is true. In a closed container liquid particles will gain enough energy to overcome the intermolecular attractive forces that hold them and escape into the gaseous phase. Once the gas phase is filled with particles, these particles will collide and lose energy and drop back down. This is the premise behind a terrarium. Statement II is true. At a constant temperature the particles will escape and return at a constant rate—this is called a state of dynamic equilibrium. Since statement II is the reason for statement I, fill in the **CE** oval.

102. **T T CE**   Phase change
Statement I is true. At higher altitudes, the boiling point of water will be lower than it is at sea level pressure. Statement II is also true. As altitude increases, the atmospheric pressure drops. Boiling point is the point at which the vapor pressure of the liquid is equal to the atmospheric pressure, so statement II is the explanation for statement I. Fill in the **CE** oval.

103. **F T**   Kinetic molecular theory
Statement I is false. During a phase change, the temperature of a substance remains constant even with added energy. The energy being added is all used to break intermolecular forces so that particles can move between phases, so the temperature does not change. Statement II is true. Particles will have a higher average kinetic energy with an increase in temperature. Since statement I is false, you should not fill in the **CE** oval.

104. **T T**   Gas laws
Statement I is true. Gas particles are mostly empty space and are therefore easily compressible. Liquid particles are very close together; pressure has no effect on a liquid. Statement II is true. Gases do expand to fill their container. With two true statements you must decide if

statement II is a reason for statement I. In this case, you just have two separate facts about gases. You should not fill in the **CE** oval.

105. **T T**   Formula writing

Statement I is true. Magnesium has a charge of +2 and Cl has a charge of –1, so this formula is correct as written. Statement II is also true. Chlorine is one of the seven diatomic molecules on the periodic table. But the fact that chlorine is diatomic has nothing to do with the formula for magnesium chloride. You would not fill in the **CE** oval.

106. **T T CE**   Periodic trends

Statement I is true: larger molecules usually have a higher boiling point. Statement II is also true: the change from liquid to gas requires the breaking of attractive intermolecular forces. Larger molecules have more electrons that can polarize; thus they have a greater chance for more attractive forces. Statement II does a good job of explaining the observable trend of the periodic table, so fill in the **CE** oval.

107. **F T**   Thermochemistry

Statement I is false. Spontaneity is a measure of free energy, while the state of being exothermic is a measure of enthalpy. Many reactions are exothermic but not all. Remember that the spontaneity of a reaction depends on enthalpy *and* entropy. Statement II is true. Energy is released during the course of an exothermic reaction.

108. **T T CE**   Kinetics

Statement I is true: temperature does affect the rate of a reaction. When temperature is increased, reactions generally will occur more quickly, and when the temperature is decreased, the reactions will occur more slowly. This is why we store food in a refrigerator. Statement II is true. When the temperature is increased, particles will collide more often and with more force; therefore more particles will have the necessary energy to overcome the energy of activation. This statement does give an explanation for statement I, so fill in the **CE** oval.

109. **T T**   Equilibrium

Statement I is true. The equilibrium constant will change with temperature. If the reaction is endothermic, the value of K will increase with an increase in temperature. If the reaction is exothermic, the value of K will decrease with an increase in temperature. Statement II is true. When temperature is increased, there will be more effective collisions between reacting particles. However, this does not explain the change in the value of K. Do not fill in the **CE** oval.

110. **T F**   Equilibrium

Statement I is true. The larger the K value, the more products are present at equilibrium compared to the amount of reactants. Statement II is false. The value of K at equilibrium is often a small number, a number less than 1.

111. **T T**   Phase change

Statement I is true: as molecules come close together and position themselves in fixed, ordered positions, they will lose energy, and this represents an exothermic reaction. Statement II is also true. When two or more elements come together and form a bond, they release energy. The reason bonds form is to minimize energy and become more stable. Statement II does not explain the first statement, however, so you would not fill in the **CE** oval.

112. **F T**   Solution formation

Statement I is false. Ionic compounds may dissolve in any polar or ionic substance, according to the "like dissolves like" rule. Statement II is true. When an ionic solid dissolves in water, this is called a hydration reaction. Water molecules actually surround the ions of the ionic compound, pull them apart, and hold them in place within the solution.

113. **T T**   Bonding

Statement I is true. Each oxygen contributes 6 electrons ($2(6e^-) = 12 e^-$ total). If only a single bond were formed, each oxygen wouldn't be able to have a stable octet, but with the creation of a double bond, the octet rule is fulfilled. Statement II is true. Oxygen is a diatomic molecule. However, the fact that it is diatomic does not explain *why* it is diatomic.

114. **T T**   Bonding

Statement I is true. The electronic geometry of a molecule refers to the number of areas of electrons around its central atom. Nitrogen does have four areas of electrons in the ammonia molecule; therefore it is tetrahedral with respect to electrons. Statement II is true. With eight electrons around nitrogen, ammonia does obey the octet rule. However, the fact that it obeys the octet rule is not the reason for its geometry. Do not fill in the **CE** oval.

115. **T F**   Bonding

Statement I is true. In carbon dioxide, carbon is the central atom, and the two oxygen atoms on either side are each connected to the oxygen with a double bond. There are no unshared pairs of electrons left on carbon after the two double bonds are created, so oxygen atoms spread as far apart as possible, which gives rise to linear shape. Statement II is false. Carbon dioxide does have three atoms, and it does have a bond angle of 180°. However, there are many other three-atom molecules that have unshared pairs on the central atom that would have different bond angles. One example of this is water, H_2O. It has a bent shape and a bond angle of 104.5°.

Part C

The remaining questions on the test are the traditional multiple choice that you know and love. Eliminate any choices that you can initially, then see which answer choice is most similar to your answer.

26. A Ionic and covalent compounds

I is true. Covalent compounds are usually gases, liquids, or solids that have low melting points. By contrast, ionic compounds are solid crystals with very high melting points. II is false: "like dissolves like," so only *polar* covalent compounds dissolve in polar solvents. Nonpolar covalent compounds only dissolve in nonpolar solvents. III is true since covalent compounds that dissolve release neutral molecules into solution rather than ions. Electrical conductivity requires that charged ions are released on melting to form a liquid or dissolved to form a solution. IV is false since it is in conflict with III, and answer choice **A** contains the correct statements.

27. D Gas density

The density of a gas is measured in g/L. To answer this question, you would first find the mass for nitrogen, N_2, from the periodic table: $2 \times 14.00 \text{ g/mol} = 28.00 \text{ g/mol}$ for diatomic nitrogen. At STP, molar volume for a gas is 22.4 L/mol. Density = $28/22.4 = 1.25$ g/L. The only possible choices would be choice **D** or **E**. 28 is not $1\frac{1}{2}$ times bigger than 22, so choice **E** must be eliminated since it is even bigger than 1.5; this leaves answer choice **D**.

28. D Conjugate acid/base pairs

HSO_4^- can act as an acid and donate a proton to form SO_4^{2-}, so you're looking for the equation that has the sulfate ion as a product, and this is answer **D**. Just to clarify, HSO_4^- can also act as a base in water solution by accepting a proton to become H_2SO_4. Chemical species that do this are called amphiprotic or amphoteric species.

29. D Nuclear chemistry

In a transmutation reaction, the superscripts on each side should be equal, as should the subscripts.

$$^{235}_{92}U + ^{1}_{0}n \rightarrow 3^{1}_{0}n + ^{139}_{56}Ba + \underline{\qquad\qquad}$$

The total for the superscripts on the reactant side is 236. The total on the product side is 142. (This is a bit tricky—the coefficient in front of the neutron multiplies through, so the neutron contributes 3.) This means that the mass number of the missing element is $236 - 142 = 94$. The total for the subscripts on the reactant side is 92, while on the product side the total is 56. Therefore, the atomic number will be $92 - 56 = 36$. This is the atomic number for krypton, so choice **D** is correct.

30. D   Percent composition

This question looks scary, but the math is not very hard. The mass of the sample is 35 + 5 + 60 = 100 g, a nice, round number. If it's a 200 g sample, it will contain twice as much oxygen, or 2(60.0 g) = 120 g.

31. C   Electron configuration

The ground state electron configuration represents the electrons at minimum energy levels. First write the electron configuration for cobalt. The cobalt atom has 27 electrons, and its electron configuration is $1s^2 2s^2 2p^6 3s^2 3p^6 4s^2 3d^7$. Statement I is true. The $3d$ sublevel is not filled: it could hold a maximum of 10 electrons, but it holds only 7. Statement II is also true. The d sublevel has five orbitals. Hund's rule says that each electron will occupy an orbital and then pairing will occur when necessary. Two of the five orbitals will have paired electrons and three orbitals will have a single electron. Statement III must be false since it opposes statement II. The answer choice that contains I and II is **C**.

32. C   Le Chatelier's principle

Oxygen is a reactant in this reaction, so if more oxygen is added, the reaction will shift toward the products to relieve the stress put on the system. This means that choice **A**, ammonia, which is also a reactant in the reaction, would decrease and not increase. The only answer choice that indicates a shift toward products is choice **C**.

33. C   Gas laws

The Kelvin temperature is directly related to the number of moles of gas present. If the volume and pressure are the same for the two gas samples but the temperature is four times greater in the first flask, then the second flask must have four times as many molecules as the first to maintain the same pressure. The ratio will be 1:4 (1 molecule in flask 1 to every 4 molecules in flask 2).

34. B   Atomic structure

The mass number of silicon is 29; the mass number represents the number of protons plus the number of neutrons. The atomic number for silicon is 14. (You can look this up in the periodic table.) The atomic number of an element is equal to its number of protons. To obtain the number of neutrons, you would subtract the atomic number from the mass number: 29 − 14 = 15.

35. B   Equilibrium constant

Since the value given to K exceeds a billion, the reaction lies very significantly on the side of the product that is formed once equilibrium is achieved. Recall that the value of K is equal to the following ratio: [product]/[reactant].

36. **D**   Equilibrium constant

K is independent of either reactant or product concentration alone. It is dependent on temperature, and since the temperature is unchanged in this question, the equilibrium constant, *K*, will remain unchanged.

37. **C**   Gas density

To answer this question, you'll need to calculate the masses of the gases given as choices and compare them to the mass of argon. The mass of argon is 40.0 g/mol, and F_2 = 38 g/mol, H_2S = 34 g/mol, NH_3 = 17 g/mol, and CO_2 = 44 g/mol. Carbon dioxide, IV, is the only gas that has a greater mass than argon; therefore it is the only gas with a greater density at STP. Choice **C** is the answer.

38. **D**   Atomic structure

The key to solving this problem is to figure out what the answer is before looking at the choices. To have a +2 charge, the ion must have two more protons than electrons. The other criterion is that the mass equal 40, and the mass number is equal to the number of protons plus the number of neutrons. There is only one answer choice with two more protons than electrons: it's choice **D**, so there's no need to calculate the mass.

39. **D**   Acid-base

An oxyacid is a polyatomic ion containing oxygen. Oxygen is very electronegative. The more oxygens found in the acid, the harder they will pull the electrons and the easier it will be for the hydrogen to be extracted from the acid. Therefore, choice **D** is the correct answer. The concentration of hydrogen ions in solution determines the strength of the acid.

40. **B**   Bonding

Nitrogen has one unshared pair of electrons after it has bonded with three hydrogen atoms, as it has in ammonia.

41. **E**   Salt hydrolysis

Solutions with a high pH are basic, so this question asks which solution would be most basic. That means that the substance you're looking for should be either a strong base or a salt that was formed from the reaction of a strong base with a weak acid. Choices **A**, **B**, and **D** can be quickly eliminated. Remember that strong bases are oxides and hydroxides of 1A and 2A metals. Since a strong base is not present among the answers, we must look for the salt of a 1A or 2A metal. The sodium salt of a weak acid is our best choice, and the answer is **E**.

42. **E**   Acid/base strength

Keep in mind that alcohols are not bases in spite of their OH^- group. Ammonia is the classic weak base, while the other answers are oxides and hydroxides of 1A and 2A metals, which form strong bases in aqueous solution.

43. D   Ionization energy
Statement I lists elements from the same period, avoiding the p^4 anomaly, so it indeed represents a correct general trend: increasing Z_{eff} corresponds with increasing ionization energy. Statement II is backward since IE decreases as you move down a family, and III is backward for the same reason. The ions listed in statement IV all have helium's electron configuration, so their IE depends solely on the Z_{eff}; the order is correct since the Z_{eff}'s increase in the series.

44. E   Predicting oxidation state
Halogens are most likely to form –1 oxidation states. Number your periodic table as soon as you open your test so that the 1A column is +1 and the 2A column is +2 until you reach the carbon family, which is ±4. Then halogens, 7A, are –1, the oxygen family is –2, and the nitrogen family is –3. This will make formula writing and oxidation state questions much easier since these numbers remind you of the most probable oxidation state for that family of elements.

45. B   Valence bond theory/hybridization
When a molecule has bond angles of 120°, it is trigonal planar. That means it has three sites of electron density: it requires one s and two p orbitals, so it is sp^2 hybridized.

46. E   Acid/base strength
The strength of the acid formed when each of these hydrogen halides is dissolved in water is dependent on the size of the molecule and the strength of the bond in the molecule. For example, the small size of F contributes to the strength of the bond that forms between it and H. F is so strongly attracted to H that the H cannot be easily removed by hydration, so HF remains primarily undissociated in aqueous solutions and is classified as a weak acid.

47. D   Mole concept
You must know that the molecular formula of ammonia is NH_3, so you can easily calculate its molar mass: round the molar mass of N to 14 and the mass of H to 1, and the molar mass of ammonia is 17. Also estimate 51.1 as 51, and your calculation is 51 g/17 g/mole = 3 moles. Then 3 moles (6.02×10^{23}) = roughly 18×10^{23}, which is 1.8×10^{24} molecules. The answer is **D**.

48. C   Equilibrium constant
If the value of K is small, meaning less than 1, then the concentration of reactants is greater at equilibrium; thus the equilibrium lies to the left. K has nothing to do with the time that a reaction takes to reach equilibrium.

49. B   Mole concept
This molecule has 14 atoms, but just slog your way through it: $(NH_4)_2CO_3$. The molar mass is $2(14) + 8(1) + 12 + 3(16) = 28 + 8 + 12 + 48 = 48 + 48 =$ slightly more than 96 g/mol.

Test II Explanations

50. **D**   Gas laws

You must combine all of your gas law knowledge here. The combination of P, V, and T into one formula results in the combined gas law.

$$\frac{P_1 V_1}{T_1} = \frac{P_2 V_2}{T_2}$$

To solve the formula quickly, plug in easy numbers. Let all of the first set be values of 1. For the second set, manipulate the values as the problem tells you to:

$$\frac{(1)(1)}{(1)} = \frac{(P_2)(2)}{(3)}$$

So you get $1 = \frac{2P_2}{3}$, and to solve for P_2, multiply both sides of the equation by $\frac{3}{2}$; your answer is $\frac{3}{2}$.

51. **C**   Mole concept

The formula for sodium hydroxide is NaOH, so its molar mass is $23 + 16 + 1 = 40$ g/mol, and 7 moles $\times$ 40 g/mol = 280 g.

52. **B**   Percent composition

Hydrofluoric acid is HF. Hydrogen weighs 1 and fluorine is 19, so the percent hydrogen is 1/molar mass of HF, or $(1/20) \times 100\%$, which is 5%.

53. **D**   Molecular chemical equations

This one is a bit tricky. If you begin with the rather scary-looking C_4H_{10}, then you soon find out that you end up with an odd number of oxygen molecules. That is your signal to double the C_4H_{10} and start again. The balanced equation is $2C_4H_{10(g)} + 13O_{2(g)} \rightarrow 8CO_{2(g)} + 10H_2O_{(g)}$, so the coefficient for oxygen is 13.

54. **C**   Thermochemistry

When a solution becomes cold over the course of a reaction, the reaction is endothermic, so statement I is true. Statement II is also true: energy is a reactant in an endothermic reaction, so increasing the temperature would result in more products. Statement III is false. As you know, $\Delta S°$ is entropy. The two driving forces of a chemical reaction are enthalpy and entropy. Exothermic reactions are favored—since this reaction is endothermic, entropy must be the driving force, and thus disorder must be increasing. Increasing entropy would have a positive value. The answer is choice **C**.

55. **B**   Acid/base dissociation

HCl, HBr, HI, HNO_3, H_2SO_4, and $HClO_4$ are the six strong acids. The strong bases are oxides and hydroxides of 1A and 2A metals. HNO_3 is a strong acid, not a weak one, so it is paired incorrectly.

56. A Laboratory/reactions
The reaction is between magnesium ribbon and hydrochloric acid. This single replacement reaction is written $Mg + 2HCl \rightarrow MgCl_2 + H_2$. Choice **A**, hydrogen, has to be the answer.

57. B Laboratory
Figure 3 shows the adjustment of the tube so that the gas level matches the water level. The purpose of this is to equalize the pressure. Air pressure and water pressure are not the same. Boyle's law is in action in this experiment. The gas that is trapped in the tube will change volume as the tube is moved in and out of the water.

58. C Laboratory/gas laws
Recall Dalton's law of partial pressure. The total pressure is given in the paragraph above the diagram, so you'll need to look back to that paragraph—the total pressure is given as 760 mmHg. The pressure of the water vapor at 25°C is given as 24 mmHg. To find the pressure of the hydrogen gas, subtract: $P_{total} = P_{H_2} + P_{H_2O} = 760 - 24 = 736$ mmHg.

59. B Laboratory
Statements I and III will result in incorrect final answers for this laboratory exercise, but they are not true sources of error from the lab. However, if there were leftover magnesium ribbon that did not react, this would cause the amount of hydrogen produced to be too low, so choice **B** is the best answer.

60. E Empirical formula
Styrene, molecular formula C_8H_8, has an empirical formula of CH; thus any other compound having that same ratio of C:H will have the same percent composition by mass as styrene. Each of the formulas listed has the same ratio of 1:1. Therefore choice **E** is the best answer.

61. D Law of conservation of mass
Both the number of atoms, II, and the total mass, III, are conserved in a chemical change. This is exactly why we balance chemical equations, and this is what allows us to perform stoichiometric calculations. Statement I is false. The number of molecules is not necessarily conserved in a chemical reaction.

62. E Net ionic equations
You must know your solubility rules to get the correct answer to this problem. Calcium chloride and sodium phosphate are both soluble. This is a double replacement reaction, and sodium chloride is soluble, but calcium phosphate is not. The balanced molecular equation is

$$3CaCl_2 + 2Na_3PO_4 \rightarrow 6NaCl + Ca_3(PO_4)_2$$

The balanced net ionic equation is

$$3Ca^{2+}_{(aq)} + 2PO_4{}^{3-}_{(aq)} \rightarrow Ca_3(PO_4)_{2(s)}.$$

63. **E**   Equilibrium

When the pressure of the system is increased, the volume is decreased, and equilibrium tends to shift in the direction that produces the fewer moles. However, in this case there are two moles of gaseous reactant and two moles of gaseous product. Therefore, no shift will occur, and the answer is choice **E**.

64. **B**   Molecular chemical equations

The balanced molecular equation is

$$MgCl_2 + 2AgNO_3 \rightarrow 2AgCl_{(s)} + Mg(NO_3)_2$$

Read the answer choices carefully since they all look similar. Only one answer choice has the correct coefficient and formula, and that is choice **B**.

65. **C**   Net ionic equations

The balanced complete ionic equation is

$$Mg^{2+}_{(aq)} + 2Cl^-_{(aq)} + 2Ag^+_{(aq)} + 2NO_3{}^-_{(aq)} \rightarrow Mg^{2+}_{(aq)} + 2NO_3{}^-_{(aq)} + 2AgCl_{(s)}.$$

The word *complete* is what makes this problem tricky. You must break apart the soluble reactants and realize that silver chloride is a precipitate, while magnesium nitrate is a soluble compound. All chlorides are soluble except silver, mercury, and lead.

66. **A**   Net ionic equations

The net ionic equation simply focuses on the substances that are actually undergoing reaction:

$$Cl^-_{(aq)} + Ag^+_{(aq)} \rightarrow AgCl_{(s)}$$

The trick here is that everything left in the net ionic equation had a coefficient of 2. Always reduce to lowest terms before stating the answer.

67. **E**   Molecular chemical equations

What makes this question difficult is that you are not given any chemical formulas. You're given a hint as to the empirical formula of sodium oxide since you're told that the O:Na ratio is 1:2. The balanced equation is $4Na + O_2 \rightarrow 2Na_2O$, so the coefficient for sodium is 4.

68. **B**   Limiting reactant

You know this is a limiting reagent problem since you were given two starting amounts, so write a balanced equation and determine the moles of each substance, hydrogen and oxygen.

Start by looking at hydrogen: we have 8 moles. Since H:O is 2:1, we need 4 moles of oxygen to use up all of our hydrogen. We do not have 4 moles of oxygen, we only have $\frac{1}{2}$ of a mole, so oxygen is clearly the limiting reagent here. If we use the $\frac{1}{2}$ mole of oxygen, we will need twice as much hydrogen, or 1.0 mole. This produces 1.0 mole of water as a product. 1 mole = a molar mass in grams = 18 g.

Molar mass	2	32	18
Balanced equation	$2H_2 +$	$O_2 \rightarrow$	$2H_2O$
Number of moles	1.0 moles used, 7 moles excess! 8 moles available	0.5 mole	1.0 mole produced
Amount	16 g	16 g	18 g

69. **D**   Percent yield and limiting reactant

Percent yield is calculated by this formula:

$$\frac{\text{actual yield}}{\text{theoretical yield}} \times 100\% = \text{percent yield}$$

The amount you calculate using stoichiometry constitutes the theoretical yield of the reaction. The moles of product should *not* go into the table, only the numbers of reactant moles. We'd need 1.5 moles of Y, and we have 2.0 moles, so X is the limiting reactant. With 1.5 moles of Y, the theoretical yield of Z is 4.5 moles.

Molar mass			
Balanced equation	$2X +$	$Y \rightarrow$	$3Z$
Mole:mole	2	1	3
Number of moles	3 moles used	1.5 moles used 2 moles	4.5 moles theoretically produced

Now we can calculate the percent yield. We were told that only 4 moles of Z was produced, so the % yield = $(4/4.5) \times 100\%$ = about 90%.

70. **D**   Predicting products

To solve this problem, you must first translate words into chemical formulas, then recognize the reaction as a double displacement reaction and predict the products. The balanced molecular equation is

$$2KCl + Pb(NO_3)_2 \rightarrow Pb_2Cl_{(s)} + 2KNO_{3(aq)}$$

The answer is choice **D**.

SAT II Chemistry Practice Test III

SAT II CHEMISTRY PRACTICE TEST III ANSWER SHEET

1	Ⓐ Ⓑ Ⓒ Ⓓ Ⓔ	15	Ⓐ Ⓑ Ⓒ Ⓓ Ⓔ	29	Ⓐ Ⓑ Ⓒ Ⓓ Ⓔ	43	Ⓐ Ⓑ Ⓒ Ⓓ Ⓔ	57	Ⓐ Ⓑ Ⓒ Ⓓ Ⓔ
2	Ⓐ Ⓑ Ⓒ Ⓓ Ⓔ	16	Ⓐ Ⓑ Ⓒ Ⓓ Ⓔ	30	Ⓐ Ⓑ Ⓒ Ⓓ Ⓔ	44	Ⓐ Ⓑ Ⓒ Ⓓ Ⓔ	58	Ⓐ Ⓑ Ⓒ Ⓓ Ⓔ
3	Ⓐ Ⓑ Ⓒ Ⓓ Ⓔ	17	Ⓐ Ⓑ Ⓒ Ⓓ Ⓔ	31	Ⓐ Ⓑ Ⓒ Ⓓ Ⓔ	45	Ⓐ Ⓑ Ⓒ Ⓓ Ⓔ	59	Ⓐ Ⓑ Ⓒ Ⓓ Ⓔ
4	Ⓐ Ⓑ Ⓒ Ⓓ Ⓔ	18	Ⓐ Ⓑ Ⓒ Ⓓ Ⓔ	32	Ⓐ Ⓑ Ⓒ Ⓓ Ⓔ	46	Ⓐ Ⓑ Ⓒ Ⓓ Ⓔ	60	Ⓐ Ⓑ Ⓒ Ⓓ Ⓔ
5	Ⓐ Ⓑ Ⓒ Ⓓ Ⓔ	19	Ⓐ Ⓑ Ⓒ Ⓓ Ⓔ	33	Ⓐ Ⓑ Ⓒ Ⓓ Ⓔ	47	Ⓐ Ⓑ Ⓒ Ⓓ Ⓔ	61	Ⓐ Ⓑ Ⓒ Ⓓ Ⓔ
6	Ⓐ Ⓑ Ⓒ Ⓓ Ⓔ	20	Ⓐ Ⓑ Ⓒ Ⓓ Ⓔ	34	Ⓐ Ⓑ Ⓒ Ⓓ Ⓔ	48	Ⓐ Ⓑ Ⓒ Ⓓ Ⓔ	62	Ⓐ Ⓑ Ⓒ Ⓓ Ⓔ
7	Ⓐ Ⓑ Ⓒ Ⓓ Ⓔ	21	Ⓐ Ⓑ Ⓒ Ⓓ Ⓔ	35	Ⓐ Ⓑ Ⓒ Ⓓ Ⓔ	49	Ⓐ Ⓑ Ⓒ Ⓓ Ⓔ	63	Ⓐ Ⓑ Ⓒ Ⓓ Ⓔ
8	Ⓐ Ⓑ Ⓒ Ⓓ Ⓔ	22	Ⓐ Ⓑ Ⓒ Ⓓ Ⓔ	36	Ⓐ Ⓑ Ⓒ Ⓓ Ⓔ	50	Ⓐ Ⓑ Ⓒ Ⓓ Ⓔ	64	Ⓐ Ⓑ Ⓒ Ⓓ Ⓔ
9	Ⓐ Ⓑ Ⓒ Ⓓ Ⓔ	23	Ⓐ Ⓑ Ⓒ Ⓓ Ⓔ	37	Ⓐ Ⓑ Ⓒ Ⓓ Ⓔ	51	Ⓐ Ⓑ Ⓒ Ⓓ Ⓔ	65	Ⓐ Ⓑ Ⓒ Ⓓ Ⓔ
10	Ⓐ Ⓑ Ⓒ Ⓓ Ⓔ	24	Ⓐ Ⓑ Ⓒ Ⓓ Ⓔ	38	Ⓐ Ⓑ Ⓒ Ⓓ Ⓔ	52	Ⓐ Ⓑ Ⓒ Ⓓ Ⓔ	66	Ⓐ Ⓑ Ⓒ Ⓓ Ⓔ
11	Ⓐ Ⓑ Ⓒ Ⓓ Ⓔ	25	Ⓐ Ⓑ Ⓒ Ⓓ Ⓔ	39	Ⓐ Ⓑ Ⓒ Ⓓ Ⓔ	53	Ⓐ Ⓑ Ⓒ Ⓓ Ⓔ	67	Ⓐ Ⓑ Ⓒ Ⓓ Ⓔ
12	Ⓐ Ⓑ Ⓒ Ⓓ Ⓔ	26	Ⓐ Ⓑ Ⓒ Ⓓ Ⓔ	40	Ⓐ Ⓑ Ⓒ Ⓓ Ⓔ	54	Ⓐ Ⓑ Ⓒ Ⓓ Ⓔ	68	Ⓐ Ⓑ Ⓒ Ⓓ Ⓔ
13	Ⓐ Ⓑ Ⓒ Ⓓ Ⓔ	27	Ⓐ Ⓑ Ⓒ Ⓓ Ⓔ	41	Ⓐ Ⓑ Ⓒ Ⓓ Ⓔ	55	Ⓐ Ⓑ Ⓒ Ⓓ Ⓔ	69	Ⓐ Ⓑ Ⓒ Ⓓ Ⓔ
14	Ⓐ Ⓑ Ⓒ Ⓓ Ⓔ	28	Ⓐ Ⓑ Ⓒ Ⓓ Ⓔ	42	Ⓐ Ⓑ Ⓒ Ⓓ Ⓔ	56	Ⓐ Ⓑ Ⓒ Ⓓ Ⓔ	70	Ⓐ Ⓑ Ⓒ Ⓓ Ⓔ

CHEMISTRY

	I	II	CE
101	Ⓣ Ⓕ	Ⓣ Ⓕ	Ⓒⓔ
102	Ⓣ Ⓕ	Ⓣ Ⓕ	Ⓒⓔ
103	Ⓣ Ⓕ	Ⓣ Ⓕ	Ⓒⓔ
104	Ⓣ Ⓕ	Ⓣ Ⓕ	Ⓒⓔ
105	Ⓣ Ⓕ	Ⓣ Ⓕ	Ⓒⓔ
106	Ⓣ Ⓕ	Ⓣ Ⓕ	Ⓒⓔ
107	Ⓣ Ⓕ	Ⓣ Ⓕ	Ⓒⓔ
108	Ⓣ Ⓕ	Ⓣ Ⓕ	Ⓒⓔ
109	Ⓣ Ⓕ	Ⓣ Ⓕ	Ⓒⓔ
110	Ⓣ Ⓕ	Ⓣ Ⓕ	Ⓒⓔ
111	Ⓣ Ⓕ	Ⓣ Ⓕ	Ⓒⓔ
112	Ⓣ Ⓕ	Ⓣ Ⓕ	Ⓒⓔ
113	Ⓣ Ⓕ	Ⓣ Ⓕ	Ⓒⓔ
114	Ⓣ Ⓕ	Ⓣ Ⓕ	Ⓒⓔ
115	Ⓣ Ⓕ	Ⓣ Ⓕ	Ⓒⓔ

THE PERIODIC TABLE OF ELEMENTS

Legend

OXIDATION STATES (MOST STABLE STATE IN BOLD)
ELECTRONEGATIVITY
ELECTRON AFFINITY (kJ/mol)
FIRST IONIZATION POTENTIAL (eV)
ATOMIC RADIUS (Å)

ATOMIC NUMBER
ATOMIC SYMBOL
ATOMIC MASS
NAME
ELECTRON SHELL CONFIGURATION

Example:
1, 3   79
EN 2.54
EA 222.737
FIP 9.23   **Au**
AR 1.44   196.96654
Gold
[Xe] 4f^{14}5d^{10}6s^1

METALS
METALLOIDS
NONMETALS

LANTHANIDE SERIES
ACTINIDE SERIES

HYDROGEN & ALKALI METALS 1 IA
ALKALINE-EARTH METALS 2 IIA
3 IIIB, 4 IVB, 5 VB, 6 VIB, 7 VIIB, 8 VIII, 9 VIII, 10 VIII, 11 IB, 12 IIB
13 IIIA, 14 IVA, 15 VA, 16 VIA, 17 VIIA, 18 0
CHALCOGENS 16 VIB VIA
HALOGENS 17 VIIB VIIA
NOBLE GASES 18 0

(Periodic table of all elements, hydrogen through ununoctium, with lanthanide and actinide series.)

SAT II CHEMISTRY TEST

<u>Note:</u> For all questions involving solutions and/or chemical equations, assume that the system is in pure water unless otherwise stated.

Time: 1 hour

Part A

<u>Directions:</u>   Each set of lettered choices below refers to the numbered questions or statements immediately following it. Select the one lettered choice that best answers each question or best fits each statement, and then fill in the corresponding oval on the answer sheet. <u>A choice may be used once, more than once, or not at all in each set.</u>

<u>Questions 1–5</u>

    (A) Mg^+ and F^+
    (B) Li^+ and Ne
    (C) O^{2-} and O^-
    (D) N and P^{3-}
    (E) Ca^{2+} and Cl^-

1. These ions have the same number of electrons.

2. These ions differ in their number of electrons by one.

3. These ions differ in their number of electrons by three.

4. These ions differ in their number of electrons by eight.

5. These ions differ in their number of electrons by 11.

<u>Questions 6–9</u>

    (A) Zinc
    (B) Iron
    (C) Tin
    (D) Aluminum
    (E) Hydrogen

6. Is combined with copper to make brass.

7. Is combined with copper to make bronze.

8. Is used to galvanize metals, making them resistant to oxidation (rusting).

9. Is combined with carbon to make steel.

<u>Questions 10–13</u> refer to the following phase diagram. The arrows refer to phase changes as the temperature is changing while the pressure remains constant.

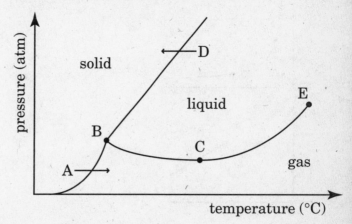

10. The set of temperature and pressure conditions where all three states of matter can exist in equilibrium.

11. The point beyond which pressure alone cannot liquefy the gas.

12. The process known as sublimation.

13. The set of temperature and pressure conditions that represents an equilibrium between the liquid and gas or vapor phase only.

GO ON TO THE NEXT PAGE

Questions 14–17

   (A) ΔH_f°

   (B) ΔH_{fus}

   (C) ΔH_{vap}

   (D) ΔH_{comb}

   (E) ΔG°

14. $C_5H_{12(g)} + 4O_{2(g)} \rightarrow 5CO_{2(g)} + 6H_2O_{(g)}$

15. $H_2O_{(l)} \rightarrow H_2O_{(g)}$

16. $H_{2(g)} + {}^1/_2\,O_{2(g)} \rightarrow H_2O_{(l)}$

17. Equals zero for an element in its standard state

Questions 18–21

   (A)

   (B)

   (C)

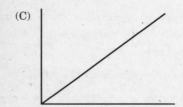

   (D)

   (E)

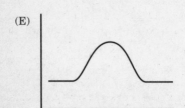

This type of graph would result if you graphed

18. Pressure versus volume for a sample of an ideal gas at constant temperature

19. Volume versus temperature for a sample of an ideal gas at constant pressure

20. Kinetic energy versus temperature for a given substance

21. Mass versus volume for a given substance

Questions 22–25 refer to the following laboratory procedures:

   (A) Distillation

   (B) Chromatography

   (C) Fractional crystallization

   (D) Filtration

   (E) Titration

22. Technique utilized to separate a precipitate from a filtrate using a porous substance

23. Technique utilized to separate a mixture of liquids based on differences in their boiling points

24. Technique utilized to determine the unknown concentration of a known acid

25. Technique utilized to separate a mixture of dissolved solids by evaporation according to individual solubilities

GO ON TO THE NEXT PAGE

SAT II CHEMISTRY TEST

PLEASE GO TO THE SPECIAL SECTION OF YOUR ANSWER SHEET LABELED CHEMISTRY AND ANSWER QUESTIONS 101–115 ACCORDING TO THE FOLLOWING DIRECTIONS:

Part B

Directions: Each question below consists of two statements, statement I in the left-hand column and statement II in the right-hand column. For each question, determine whether statement I is true or false and whether statement II is true or false and fill in the corresponding T or F ovals on your answer sheet. Fill in oval **CE** only if statement II is a correct explanation of statement I.

	Statement I	BECAUSE	Statement II
101.	The alkali metals have a large increase between their first and second ionization energies.	BECAUSE	It takes more energy to remove an electron from a principal energy level since it is closer to the nucleus.
102.	Metals have higher electronegativity values than nonmetals.	BECAUSE	Metals conduct an electric current.
103.	Water is a polar molecule.	BECAUSE	Water has polar covalent bonds.
104.	Water has a low vapor pressure.	BECAUSE	Water molecules form hydrogen bonds with other water molecules.
105.	C_2H_5OH is as an Arrhenius base.	BECAUSE	C_2H_5OH donates its OH^- in aqueous solutions.
106.	The entropy of steam is greater than the entropy of liquid water.	BECAUSE	At 100°C, the average kinetic energy of the steam molecules is greater than the average kinetic energy of the liquid water molecules.
107.	All atoms of the same element are identical.	BECAUSE	All atoms of the same element have the same number of protons.
108.	At the same temperature lighter gas molecules have a higher average velocity than heavier gas molecules.	BECAUSE	At the same temperature lighter gas molecules have a higher average kinetic energy than heavier gas molecules.
109.	CH_3Cl is a polar molecule.	BECAUSE	The Lewis diagram of polar molecules always has at least one lone pair of electrons.
110.	Ammonia has trigonal planar molecular geometry.	BECAUSE	Ammonia has a central nitrogen atom surrounded by three hydrogen atoms and one unshared electron pair.
111.	The two products formed by the reaction of $NaCl_{(aq)}$ and $AgNO_{3(aq)}$ can be separated by filtration.	BECAUSE	When sodium chloride and silver nitrate react, a precipitate is formed.
112.	Zinc metal is the reducing agent in the following reaction: $Cu^{2+}_{(aq)} + Zn_{(s)} \rightarrow Cu_{(s)} + Zn^{2+}_{(aq)}$.	BECAUSE	The reducing agent causes reduction but is itself oxidized in an oxidation-reduction reaction.
113.	Calcium oxide is a covalent substance.	BECAUSE	When a metal reacts with a nonmetal, a covalent bond is formed.
114.	Zinc oxide is a covalent substance.	BECAUSE	All oxides are covalent compounds.
115.	The Cl^- ion is larger than the K^+ ion.	BECAUSE	The ionic radii in a series of isoelectronic ions increase as the nuclear charge increases.

RETURN TO THE MAIN SECTION OF YOUR ANSWER SHEET AND ANSWER QUESTIONS 26–70.

GO ON TO THE NEXT PAGE

SAT II CHEMISTRY TEST

Part C

26. An atom contains 12 protons, 12 electrons, and 13 neutrons. Which of the following combinations of particles is an isotope of that atom?

Protons	Electrons	Neutrons
(A) 12	12	12
(B) 12	13	13
(C) 13	12	12
(D) 13	13	12
(E) 14	12	12

27. $C_6H_{6(l)} + O_{2(g)} \rightarrow CO_{2(g)} + H_2O_{(g)}$

    When the equation for the reaction represented above is balanced and all coefficients are reduced to lowest whole-number terms, the coefficient for $H_2O_{(g)}$ is

    (A) 2
    (B) 3
    (C) 4
    (D) 5
    (E) 6

28. Which of the following would have the highest pH?

    (A) HNO_3
    (B) C_2H_5OH
    (C) MgO
    (D) SO_2
    (E) CO_2

29. Which of these actions will cause more potassium nitrate to dissolve in a saturated potassium nitrate solution?

    I. Grind the potassium nitrate and then add to the solution while stirring
    II. Add more potassium nitrate while using a magnetic stirrer
    III. Add more potassium nitrate and heat the solution

    (A) I only
    (B) II only
    (C) III only
    (D) I and III only
    (E) I, II, and III

30. What is the molarity of a hydrofluoric acid solution, $HF_{(aq)}$, if 4.0 g of HF is dissolved in enough water to make 1.0 L of solution?

    (A) 0.10 M
    (B) 0.20 M
    (C) 0.40 M
    (D) 0.50 M
    (E) 0.60 M

31. Which of the following is the set of products formed when propanol, C_3H_7OH, undergoes a combustion reaction?

    (A) $CO_{2(g)}$ and $H_2O_{(l)}$
    (B) $CO_{2(g)}$ and $H_2O_{(g)}$
    (C) $C_{(s)}$, $O_{2(g)}$, and $H_2O_{(g)}$
    (D) $C_{(s)}$, $H_{2(g)}$, and $H_2O_{(g)}$
    (E) $CO_{2(g)}$, $H_2O_{(g)}$, and $O_{2(g)}$

32. $AlCl_2 \rightarrow AlCl_3$

    When the equation for the reaction represented above is balanced and all coefficients are reduced to lowest whole-number terms, the coefficient for Al is

    (A) 1
    (B) 2
    (C) 3
    (D) 4
    (E) 5

33. What is the concentration of ammonium ions in a 0.25 M solution of ammonium chloride?

    (A) 0.13 M
    (B) 0.25 M
    (C) 0.50 M
    (D) 0.75 M
    (E) 1.00 M

GO ON TO THE NEXT PAGE

34. The correct formula for barium sulfate is

    (A) BaS
    (B) BaS$_2$
    (C) BaSO$_3$
    (D) Ba$_2$SO$_4$
    (E) BaSO$_4$

35. The expected products of the decomposition of sodium oxide are

    (A) Na$_{(s)}$ and O$_{(g)}$
    (B) Na$^+_{(s)}$ and O$^{2-}_{(g)}$
    (C) Na$^+_{(s)}$ and O$_{2(g)}$
    (D) Na$_{(g)}$ and O$^{2-}_{(g)}$
    (E) Na$_{(s)}$ and O$_{2(g)}$

36. Which of the following sets of conditions best describes a solution of potassium iodide as compared to pure water?

	Vapor pressure	Freezing point	Boiling point
(A)	higher	higher	higher
(B)	higher	higher	lower
(C)	higher	lower	lower
(D)	lower	lower	higher
(E)	lower	higher	higher

37. The elements known for their limited chemical reactivity are the

    (A) Alkali metals
    (B) Alkaline earth metals
    (C) Transition metals
    (D) Halogens
    (E) Noble gases

38. Which of the following combinations of 0.20 M aqueous solutions will form a precipitate on mixing?

    I.   AgNO$_3$ and HCl
    II. BaC$_2$H$_3$O$_2$ and MgSO$_4$
    III. KI and Pb(NO$_3$)$_2$

    (A) I only
    (B) I and II only
    (C) I and III only
    (D) II and III only
    (E) I, II, and III

39. The oxidation number for sulfur is highest in which of the following ions or compounds?

    (A) SO$_2$
    (B) SO$_3^{2-}$
    (C) SO$_4^{2-}$
    (D) S$_2$O$_3^{2-}$
    (E) HSO$_3^-$

40. Given the equation $3X + Y \rightarrow Z$, you react 2 moles of X with 1 mole of Y. Which of the following is true?

    (A) X is the limiting reactant because of its higher molar mass.
    (B) X is the limiting reactant because you need 3 moles of X and have 2.
    (C) Y is the limiting reactant because you have fewer moles of Y than X.
    (D) Y is the limiting reactant because $3X$ molecules react with 1 Y molecule.
    (E) Neither reactant is limiting.

41. Which of these statements best describes a galvanic cell?

    (A) Reduction occurs at the anode.
    (B) Oxidation occurs at the anode.
    (C) Energy is required from an external source.
    (D) The cathode is negative.
    (E) E°_{cell} is negative.

42. Which of these half-reactions represents an oxidation?

    I.   Sn^{4+} → Sn^{2+}
    II. MnO$_4^-$ → Mn^{2+}
    III. Cl$_2$ → ClO$_3^-$

    (A) I only
    (B) II only
    (C) III only
    (D) I and II only
    (E) II and III only

43. Which of the following compounds has more than three isomers?

    (A) C$_2$H$_6$
    (B) C$_3$H$_8$
    (C) C$_4$H$_{10}$
    (D) C$_5$H$_{12}$
    (E) C$_6$H$_{14}$

44. Which of these types of chemical reactions is NOT a redox reaction?

    (A) Decomposition into elements
    (B) Single replacement
    (C) Double replacement
    (D) Combustion
    (E) Synthesis of two elements

GO ON TO THE NEXT PAGE

45. Based on the structure below, what is the empirical formula for this compound?

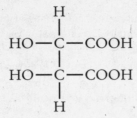

   (A) CHO
   (B) $C_2H_3O_3$
   (C) $C_2H_3O_4$
   (D) $C_2H_6O_6$
   (E) $C_4H_6O_8$

46. A reaction occurs between potassium carbonate and hydrochloric acid producing potassium chloride, carbon dioxide, and water. The correct set of coefficients, respectively, for the balanced reaction is

   (A) 1, 1, 1, 1, 1
   (B) 1, 2, 2, 1, 1
   (C) 3, 6, 6, 3, 4
   (D) 8, 6, 5, 10, 5
   (E) 5, 10, 10, 5, 5

47. Which of the following is true for a system whose equilibrium constant is relatively small?

   (A) It will take a short time to reach equilibrium.
   (B) It will take a long time to reach equilibrium.
   (C) The equilibrium lies to the left.
   (D) The equilibrium lies to the right.
   (E) It requires a higher concentration of reactants to reach equilibrium.

48. Iron (III) oxide is formed according to the following balanced chemical equation:

$$4Fe_{(s)} + 3O_{2(g)} \rightarrow 2Fe_2O_{3(s)}$$

   The reaction of 8.0 moles of solid iron with 9.0 moles of oxygen gas produces

   (A) 4.0 moles of Fe_2O_3 and 3.0 moles excess O_2
   (B) 4.0 moles of Fe_2O_3 and 6.0 moles excess O_2
   (C) 6.0 moles of Fe_2O_3 and 2.0 moles excess Fe
   (D) 6.0 moles of Fe_2O_3 and 3.0 moles excess Fe
   (E) 6.0 moles of Fe_2O_3 and 4.0 moles excess Fe

49. Which of the following statements is true about a balloon filled with 1.00 mol of CO_2 at STP?

   I. The contents of the balloon have a mass of 44.0 g.
   II. The balloon has a volume of 22.4 L.
   III. The balloon contains 6.02×10^{23} molecules.

   (A) I only
   (B) III only
   (C) I and II only
   (D) II and III only
   (E) I, II, and III

50. Which of the following processes shows an increase in entropy?

   (A) A pond freezes in winter.
   (B) Solid iodine sublimes.
   (C) Condensation occurs on the bathroom mirror.
   (D) Gaseous hydrogen and oxygen react to form water.
   (E) A sugar solution crystallizes.

51. Which of the following has the lowest ionization energy?

   (A) Li
   (B) Na
   (C) K
   (D) Rb
   (E) Cs

52. Chloral hydrate, $C_2H_3Cl_3O_2$, is a drug formerly used as a sedative and hypnotic. A sample of chloral hydrate contains 3.0×10^{18} atoms of carbon. How many atoms of hydrogen does this sample contain?

   (A) 1.5×10^{18}
   (B) 3.0×10^{18}
   (C) 4.5×10^{18}
   (D) 6.0×10^{18}
   (E) 9.0×10^{18}

53. Which of the following has the smallest radius?

   (A) P
   (B) S
   (C) Cl
   (D) Cl^-
   (E) S^{2-}

54. Which reaction is represented by the following expression for the law of mass action?

$$K_{eq} = \frac{[N_2O_4]}{[N_2][O_2]^2}$$

   (A) $N_2 + O_2 \rightarrow N_2O_4$
   (B) $N_2 + 2O_2 \rightarrow N_2O_4$
   (C) $N_2O_4 \rightarrow N_2 + O_2$
   (D) $N_2O_4 \rightarrow N_2 + 2O_2$
   (E) $N_2O_4 \rightarrow 2N + 4O$

GO ON TO THE NEXT PAGE

55. The balanced net ionic reaction for the neutralization reaction between solutions of sodium hydroxide and hydrochloric acid is

   (A) $Na^+_{(aq)} + OH^-_{(aq)} + H^+_{(aq)} + Cl^-_{(aq)} \rightarrow H_2O_{(l)} + NaCl_{(aq)}$

   (B) $Na^+_{(aq)} + Cl^-_{(aq)} \rightarrow NaCl_{(aq)}$

   (C) $OH^-_{(aq)} + H^+_{(aq)} \rightarrow H_2O_{(l)}$

   (D) $NaOH_{(aq)} + NaCl_{(aq)} \rightarrow H_2O_{(l)} + NaCl_{(aq)}$

   (E) $Na^+_{(aq)} + OH^-_{(aq)} + H^+_{(aq)} + Cl^-_{(aq)} \rightarrow H_2O_{(l)} + Na^+_{(aq)} + Cl^-_{(aq)}$

56. Complete the following nuclear equation:
   $$^{59}_{26}Fe \rightarrow ^{\ 0}_{-1}\beta + \underline{\quad}$$

   (A) $^{58}_{25}Mn$

   (B) $^{58}_{27}Co$

   (C) $^{59}_{25}Mn$

   (D) $^{59}_{27}Co$

   (E) $^{60}_{25}Mn$

57. Which of the following is the most chemically reactive?

   (A) Li
   (B) Na
   (C) K
   (D) Rb
   (E) Cs

58. Which of the following best describes the salt formed from the neutralization reaction between aqueous solutions of NaOH and $HC_2H_3O_2$?

   I. Acidic
   II. Basic
   III. Soluble

   (A) I only
   (B) II only
   (C) III only
   (D) I and III only
   (E) II and III only

59. What is the oxidation number for As in the chemical formula for arsenic acid, H_3AsO_4?

   (A) +1
   (B) +2
   (C) +3
   (D) +4
   (E) +5

GO ON TO THE NEXT PAGE

Questions 60–61 refer to the graph below.

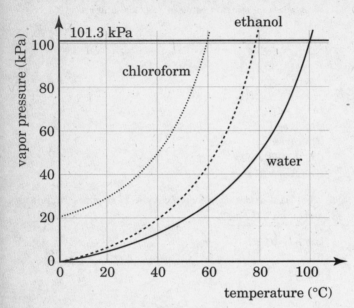

60. What is the normal boiling point for chloroform?

    (A) 40°C
    (B) 50°C
    (C) 60°C
    (D) 70°C
    (E) 80°C

61. To what temperature should water be heated so that its vapor pressure equals the vapor pressure of chloroform at 40°C?

    (A) 40°C
    (B) 50°C
    (C) 60°C
    (D) 70°C
    (E) 80°C

62. $AgNO_{3(aq)} + H_2S_{(aq)} \rightarrow Ag_2S_{(s)} + HNO_{3(aq)}$

    When the equation for the reaction represented above is balanced and all coefficients are reduced to lowest whole-number terms, the coefficient for $AgNO_{3(aq)}$ is

    (A) 1
    (B) 2
    (D) 3
    (D) 4
    (E) 5

63. Which of the following is the least electronegative?

    (A) Hydrogen
    (B) Lithium
    (C) Nitrogen
    (D) Sulfur
    (E) Phosphorus

GO ON TO THE NEXT PAGE

Questions 64–66 refer to the following heating curve and table of values:

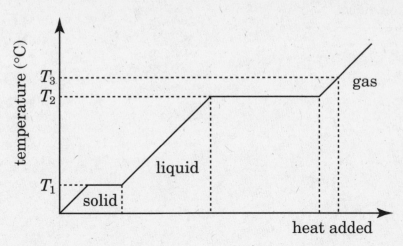

substance	freezing point (K)	ΔH_{fus} (kJ/mol)	boiling point (K)	ΔH_{vap} (kJ/mol)
neon	25	0.33	27	1.76
methanol	176	3.16	337	35.3
ammonia	195	5.65	240	23.4
water	273	6.01	373	40.7
benzene	279	9.87	353	30.8

64. What is the ΔH_{rxn} when one mole of ammonia undergoes the following reaction:

$$NH_{3(l)} \rightarrow NH_{3(g)}$$

(A) 3.16 kJ
(B) 5.65 kJ
(C) 23.4 kJ
(D) 35.3 kJ
(E) 40.7 kJ

65. Which of the following would have the lowest value for T_3?

(A) Neon
(B) Methanol
(C) Ammonia
(D) Water
(E) Benzene

66. Which of the following substances would you expect to require the most energy while vaporizing at 1.0 atm pressure?

(A) Neon
(B) Methanol
(C) Ammonia
(D) Water
(E) Benzene

67. The pH of a sample of orange juice is 3.7. A sample of lemonade has a pH of 4.7. Compared to the [H⁺] of lemonade, the [H⁺] of orange juice is

(A) Two times higher
(B) Half as much
(C) Ten times higher
(D) One-tenth as much
(E) One hundred times higher

GO ON TO THE NEXT PAGE

68. Which of the following salts would have the greatest effect on the freezing point of a solution if 0.10 mole of the salt was dissolved in enough water to make 100.0 mL of solution?

    (A) NaCl
    (B) KCl
    (C) $CaCl_2$
    (D) $MgCl_2$
    (E) $AlCl_3$

69. How many moles of NaOH are required to neutralize 1.2 moles of H_2SO_4?

    (A) 0.6 mole
    (B) 1.2 moles
    (C) 2.4 moles
    (D) 3.6 moles
    (E) 4.8 moles

70. Which of the following compounds is named *n*-butane?

    (A) CH_4
    (B) C_2H_6
    (C) C_3H_8
    (D) C_4H_{10}
    (E) C_5H_{12}

S T O P

IF YOU FINISH BEFORE TIME IS CALLED, YOU MAY CHECK YOUR WORK ON THIS TEST ONLY.
DO NOT TURN TO ANY OTHER TEST IN THIS BOOK.

SAT II Chemistry
Practice Test III
Explanations

Answers to SAT II Chemistry Practice Test III

Question Number	Answer	Right	Wrong	Question Number	Answer	Right	Wrong
Part A				**Part C**			
1.	E			26.	A		
2.	C			27.	E		
3.	A			28.	C		
4.	B			29.	C		
5.	D			30.	B		
6.	A			31.	B		
7.	C			32.	B		
8.	A			33.	B		
9.	B			34.	E		
10.	B			35.	E		
11.	E			36.	D		
12.	A			37.	E		
13.	C			38.	E		
14.	D			39.	C		
15.	C			40.	B		
16.	A			41.	B		
17.	A			42.	C		
18.	A			43.	E		
19.	C			44.	C		
20.	E			45.	B		
21.	C			46.	B		
22.	D			47.	C		
23.	A			48.	A		
24.	E			49.	E		
25.	C			50.	B		
Part B				51.	E		
101.	T T CE			52.	C		
102.	F T			53.	C		
103.	T T			54.	B		
104.	T T CE			55.	C		
105.	F F			56.	D		
106.	T F			57.	E		
107.	F T			58.	E		
108.	T F			59.	E		
109.	T F			60.	C		
110.	F T			61.	E		
111.	T T CE			62.	B		
112.	T T CE			63.	B		
113.	F F			64.	C		
114.	F F			65.	A		
115.	T F			66.	D		
				67.	C		
				68.	E		
				69.	C		
				70.	D		

Calculating Your Score

Your raw score for SAT II Chemistry test is based on the number of questions you answer correctly and incorrectly. Once you have determined your raw score, use the conversion table on page 14 of this book to calculate your scaled score.

To Calculate Your Raw Score

1. Count the number of questions you answered correctly: _____ (A)
2. Count the number of questions you answered incorrectly, and multiply that number by $1/4$: _____ (B) × $1/4$ = _____ (C)
3. Subtract the value in (C) from value in (A): _____ (D)
4. Round the number in (D) to the nearest whole number. This is your raw score: _____ (E)

Part A

The first 25 questions on this exam are classification set questions. These should be some of the easier points to obtain on the exam. You need to read only one set of answer choices to complete several questions. Approach these questions by reading all of the choices, read each statement that follows, answer, and then match your answer with the best answer choice.

1. **E** Periodic table
You should first figure out how many electrons each ion has, then go through this set of questions. If you've done so, you'll see that Ca^{2+} and Cl^- are isoelectronic, meaning that they have the same number of electrons. Both have Ar's electron configuration, or a total of 18 electrons.

2. **C** Periodic table
The oxide ion, O^{2-}, has gained two electrons while the O^- has gained only one electron; therefore these two ions differ by one electron.

3. **A** Periodic table
Mg^+ and F^+ have each lost one electron. Mg^+ now has 11 while F^+ has eight: this is a difference of three electrons.

4. **B** Periodic table
Li^+ has lost one electron and now has two electrons. Ne has not ionized and thus has 10 electrons: this is a difference of eight electrons.

5.   **D**   Periodic table
N is a neutral atom and has seven electrons. P^{3-} has gained three electrons to add to neutral phosphorus's 15 electrons for a total of 18. N and P^{3-} differ by 11 electrons.

6.   **A**   Descriptive chemistry
Zinc is combined with copper to make the alloy brass. This is something you will just have to memorize.

7.   **C**   Descriptive chemistry
Tin is combined with copper to make the alloy bronze. Again, this question is testing your ability to memorize facts.

8.   **A**   Descriptive chemistry
Zinc is used to galvanize metals, and galvanization makes metals resistant to oxidation (rusting). This is a useful process since it does things like make nails or screws suitable for use outdoors.

9.   **B**   Descriptive chemistry
Iron can be combined with carbon to make steel. Other substances can be added to the alloy to make the many different varieties of steel.

10.   **B**   Phase diagrams
The set of temperature and pressure conditions where all three states of matter can exist in equilibrium is known as the triple point. On a phase diagram, all of the curves coincide at the triple point, which is point *B* here.

11.   **E**   Phase diagrams
The point beyond which pressure alone cannot liquefy the gas is known as the critical point. It is a specific set of temperature and pressure coordinates on a phase change diagram. The temperature coordinate is the critical temperature, while the pressure coordinate is called the critical pressure. It is always found at the top of the liquid-gas curve. At the critical point, the average kinetic energy of the molecules is too great for pressure alone to liquefy the gas; it must also be cooled to below the critical temperature.

12.   **A**   Phase diagrams
The direct change of state from solid to vapor is known as sublimation. This process bypasses the liquid phase. At 1 atm and room temperature, for example, CO_2 sublimates; it is called "dry" ice for this reason.

13. **C**   Phase diagrams

The set of temperature and pressure conditions that represents an equilibrium between the liquid and gas or vapor phase can be found anywhere along the curve from *B* to *E*. Point *C* is on this line, so it is the answer. Again, equilibrium of phases occurs anywhere along the curves on the diagram.

14. **D**   Enthalpy

This bunch of questions is a bit difficult since you have to apply the definitions of the various types of enthalpy to chemical equations. The subscripts on the enthalpy symbols give you a hint as to what's going on in the problem. Answer **D** is a classic example of the combustion of one mole of a hydrocarbon.

15. **C**   Enthalpy

This reaction is a simple phase change from liquid to vapor, which is known as vaporization.

16. **A**   Enthalpy

The definition for enthalpy of formation states that you form one mole of a compound from its elements in their standard states. Don't let the reactant coefficient of $\frac{1}{2}$ throw you off! One mole of water is still the product in this reaction.

17. **A**   Enthalpy

Elements are assigned an enthalpy of formation of zero when in their standard states.

18. **A**   Pressure-volume relationships for gases

This set is easier if you remember that "vs." is always stated as "*y* variable vs. *x* variable" and actually put those labels on these generic graph shapes! Since the question states that the gas is ideal and at a constant temperature, we know that as volume is increased, pressure decreases. The graph is a curve since this is not a direct, linear relationship.

19. **C**   Volume-temperature relationships for gases

Here a sample of an ideal gas is held at constant pressure. This is a direct relationship. The volume of a gas expands by 1/273 of its original volume for every 1°C increase in temperature.

20. **E**   Kinetic energy–temperature relationships

This graph is a normal distribution, so it will usually represent an average between the variables. Drop a straight vertical line from the top of the "bell" to the *x* axis and read the graph to determine the average (or the optimum) for the sample. It's exactly what we mean when we say that the temperature is the "average kinetic energy" of the molecules in a given sample of matter.

21. C Density
To answer this question, you must first recognize that mass vs. volume *is* density. Since you know that the density of a substance is a constant, you now know you are looking for a direct or linear relationship. Since as volume increases, so does mass, the answer is choice C.

22. D Laboratory
Filtration is the technique used to separate a precipitate from a filtrate (the liquid part of the mixture). Porous filter paper is used to filter the solution.

23. A Lab processes
Distillation is the technique used to separate a mixture of liquids based on differences in their boiling points. In distillation, a device called a condenser is used. A condenser is a glass tube within a tube: the outer tube has cold water circulating throughout it, while the inner tube contains the vapor of one of the liquids in the mixture. The liquid with the lowest boiling point vaporizes first. Its vapor is less dense, so it rises and travels through the inner tube of the condenser. Next it is cooled, re-condenses, and then drips out the other end of the condenser into a collection flask.

24. E Lab processes
A titration is the technique used to determine the unknown concentration of a known acid. Usually an indicator is used that has been carefully selected so that its color change coincides with the equivalence point in the reaction, where moles of acid equal moles of base. From this relationship and from the very carefully measured quantities of both the acid and the base, you can calculate the unknown molarity.

25. C Lab processes
Fractional crystallization is the technique used to separate a mixture of dissolved solids by evaporation. This technique relies on differences in the individual solubilities at different temperatures.

Part B

By now you are well versed in how these questions work. Remember that to be successful on this type of question, you should read each statement individually and decide whether it is true or false. Then if both statements are true, read the second statement again and see if it is the *reason* the first statement is true.

101. T T CE Ionization energy
Statement I is true. The alkali metals have an electron configuration of ns^1 and an effective nuclear charge of 1. The removal of the outer s^1 electron requires energy, but the removal

of a second electron requires an enormous input of energy since the second electron is from a different principal energy level, one that's closer to the nucleus; thus it is more tightly held. Statement II is also true, and it is the correct explanation for statement I, so you would fill in the **CE** oval.

102. **F T**   Metallic character
Statement I is false. Nonmetals are generally higher in electronegativity than metals, and fluorine and its neighbors have the highest electronegativity of all. Statement II is true: metals exist as cations in a "sea" of delocalized electrons. Statement II is not an explanation of statement I, so do not fill in the CE oval.

103. **T T**   Bonding—polarity
Statement I is true: water is indeed a polar molecule due to the two pairs of unshared electrons on the oxygen atom. Statement II is also true: water has polar covalent bonds. It is not a correct explanation of statement I. Many nonpolar molecules contain polar covalent bonds. Molecular polarity occurs when the dipole moments of the polar covalent bonds do not cancel each other out—so you must take the geometry of the molecule into consideration. Do not fill in the **CE** oval.

104. **T T CE**   Water's IMFs
Statement I is true: water has a low vapor pressure, as evidenced by its slow rate of evaporation. Statement II is also true: hydrogen bonds form between water molecules, specifically between the H of one water molecule and the unshared electron pair on the oxygen of an adjacent water molecule. These intermolecular forces contribute to the low vapor pressure of water, so statement II is the correct explanation for statement I, and you would fill in the **CE** oval.

105. **F F**   Acid-base theory
Statement I is false. It's a trap—don't fall for it. Indeed, Arrhenius bases donate an OH^- ion in water, but this molecule, C_2H_5OH, is an alcohol (ethanol, to be exact), and the OH is a neutral functional group called a hydroxyl group; it is not a hydroxide ion at all. Statement II is also false since ethanol does not dissociate in water, so do not fill in the **CE** oval.

106. **T F**   Entropy and energy
Statement I is true, since steam is water vapor, which is much more energetic and chaotic than water in the liquid phase. Statement II is false since both samples are at the same temperature; their average kinetic energies are the same. Do not fill in the **CE** oval.

107. **F T**   Atomic theory
Statement I is false because of the existence of isotopes. Statement II is true since it is the number of protons that defines the element.

108. **T F**   Behavior of gases

Statement I is true. At the same temperature, lighter gas molecules move at a faster rate than heavier gas molecules, according to Graham's law. Statement II is false: again, if the temperature is the same, the average kinetic energy will be the same.

109. **T F**   Bonding and polarity

Statement I is true. CH_3Cl is a polar molecule since the C—Cl bond has a higher dipole moment (it is a stronger dipole since Cl is more electronegative than H) than the three C—H bonds. Statement II is false and is a common misconception. Yes, lone pairs of electrons often contribute to the polarity of a molecule, but not in this case. Lone pairs are not necessary for a molecule to be polar: molecules are polar when their dipole moments do not cancel each other out.

110. **F T**   Bonding and molecular geometry

Statement I is false. Draw this structure. In the ammonia molecule, the nitrogen atom obeys the octet rule: it is surrounded by three bonded H atoms and a lone, unshared pair of electrons. The H—N—H bond angles are approximately 107° rather than the 120° that would be found in a trigonal planar molecule. Statement II is true as is evidenced by the Lewis structure. Do not fill in the **CE** oval.

111. **T T CE**   Chemical reactions

You have to know basic solubility rules and apply them correctly to answer this question. All nitrates are soluble, and chlorides are soluble except silver, mercury, and lead. This means that both of these reactants dissolve in water. The two products formed from the double displacement reaction are $NaNO_3$, a very soluble compound, and AgCl, a very insoluble compound. Therefore, our precipitate can indeed be separated by filtration. Statement II is correct and the explanation for statement I, so fill in the **CE** oval.

112. **T T CE**   Redox reactions

Statement I is true since the half-reaction involving zinc, $Zn_{(s)} \rightarrow Zn^{2+}_{(aq)}$, is an oxidation, which means zinc metal is the reducing agent (it accepts electrons). Whichever reactant is oxidized causes the other reactant to be reduced. Statement II is thus true and a correct explanation.

113. **F F**   Bonding

Statement I is false. Remember that compounds formed from elements from the far ends of the periodic table are ionic. Statement II is also false. Metals that react with nonmetals form electrostatic attractions that we refer to as ionic bonds.

114. F F   Bonding

Statement I is false here too. Metal oxides are not covalent compounds. Statement II is false and is a common misconception. Nonmetal oxides are covalent compounds, but metal oxides are not.

115. T F   Periodic trends

Statement I is true. K^+ and Cl^- are isoelectronic: they both have 18 electrons. The chloride ion has 17 protons, while the potassium ion has 19 protons. K^+'s 19 protons mean it has a stronger attraction for the electron cloud, thus causing it to be smaller than Cl^-. Statement II is false: as the nuclear charge increases, the increased number of protons attracts the electron cloud more strongly, causing the ionic radii within the series to shrink.

Part C

The remaining questions on the test are the traditional multiple choice that you know and love. Eliminate any choices that you can initially, then see which answer choice is most similar to your answer.

26. A   Isotopes

If an atom contains 12 protons, 12 electrons, and 13 neutrons, then an isotope of that element would contain 12 protons, 12 electrons, and a different number of neutrons, in this case, 12.

27. E   Balancing chemical equations

The correctly balanced equation is $2C_6H_{6(l)} + 15O_{2(g)} \rightarrow 12CO_{2(g)} + 6H_2O_{(g)}$. The coefficient for $H_2O_{(g)}$ is thus 6.

28. C   pH concept

Start by translating the question. The compound with the highest pH would be the most basic compound. The stronger the base, the higher the pH. Don't be confused by the presence of an alcohol on this list. Strong bases are oxides and hydroxides of 1A and 2A metals, so MgO is the best choice.

29. C   Solutions and reaction rate

Since this is a saturated solution, changing the temperature is the only action listed that will allow more solute to dissolve. The other two actions affect the rate of solution formation but have no effect on the amount of solute that can dissolve at a given temperature.

30. **B**   Molarity
HF has a molar mass of 20 g/mol. Do the math: 4.0 g is 1/5 of a mole, which is equal to 2/10, which is the same thing as 0.20 M since a liter of solution is formed.

31. **B**   Predicting products
Since propanol, C_3H_7OH, consists entirely of C, H, and O, the products will be the normal products of a combustion reaction, $CO_{2(g)}$ and $H_2O_{(g)}$.

32. **B**   Balancing chemical reactions
The balanced equation is $2Al + 3Cl_2 \rightarrow 2AlCl_3$, so the correct coefficient for Al is 2.

33. **B**   Solution stoichiometry
First write the correct formula for ammonium chloride, NH_4Cl. Since this molecule contains one ammonium ion, the concentration of the ammonium ion is the same as the concentration of the solution, or 0.25 M.

34. **E**   Chemical formulas
The correct formula for barium sulfate is $BaSO_4$ since the barium ion has a +2 oxidation state and the sulfate ion has a –2 oxidation state.

35. **E**   Predicting products
The expected products of the decomposition of any metal oxide are the metal itself and oxygen gas.

36. **D**   Properties of solutions
You are forced to think through several relationships here. All of the colligative properties are due to vapor pressure lowering. A lowering of vapor pressure generally occurs when a solute is added to a pure solvent. The only two answers listed that have a drop in vapor pressure are **D** and **E**. Adding a solute to a solution depresses (lowers) the freezing point and elevates the boiling point, so **D** is the correct answer.

37. **E**   Descriptive chemistry
The noble gases are known for their extremely limited chemical reactivity.

38. **E**   Predicting products
You must know and correctly apply the solubility rules to get the correct answer here. All of these reactions constitute double replacement reactions. First figure out what ions the compounds will dissociate into and then apply the solubility rules as appropriate to determine whether the new compounds are soluble and thus will ionize or whether they are insoluble and will form a precipitate. Combination I forms HNO_3 and AgCl; HNO_3 is a strong acid that completely dissociates on formation, while all chlorides, bromides, and iodides are

soluble except silver, mercury, and lead. Therefore, AgCl is a precipitate. Combination II forms $MgC_2H_3O_2$ and $BaSO_4$. All acetates are soluble and all sulfates are soluble except Ca, Sr, Ba, and Pb. Therefore, $BaSO_4$ is a precipitate. Combination III forms PbI_2 and KNO_3. All nitrates are soluble and all chlorides, bromides, and iodides are soluble except silver, mercury, and lead. Therefore PbI_2 is a precipitate.

39. **C** Oxidation numbers

This question is time consuming. Start by applying the oxidation rules. O is usually 2–, and the sum of the oxidation states in a neutral compound must be zero, while the sum of the oxidation states in a polyatomic ion must be equal to the charge on the ion. For SO_2, which is neutral, a –4 number is attributed to the two oxygen atoms, so S must have a +4 number so that $(-4) + (+4) = 0$. For SO_3^{2-}, the sum of the oxidation numbers must equal –2. Negative 6 is attributed to the three oxygen atoms, so again, sulfur must have a +4 number so that $(+4) + (-6) = -2$, the charge on the ion. For SO_4^{2-}, the sum must equal –2. Negative 8 is attributed to the four oxygen atoms, so S must be a +6 (we have a winner!) so that $(-8) + (+6) = -2$, the charge on the ion. For $S_2O_3^{2-}$, the sum must equal –2. Negative 6 is attributed to the three oxygen atoms, so the remaining +4 is split between the two S atoms for a +2 each, so that $(-6) + 2(+2) = -2$. For HSO_3^-, the sum must be –1. Negative 6 is attributed to the three oxygen atoms, and +1 is attributed to the hydrogen atom, so S must be +4 so that $(-6) + (+1) + (+4) = -1$.

40. **B** Limiting reactant

Refer to the equation $3X + Y \rightarrow Z$. The mole:mole ratio is 3:1:1. The question says you react 2 moles of X with 1 mole of Y. What if you use all of Y? You'd need 3 moles of X due to the mole:mole ratio. You only have 2 moles of X, so X is the limiting reactant, and the answer is **B**.

41. **B** Electrochemistry

Galvanic cells, voltaic cells, and batteries all have a $+E^\circ_{cell}$ and convert chemical energy into useful electrical energy. Rely on the mnemonic devices. <u>Red cat</u>—reduction occurs at the cathode. <u>An ox</u>—oxidation occurs at the anode. The cathode is the positive electrode; to help you remember that you might think of the *t* in the word *cathode* as a plus sign in the middle of the word. By default the anode must be negative. The only correct statement given is **B**.

42. **C** Redox reactions

Remember, an oxidation is an increase in the oxidation number. The first two reactions show reductions. Tin's oxidation state reduces from +4 to +2; Mn's reduces from +7 to +2. In the half-reaction $Cl_2 \rightarrow ClO_3^-$, Cl is oxidized from Cl^0 (element in its standard state) to +5.

43. E Isomers

Again, this is a time-consuming problem. Isomers have the same chemical formula (meaning the same numbers and kinds of atoms) but different structural formulas. Concentrate on the carbon skeletons. Generally, as the number of carbons increase, so does the number of isomers. Examine the carbon skeleton formulas below:

C₂H₆: C—C There is no other way to connect these carbons, so it has no isomers.

C₃H₈: C—C—C There is no other way to connect those carbons, so it has no isomers.

C₄H₁₀: C—C—C—C and C—C—C with C dangling below Putting the carbon "dangling" above results in the same structure. Hanging it off either end, C is just a bend in the chain.

C₅H₁₂: C—C—C—C—C and C—C—C—C with C below and C—C—C with C above and below

C₆H₁₄: C—C—C—C—C—C and C—C—C—C—C with C below and

C—C—C—C—C with C below and C—C—C—C with two C below and C—C—C—C with C above and below

44. C Types of chemical reactions

All redox reactions involve a change in oxidation state. Let's break it down. Compounds usually undergo decomposition into elements—the oxidation numbers of the elements in a compound are not usually zero. However, the products of a "decomposition into elements" reaction—meaning the elements—have oxidation numbers of zero. This represents a clear change in oxidation state. Next, in a single replacement reaction, an element with an oxidation number of zero is "bumping" out a member of a compound to take its place. The element now has an oxidation state that is *not* zero; again, a clear change in oxidation state. In a combustion reaction, the element oxygen has an oxidation state of zero as a reactant but –2 as a member of either water or carbon dioxide. Synthesis of two elements with oxidation states of zero forms compounds with oxidation states that are rarely zero. The only choice that shows a type of reaction in which there is usually not a change in oxidation state is the double replacement reaction.

45. B Empirical formulas

Rewrite the structural formula below as a chemical formula. Reduce to the lowest terms and you have the empirical formula: four C's, six H's, and six O's; the empirical formula is $C_2H_3O_3$.

46. B Molecular chemical equations

This one is a triple whammy. First, you'll need to determine the correct chemical formula. Second, you'll need to balance the equation. Finally, you'll need to determine the order of the coefficients, being careful to write the chemical formulas in the correct order. The balanced equation is $K_2CO_3 + 2HCl \rightarrow 2KCl + CO_2 + H_2O$. The coefficients, in order, are 1, 2, 2, 1, 1.

47. C Equilibrium constants

Recall that the equilibrium constant, K, is a ratio of [products]/[reactants]. For a system whose equilibrium constant is relatively small, the [reactants] must be larger than the [products]. That means the equilibrium lies far to the left. Do not confuse rate with equilibrium; equilibrium has nothing to do with the rate of the reaction.

48. A Limiting reactant

Consider the balanced equation $4Fe_{(s)} + 3O_{2(g)} \rightarrow 2Fe_2O_{3(s)}$. The mole:mole:mole ratio is 4:3:2. If you use all 8 moles of iron, you'd need 6 moles of oxygen to produce 4 moles of iron (III) oxide. You'd have an excess of 3 moles of oxygen gas since you'll use 6 moles and you started with 9 moles.

49. E The mole concept

A balloon filled with 1.00 mol of CO_2 at STP contains a molar mass of gas in grams (44.0 g/mol), occupying a volume of 22.4 L. This balloon contains Avogadro's number of molecules.

50. B Entropy

Always think of an increase in entropy as an increase in chaos. Freezing or crystallizing and condensing represent an increase in order of a system. Any reduction in the number of moles of gas also brings more order and less chaos to the system. Sublimation involves the formation of a gas, which represents an increase in chaos, or less order to the system, and is the correct answer.

51. E Ionization energy

Cesium, Cs, has the lowest ionization energy. All of the choices are alkali metals, and thus an s^1 electron is being removed from each. However, it takes less energy to remove the s^1 electron from Cs since it is the largest, so the valence electron resides far from the nucleus and is heavily shielded.

Test III Explanations

52. C   Stoichiometry
If a sample of chloral hydrate, $C_2H_3Cl_3O_2$, contains 3.0×10^{18} atoms of carbon, then it contains 4.5×10^{18} atoms of hydrogen since the ratio of C:H in the molecule is 2:3.

53. C   Atomic vs. ionic radii
Two trends are at work here. First, atomic radii generally decrease as you move from left to right within a period, due to an increase in effective nuclear charge. Second, gaining electrons, or forming negative ions, increases atomic radii with the addition of each electron. This means that the negative ions are the largest in the list. Among the neutral atoms, chlorine has the highest effective nuclear charge; therefore it is the smallest.

54. B   Equilibrium constant expression
Work backward from the expression and reconstruct the balanced chemical equation. Begin with the idea that K is [products]/[reactants]. The correct equation must begin with $N_2 + 2O_2$. Why the coefficient of 2? Oxygen's concentration is squared. N_2O_4 is the product, so the complete, balanced chemical reaction is $N_2 + 2O_2 \rightarrow N_2O_4$.

55. C   Net ionic reactions
You must apply the solubility rules and realize that both the acid and base are strong, so they completely ionize. Next you must realize that the salt formed is soluble, so the ions forming the salt are both spectator ions. Here's the reaction: $OH^-_{(aq)} + H^+_{(aq)} \rightarrow H_2O_{(l)}$.

56. D   Nuclear
Just apply the law of conservation of mass and charge. The mass numbers and atomic numbers must be equal on both sides of the equation. The correctly balanced equation is $^{59}_{26}Fe \rightarrow ^{0}_{-1}\beta + ^{59}_{27}Co$.

57. E   Periodicity
All of the answer choices are alkali metals, so all react violently with water. The larger they are, the more violent the reaction. This is because in larger atoms, the valence electrons are less tightly held due to increased distance from the nucleus and increased shielding.

58. E   Predicting products
First you must realize that this question represents a mixture of a strong base with a weak acid. This will result in a basic salt, sodium acetate, which is very soluble.

59. E   Oxidation numbers
Apply the oxidation rules and be careful with your arithmetic. This is a neutral compound, so the sum of the oxidation numbers must be zero. H is +1 and O is –2. That means that –8 is attributed to the 4 oxygens, while +3 is attributed to the 3 hydrogens. That leaves As with an oxidation state of +5, so that $4(-2) + 3(+1) + (+5) = 0$.

60. **C**   States of matter
The normal boiling point is defined as the temperature at which the vapor pressure of the liquid equals 1.0 atm or 101.3 kPa. For ethanol, we see that this occurs at 60°C.

61. **E**   States of matter
First determine the vapor pressure of chloroform at 40°C from the graph. The vapor pressure is about 50 kPa. Then read across to the point on the water curve that corresponds and then drop down and read the temperature. The temperature should be about 80°C.

62. **B**   Balancing chemical equations
The correctly balanced equation is

$$2AgNO_{3(aq)} + H_2S_{(aq)} \rightarrow Ag_2S_{(s)} + 2HNO_{3(aq)}$$

The correct coefficient for $AgNO_{3(aq)}$ is 2.

63. **B**   Periodic trends
The element that has the lowest electronegativity value is the one that lies farthest to the left on the periodic table, since electronegativity increases as you move from left to right across a row of the periodic table. Of the answer choices, Lithium is farthest to the left, so **B** is the correct answer.

64. **C**   States of matter and enthalpy
The ΔH_{rxn} can calculated by multiplying the ΔH_{vap} for ammonia by the number of moles reacting. That means 23.4 kJ/mol × 1 mol = 23.4 kJ.

65. **A**   States of matter
T_3 is above the boiling point, so look through the list for the substance that has the lowest boiling point. Neon is the correct answer.

66. **D**   States of matter
The substance with the highest ΔH_{vap} will require the most energy to vaporize at constant pressure, and water has the highest ΔH_{vap}.

67. **C**   pH
You must recall that the pH scale measures the $[H^+]$ and is base 10 logarithmic. This means that a difference of 2 pH units is really a difference in $[H^+]$ of 10^2, and a difference of 5 units is really a difference of 10^5, etc. Furthermore, acids have a pH less than 7.0, while bases have a pH greater than 7.0. The farther the pH is from 7.0, the stronger the acid or base: *acid* 0 ← 7.0 → 14 *basic* Since the pH of the orange juice is lower, it contains more $[H^+]$ than the lemonade. Since the pH values differ by one unit, a power of 10 is involved, so the $[H^+]$ of the orange juice is 10 times greater than the $[H^+]$ of the lemonade.

68.　**E**　Properties of solutions

When a solute is added to a solvent, the freezing point of the resulting solution is depressed (lowered) due to the drop in vapor pressure. If the solute ionizes, this effect is even greater, and the more ions released, the larger the drop in the freezing point. $AlCl_3$ releases four ions, one Al^{3+} and Cl^-, which means it will have the greatest effect on the lowering of the freezing point.

69.　**C**　Acid-base neutralization

H_2SO_4 is a strong diprotic acid: it completely ionizes. Since sulfuric acid is diprotic, it takes two hydroxides to neutralize one molecule of sulfuric acid. Sodium hydroxide releases only one hydroxide at a time, so twice as many moles are needed for neutralization to occur. Therefore, it will require 2.4 moles of NaOH to neutralize 1.2 moles of H_2SO_4.

70.　**D**　Chemical formulas

Butane is an alkane that has four carbons. Alkanes follow the general formula C_nH_{2n+2}. The *-ane* in the word means all of the carbons are singly bonded. Either apply the generalized formula or draw out the four carbons and obey the octet rule for each carbon. When you saturate the chain, you'll have 10 H's. The correct formula is C_4H_{10}.

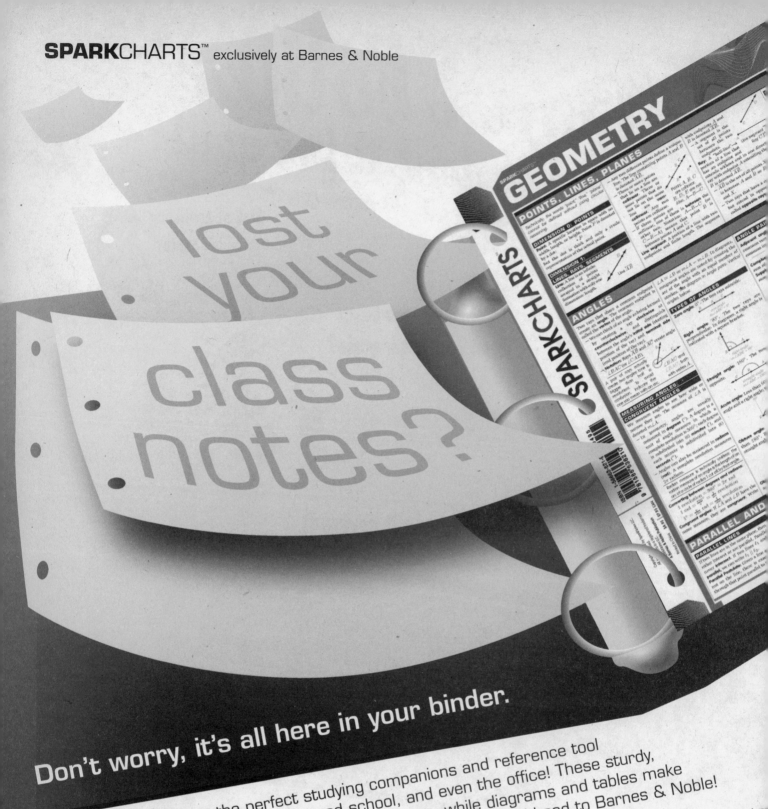